SOUTHWEST

A CONTEMPORARY ANTHOLOGY

SOUTH

Karl and Jane Kopp, general editors
Bart Lanier Stafford III, fiction edit

NEST

A CONTEMPORARY ANTHOLOGY

Red Earth Press
P.O. Box 26641
Albuquerque, N.M. 87125

RED EARTH PRESS
P.O. Box 26641
Albuquerque, N.M. 87125

We are grateful for permission to reprint — from books, anthologies, and periodicals
— the materials listed below.

ACKNOWLEDGEMENTS: Paula Allen, "Wool Season: 1973": from *American Poetry Review*.
Copyright © 1975 by Paula Allen. Bert Almon, "Fishing on the Sea Wall . . .": from *TAWTE* and
Travois (Contemporary Arts Museum of Houston/Thorp Springs Press); also in *Taking Possession*
(Solo Press) Copyright © 1976 by Bert Almon; "Albuquerque Landing": from *Blue Fife*. Jim Barnes,
"A Season of Loss": from *Dacotah Territory*; "Postcard to Brian Bedard . . .": from *Greenfield
Review*; "Four Choctaw Songs": from *Oakwood*. William D. Barney, "To Be A Bull": from *The
Killdeer Crying* (Prickly Pear Press) Copyright © 1977 by William D. Barney. Charles Behlen,
"Bastards": from *TAWTE*. Leonard Bird, "Mourning Dove": from *Rocky Mountain Review*;
quotation in the introduction to this book: from an unpublished essay, "Contemporary Southwest
Poetry and the Mythopoeic Tradition"; "Mourning Dove", "Lonely Woman at Tsaile," and "Above
Arch Canyon": from *River of Lost Souls* (Tooth of Time Press) Copyright © 1977 by Leonard Bird.
Robert Bonazzi, "Houston's Adolescence was my Adolescence": from *Travois*. Jon Bracker, "Yard
Sale": from *The Salt Creek Reader*; "Flowers": from *TAWTE* and *Travois*. Haldeen Braddy, "Joe
Lafferty Ought to be Ashamed of Himself": from *Stories Southwest*, ed. A. Wilber Stevens, reprinted
with permission of Prescott College Press. John Brandi, "At Mesa Verde": from *Voices from the Rio
Grande* (Rio Grande Writers Association). besmilr brigham, "They Got Wet, Mojada": from *Monk's
Pond*; "The Sky is a Circumference": from *Puerto del Sol*. Susan Bright, "texas lady . . .": from
Wood Ibis; Robert Burlingame, "El Paso Morning": from *Kansas Magazine*; "Northwest at
Christmas": from *Outlet*. Johanna Cinader, "The Gardener": from *New Mexico Magazine*. Naomi
Clark, "Found Poem: First Letter to Aunt Cat": used with permission of the editors of *Poetry
Northwest*. Thomas Cobb, "Breaking the Drought": from *Nitty Gritty*. James Cody, "The Heart of
Texas," "The Neches River," and "Needles": from *Return* (Place of Herons Press) Copyright ©
1976 by James Cody; Cody; "The Neches" and "Needles": also in *Travois*. Joseph L. Concha, "Deer
Mother": from *Chokecherry Hunters and Other Poems* (The Sunstone Press) Copyright © 1976 by
Joseph L. Concha. Victor Contoski, "Prairie Wind": from *Gallimaufry*. Hisaye Yamamoto DeSoto,
"The Pleasures of Plain Rice": from *The Rafu Shimpo Supplement*. R.P. Dickey, "Indians": from
Oakwood; "Santo Domingo Corn Dance": in *Traveling America with Today's Poets* (Macmillan
Publishing Company) Copyright © 1977 by David Kherdian. Doug Flaherty, quotations in the
introduction to this book: from preface to *Circle the Earth Before Noon*, a collection of poems.
Michael C. Ford, "Pasadena Poem": from *Rounding Third* (Permanent Press/Biographies of
Beverley Hills) Copyright © 1974, 1975, 1976 by Michael C. Ford. Paul Foreman, "Impressionist"
and "Pecans": from *Texas Liveoak* (Thorp Springs Press) Copyright © 1977 by Paul Foreman;
"Pecans" and "L.A. A Lament": from *Redwing Blackbird* (The Headstone Press) Copyright © 1973
by Paul Foreman; "Impressionist" and "Pecans" also in *Travois*. Nia Francisco, "With Endless
Curved Walls": from *Cafe Solo*, Copyright © 1976 by Nia Francisco; "iridescent child": Copyright
© 1977 by Nia Francisco. Gene Frumkin, "Indian Corn": from *Puerto del Sol*; "The
Anglo-Coordinator" from *Quetzal*; "Soulfeathers for Albert Camus": from *Dacotah Territory*.
Dwight Fullingim, "Vehemence of the Wind": from *Travois*. Rita Garitano, "Exterior Landscapes":

When I go out of the house for a walk, uncertain as yet whither I will bend my steps, and submit myself to my instinct to decide for me, I find, strange and whimsical as it may seem, that I finally and inevitably settle southwest, toward some particular wood or meadow or deserted pasture or hill in that direction. My needle is slow to settle — varies a few degrees, and does not always point due southwest, it is true, and it has good authority for this variation, but it always settles between west and south-southwest. The future lies that way to me, and the earth seems more unexhausted and richer on that side.

—H.D. Thoreau
(from "Walking")

This book is dedicated to the land of the Southwest
and to its living spirit

For this anthology we have chosen poems and prose that focus on "place." The very best American writing — **Walden**, the work of Herman Melville and Mark Twain, Whitman's poetry, and more recently the novels of William Faulkner and the poetry of William Carlos Williams — has always had this emphasis. Through a close and deep involvement with the places they knew best and wrote about, these writers made those parts of America — whether New Bedford in the 1840's or a small county in rural Mississippi — exist for us permanently.

But an emphasis on "place" has not been limited to great American writing only. Without the names and detailed descriptions of the Achaian sea-coasts and cities, **The Odyssey** would lose much of its power even for twentieth century readers. And the same is true for **The Canterbury Tales** — stories of real people undergoing a real as well as a symbolic journey. There is power in any place on earth, but it takes someone conscious to see it, and his skill as an artist to transcribe it for others' eyes. As Frank Waters puts it:

> . . . The rootless artist has no place to stand. He has never found his own center. So his work is diffusive, constantly changing points of view, often pandering to the popular taste of the moment. The rooted artist, on the contrary, has found his own center: his geographic homeland, his race, his time. From this vantage point, which is primarily psychical or psychological, he interprets the world outside. And here happens the miracle of art. For just as his work faithfully reflects his own microcosmic background, so does it reflect the macrocosmic; the human, emotional, psychic background of all humanity. It portrays the inner **essence** of life, rather than its outer **envelope**.

"Place" writing — is rooted art, an outward looking **from** the artist's personality and psyche **into** the place, and into the behavior and speech and history of other people besides himself or herself.

The American writer is still discovering where he is. "Rootlessness" — for most of us — is a fact of contemporary life. Both the business and the entertainment "worlds" exacerbate this condition — which, perhaps, is not so much "American" as it is "modern." Hence, the identification (inevitably) of "regionalism" with "the good old days down on the farm" or with rural areas only. Large corporations insist that their employees shift locale every so often. So does the military. And I think of how most universities refuse to hire their own graduates, but pea-shoot them all over the country. Our economic system is consciously geared to rootlessness and fluctuation. Like the stock market. But this need not be a condition or our Art. Whitman gave us the vast American panorama, challenging others, "poets to come," to see it more closely and to "tally" it. Williams, in recent years, has come closest to meeting this challenge, presenting his Paterson, New Jersey, the first industrial city on the continent (and hence historically and symbolically important) as a micrososm of the United States. **Paterson** is a "place poem" par excellence, all the more awesome for taking an industrial wasteland as its subject. And it is a symbolic poem that captures "the inner essence of life."

The original inhabitants of the Southwest, the Anasazi, and their descendants, plus other native peoples who journeyed to the New World long before Cortez or Columbus, have shaped a rich tradition of close involvement with "place." Frank Waters proposes, in **Book of the Hopi**, that the original peoples covered the entire continents of North and South America and left signs of their travels — in mounds, abandoned cities, and inscriptions — from California to New England, and from the Arctic Circle to Patagonia, before their remnant settled in the spiritual center of the two land masses, in north-central Arizona. Gary Snyder calls the whole place "Turtle Island," refusing names imposed by European colonists and governments. "Place," he writes, "means in the largest sense that area I have traveled and lived in enough to know its plants, birds, and yearly weather." His place "is thus the area from the crest of the Cascades in the Sierra Nevada from British Columbia to Baja California westward across the North Pacific and including the islands of Japan . . ."

To embody a pre-European, or even a mythological "sense of place" is in fact one aim of the new writing. The attempt by many writers to absorb a vision of "place" commonly associated with that of the American Indian is an obvious feature of this aim. "I went to the Indian legends as a way to be led back," writes the poet Doug Flaherty, ". . . to a reaffirmation of life — simple, mythic, spiritual, and physical." And a strong sense of urgency marks his attempt:

> . . . Until we are able to identify with the created objects, animals, plants of our own environment, we will not be free to even see ourselves as part of the natural order. Until we recapture language for ourselves or refashion language from the past, we will remain as we are now — caught in the midst of war, pollution, racism and alienation.

Another "place poet," Leonard Bird, has written of the need to find a "mythopoeic tradition" native to this soil, and not one imported from Europe.

> Although the music of contemporary western/southwestern poetry reflects a wide variety of themes, schools and forms, one single theme throbs more steadily than the rest: the beautiful, fragile and necessary relationship between man and place, man rooted in place. Because the Indians of the Southwest have traditionally valued this relationship, increasing numbers of poets, both Indian and Anglo, are turning to indigenous myth for

metaphorical direction. Hence the double-edged relationship between myth and western poetry. Double-edged because the mythic element looks both forward and backward: in order to create and communicate a vision where we **could be** as responsible citizens of Turtle Island, western poetry, particularly southwestern poetry, tends to borrow heavily from southwest Indian religion and lore.

So you will find in these pages not only works by native American writers with their own deep-rooted feelings for the land (Simon J. Ortiz, Leslie Silko, Jim Barnes, Paula Allen, Harold Littlebird, Gearld Hobson, Joy Harjo, Norman Russell) but also work from non-Indian writers who share a similar consciousness (Will Inman, Doug Flaherty, John Brandi, Jim White.)

The best of the new "place" writing exists west of the Mississippi — particularly, we believe, in the Southwest. To give a good example of this writing, we have defined "Southwest" to include western Arkansas and Los Angeles as its eastern and western boundaries.

That western Arkansas is a part of the Southwest is to me clear. My neighbors in the Ozarks look west — to Oklahoma, New Mexico, and to southern California for any kind of cultural interest or economic change — and not to Little Rock. Their speech is western — laconic, dry, colorful, twangy — not southern. Most of them, in Johnson and Franklin Counties in Arkansas, have traveled — as migrant workers or servicemen or just to visit kinfolk — only west, to Tulsa, Dallas, Albuquerque, Los Angeles, and to the oil-fields, coal-mines, orchards, and forests of Oklahoma, the Texas panhandle, Utah, California, and Oregon. And all share a dependence on rain — the single biggest fact of rural southwestern life — as essential to poverty or plenty in the Ozarks as it is in central New Mexico, and often just as scarce. The Southwest begins in the hardwood forests and red sandstone earth of western Arkansas (the easternmost limit, incidentally, of the roadrunner and armadillo.)

The center of the Southwest (or "epicenter," as David Remley calls it in his introduction to southern Colorado and New Mexico writing) is located in an area of Arizona and New Mexico that transcends the state boundaries, coincidental with an ancient kingdom or nation of the Anasazi. The spectacular beauty and power of this part of the Southwest have challenged human response for centuries. It's where the fabulous Seven Cities of Cibola were located, and Great Quivira, and El Dorado. It's where one finds the **Grand** Canyon, the Rio **Grande**, and the continent's largest meteor crater. And it's the only area in the United States where rich and extensive ruins of earlier city-civilizations are visible, and where exist the oldest continuously inhabited villages — Acoma, 50 miles west of Albuquerque, and old Oraibi, center of the Hopi nation, in Arizona.

Los Angeles, on the other hand, is where the Southwest ends and funnels back on itself. Route 66. Interstate 40. Fort Smith. Oklahoma City. Amarillo. Albuquerque. Gallup. Flagstaff. Kingman. Needles. Barstow. San Berdoo — to the end of the line. Most of us have traveled that road often, driving or hitching. And we've been hopeful of what we'd find at the end — discovered, befriended, loved, our fortunes made. And we come back, only to return over the same road. The direction is west, and that's where the writing goes.

And west is also where the new and most vital publishing is being done. More western writers are discovering today that their audiences (as well as their subject matter) are here — in the region — and can best be reached through regional presses. The newly established Texas Center for Writers Press is one example of this movement away from the traditional publishing centers of New York and Boston. They believe that the "twelve million people of Texas are certainly enough to support a quality press dedicated to publishing outstanding fiction and poetry." A press to serve the audience and writers of New Mexico has been established by the Rio Grande Writers Association.

No large eastern press (we wrote to all of the major New York and Boston establishments) was interested in even seeing the manuscript of this book. Anticipating this response, we also wrote to the few southwestern academic presses. But the policy of the University of New Mexico Press, as stated to us in a letter from Carl J. Mora, their director, we found to be typical:

> Without expressing any doubts as to the quality of the contributions by individual writers, this book remains an anthology of previously unpublished original fiction and poetry. For the past decade, it has been the policy of the UNM Press to publish no original fiction and poetry, and to publish reprints in these fields only when they have received academic approval as approaching the status of regional classics already in classroom use.

So we did it ourselves, with no financial help, no government or state grants, no "angels" — although we have profited greatly from the advice, encouragement, and help of indigent poets, writers, and friends.

CONTENTS

Northwestern Arkansas and the Ozark mountain country of eastern Oklahoma near Tulsa and Tahlequah form one natural boundary of the Southwest region. The Arkansas River cuts sharply down from the north through Tulsa and Fort Smith and then swings south and east in a tornado track between steep bluffs to Little Rock. Its tributaries (or "bayous" as they're sometimes called in Arkansas) include the Illinois and the Poteau, both in Oklahoma, and the White River, which winds across the mountainous northern half of Arkansas. Unlike the rest of the Southwest, the land here is lucky in water. There is adequate yearly rainfall (in spite of occasional summer-long droughts) and abundant sub-surface water trapped in limestone and shale. Extensive flood-control measures, taken since the 1930's, provide a number of dams and artificial lakes. The land is rugged, heavily timbered, and green. Warm moist air from the Gulf makes for high humidity in summer (whether it rains or not) and keeps the winters mild.

The soil is ancient. Once submerged beneath a prehistoric ocean, then uplifted volcanically, the Ozarks were once as high as or higher than the present Himalayas. Their relatively low altitude now (1500-3000 feet) has been caused by centuries of erosion and weathering. Their soft sandstone and limestone formations are cut by numerous rivers and streams. The region abounds in caves, caverns, springs, reservoirs of natural gas and oil, and water.

Western Arkansas is still primarily rural and agricultural. Small farms and sawmills are to be found on practically each mountain — which are more or less flat on top, having been eroded down to their broad but steep bases. The same families (predominantly of English, Scottish, and Irish stock) have lived here for several generations — since the turn of the century, at least, when the Ozarks began to be more widely settled. Farming is hard in the shallow sandy soil. The raising of livestock for profit — beef cattle, chickens, turkeys, pigs — is a common source of income. Most Ozark farmers look west or southwest for their markets — and away from Little Rock and central Arkansas —

to Tulsa, Muskogee, and Fort Smith. Most are fundamentalist in religion — Assembly of God, Church of Christ, Southern Baptist — and attend services and revivals within miles of their farms without having to descend from their mountains. They are clannish, inclined to be mistrustful of strangers and people who live in "the valley." They think of themselves as "mountain folk" — never as "hillbillies."

But the old ways in the Ozarks are changing: foodstamps, more and more roads, the land purchased by absentee owners for investment and speculation, the sons and daughters leaving the farms, mechanization with its inevitable piles of cast-off rusted junk, the higher and higher costs of feed, of fertilizer, of gasoline, of sugar, of flour . . . but, paradoxically, with the highest population growth rate in the state. The "energy crisis" has caused a resurgence in drilling for gas and oil. The water resources have attracted industry — even though these resources are limited, and storage is difficult in the fragile limestone easily cracked and broken by drilling explorations.

Wood remains the most practical product (and source for employment) in the Ozarks. Hard wood — hickory, walnut, several varieties of oak — and many different kinds of pine and cedar are still, miraculously, plentiful. Wildlife, once much more varied, is still visible. Hunting is a way of life (not just a pastime) in the mountains. Deer, raccoon, possum, squirrels, rabbits. The humidity and the thick vegetation also mean snakes — copperheads, timber-rattlers, king snakes, cottonmouths, spreading adders — and insects. Bird life is richly varied and colorful. Bluebirds, mocking birds, cardinals, jays, wood-peckers, road-runners (imported to combat the rattlers), robins, purple martins, swallows, sparrows, whip-poor-wills, bob-white quail, hawks, buzzards, crows — on and on, many of them all year round.

This lovely land has been a violent one. Bands of guerrillas roamed the Ozarks throughout the U.S. Civil War — looting, murdering, burning. After the war "soldiers" from these free-lance armies — particularly from the infamous "Quantrill's Raiders" — turned bona-fide outlaws. The mountains gave hideouts to Frank and Jesse James, the Dalton Boys, and the Youngers. In more recent years eastern Oklahoma and western Arkansas have been the stamping grounds of Pretty Boy Floyd, Clyde Barrow and Bonnie Parker. In the glove compartment of many a mountain pickup rides a pistol — and rifles are as common here as umbrellas are in London. No road sign, no political nor religious poster (nailed to tree or telephone pole), lacks at least a dozen bullet holes surely placed.

In Oklahoma, although the landscape and soil share the same features and history as those in western Arkansas, the human history and the economy are much different. Two words — Indians and Oil — account for the differences. Long known as "Indian Territory,"

2

Oklahoma was not admitted as a state until 1907 — almost 75 years after the entry of Arkansas. The name derives from a Choctaw word, meaning "red people." Eastern Oklahoma — with good soil (black limestone) for agriculture, with ample water and drainage, and with a fortunate supply of timber and game — has been for over a century the home of the so-called "Five Civilized Tribes": Choctaw, Cherokee, Creek (or Muskogean), Seminole, and Chickasaw, who were forcibly moved to the region through Arkansas (up the Arkansas River on boats, many of them) from their original homes in the Southeast. Descendants of those who survived "the trail of tears" are now mostly of mixed "white" and Indian ancestry, and form the majority of the population — a very different one from the homogeneous Anglo families whose ancestors fled, in Daniel Boone fashion, to Arkansas voluntarily from the more mountainous southern and coastal states.

Oil was discovered in 1905 (shortly before Oklahoma was admitted as one of the United States, coincidentally) ten miles south of Tulsa. Consequently, perhaps, there are more large cities and towns today in northeastern Oklahoma than in the entire western half of Arkansas. Tulsa is a new city — very different from Little Rock, which still maintains its ante-bellum relics and sense of the past. Tulsa is a southwestern city, young, daily growing, and means Oil.

The area has produced and inspired many poets, writers, and artists. One thinks of Woody Guthrie, from Okemah; Will Rogers, from Oologah (both in northeastern Oklahoma); the great chief Sequoyah, who invented "the Indian alphabet"; John Gould Fletcher, in Arkansas; and the "regionalist" painter Thomas Hart Benton, from Neosho, Missouri, slightly north of Fayetteville.

— Karl Kopp

Mad Dog

A powerful dog, something of a mixture between a redbone hound and a bloodhound, lay under his master's porch. From time to time a shiver would run the length of his body, seeming to start somewhere in his brain and ending with a twitching of the tail. Occasionally the dog would whine low and try to get up, bumping his head against the porch.

"You seed Old Red today?" Cora Blalock asked her husband as she swatted another fly.

"Naw, but I hear him down under the porch fussing at the flies. I guess he's ashamed of that smell of skunk on him. He ain't much for coming around during hot spells," Lester Blalock answered as he looked wistfully out toward the barn. A mournful bellowing came from the barnlot where dust could be seen rising from the sick cow chained to the big oak.

"That cow is mad, I tell you Lester, and you'd best shoot her and get it over with," Cora asserted.

"They's likely lots of things that would make a cow act like that. I'm a-gonna wait a little longer and see if she don't get better," Lester countered.

"There ain't nothing that makes a cow act like that that she gets well from. Nothing! You're just too soft-hearted to kill anything 'cepting squirrel and rabbits. You was the same way when that old white horse broke his leg. You let him lay around and suffer for days before you finally shot him," Cora accused.

There was a series of thumpings under the house as Old Red, bumping each floor joist, crawled out from under it. The dog stood in the yard and faced up toward his master on the porch. His eyes seemed to be glazed over. He stood uncertainly on his legs, his tail drooping, a greenish froth dripping from his mouth.

"What's the matter, Red? Get a little hot for you under there?" Lester asked. "Think by now he'd learned to duck his head when he comes out from under there."

"As a general rule he don't bump his head," Cora said. "They's something wrong with that dog too. Just you wait and see. If you was a-doing what you ought, you'd shoot that dog right now."

"You always been against my hunting so you ain't never liked my dogs," Lester said as he got up to go down and take a closer look at Old Red.

Red faced his master unsteadily and, for the briefest moment, seemed almost to recognize him. But as Lester approached, the dog turned aside and trotted slowly toward the front gate.

"Here, Red!" Lester called.

The dog did not stop, but bumped into one of the gate posts, backed up, and then ran into the other post before making its way through the gate towards the wood lot.

As a crow flies, it is ten miles from Lester Blalock's to the Pine Grove community. The hound was traveling in a straight line when Winerfred Gray first saw it. It seemed reluctant to go around anything and bumped into several things that were in its way. Each time it bumped into something it would snap out with its teeth, slobbering all the time.

"I guess I could of shot it easy as not," Winerfred said later, "but you don't just go around shooting a fine-looking hound like that, 'specially when it's got on a collar and all."

As the hound passed by Winerfred's place, his three dogs came out and gave chase, all jumping on the hapless creature before they could stop themselves. The strange dog didn't really fight off his dogs, Winerfred later recalled, but simply nipped at them from side to side as he went on his way, pulling the other dogs along. After only a brief contact, Winerfred's dogs, seeming to sense something wrong, gave up the struggle and returned to their front porch, whining, their tails between their legs.

"They looked and acted like they had been caught sucking eggs," Winerfred said. "I guess the word mad dog came to me but I didn't ever quite say it."

The second person to see the dog was Mr. Fredman, the mailman. "He was standing right on top of the bank as I came across that low-water bridge down there on Honey Creek. I guess he was standing there on account of the water in the creek 'cause I've heard tell that mad dogs don't like water. 'Course I didn't have no way of knowing that he was mad at the time. If I'd knowed it I would of just run over him. Could of done it easy. Instead, I got out and went over and took a hold of his collar to see if there was some kind of tag on it. Just had a tag that said, 'Carroll County Coon Hunting Association, Box 48, Berryville, Arkansas.' When I turned him loose he just sorta snapped at me as if he was snapping at a fly. Didn't touch me or nothing. Just went on down the road ditch bumping into things and snapping at them. I kind of wondered if he might be mad but I don't guess I'd of thought any more about it 'cepting when I got around to Winerfred Gray's place he was waiting for me and he got to telling me about a dog that had come through his place earlier and it sounded like that same dog so we got to wondering out loud if it wasn't maybe mad. So I started telling people along the route to watch out for a dog that was acting kind of strange

5

but I didn't tell nobody it was mad, 'cause I didn't know for a fact if it was mad. They'd just have to come to their own way of thinking about that when they seed it."

Mr. Fredman had already passed the schoolhouse before he saw the dog, so no one had told the school about the strange dog.

The teacher, Mr. Bates, didn't think much about it when he first looked out during the noon hour and saw a dog standing in the school yard. He remembered he did think the dog looked like it had been running hard and was tired and had maybe got lost on some all-night fox hunt. The children weren't paying any attention to it and it didn't seem to be bothering anybody so Mr. Bates just left it alone at first. A little while later, he looked out and saw some of the smaller children trying to feed the dog some leftover lunch. He thought it was strange the dog was not eating the food. Then a strange sensation went through him and the words "mad dog" began to form on his lips.

"My first instinct," Mr. Bates testified later at a Board of Directors' meeting, "was to cry out a warning, **mad dog!** But I figured it would frighten the children causing them to panic in all directions. So I decided to go to the hallway and ring the bell. It wasn't quite time for the bell but maybe none of the children would suspect anything. So I began ringing the bell. Luckily the children all began moving toward the schoolhouse like usual. But so did the dog. I remembered then that I had heard somewhere that mad dogs were attracted to sound. I became terrified. It was like a nightmare. They all seemed to be moving toward me together — the dog and the children. I didn't know what to do so I stopped ringing the bell. I usually keep ringing until they are all in the schoolhouse. Since there were children behind the dog and there were children in front of the dog, I did the first thing that came to my mind. I closed the door on the girls' side and stood in the boys' side and called out as loud as I could, 'the last one in eats dirt!' I shouted it over again and again as I motioned the children in the one door. The dog was coming also, but not so fast as the children now. Everyone except Teddy Collins made it to the door before the dog. The dog was just ahead of Teddy so I had to slam the door on both of them. The dog bumped into the closed door and then swerved and started back down the steps. But just as it did that it brushed against Teddy, coming up, and reached out and nipped him on the ear. Then I let Teddy in and started ringing the bell again so everyone would know that there was something wrong at the school. Of course, you know the rest of what happened."

The ringing of the school bell alerted the Pine Grove community that something was amiss up at the grammar school. Since many people had already heard of the possibility that there might be a mad dog on the loose they were fearful that the dog had gone to the school. Their worst fears were proven true when they all gathered in the school yard and word passed from person to person, "There's a mad dog loose and it's

6

done been here and bit the little Collins boy."

Sam Blevins, who was the chairman of the Board of Directors of the school, and thus the highest-ranking elected official in the community, took over the meeting at the school house.

"The first thing we got to do is to get a mad stone for Teddy," Mr. Blevins announced.

"That's not going to do any good —" said the teacher, "what that boy needs is a doctor."

"I ain't against doctors when they is needed," said Mr. Blevins, "but what we need now is a mad stone. Does anybody know where there's a mad stone ?'

Several people had heard of a mad stone over in Eureka Springs that had worked on other people. Mr. Fredman said that since he had the only car in the community he would be glad to take young Collins to Eureka Springs to the mad stone. He was quite sure he could be back by nightfall.

"That'll be soon enough," Mr. Blevins assured everybody. "If we get that boy to that mad stone and it sticks to the boy's ear we'll know it took and that boy'll be out of the woods. What we need to do now is to get these children all home without anybody else getting bit and put up our livestock and then hunt down this mad dog and kill it."

The people all agreed that the best way to get the children home was to find enough wagons to haul them and to have an armed man accompanying each wagon.

While they were still discussing how they might best hunt down the mad dog, Lawrence Lane rode up on a horse and announced that he had already killed the dog over near the store. It had been coming at him right down the middle of the road when he shot it. Winerfred Gray asked Lawrence to describe the dog.

"It was a big shepherd dog," Lawrence explained.

"That's not the mad dog —" Winerfred said, "fact is, it sounds like **my** dog."

"Don't matter none whether it is or it ain't," Sam Blevins said. "We're going to have to kill all our dogs that ain't been put up long as this is going on."

"Don't make no sense going around a-killing dogs that ain't mad," Winerfred retorted, getting quite riled up.

"Don't matter none. You'd have to kill him anyway if he's been loose," Sam repeated and most everyone agreed. Winerfred cast his troubled eyes toward town.

By the time the children were all gotten home and the livestock secured, darkness had settled over the community. Some of the menfolk had gathered up at the Collins' place to wait for Mr. Fredman to return with the boy. They could hear the Ford coming up the hollow for a couple of miles before they could see its lights.

"It worked," Mr. Fredman announced as he climbed out of his machine and brought the boy up onto the porch and into the glow of a kerosene lamp. "The mad stone belonged to that old Indian, Mr. Gott, over in Eureka. He says he got it out of a stomach of a all-white deer. They say it's a ball of hair that has done turned to stone.

"Well, anyhow, I took the boy to that old Indian and we laid him out there on the ground and Mr. Gott he went to soaking that mad stone in some fresh warm milk from a fresh cow. Then he lays that stone on that cut on Teddy's ear. Well it lays there a spell and then the old Indian tries to pull it off and they is stuck together tight as you please. So he leaves it on a spell longer so as to draw out all that poison."

Most people felt better about the boy, but the teacher told them that he had read about a scientist who had found a cure for rabies and that a good doctor would know about such things. But the Collinses and most of the others were pleased with the treatment and spoke of similar cases where the mad stone had worked.

Night settled over Pine Grove. Here and there dogs would set to barking and a frightened farmer would go to his cabin door and look out into the night. There seemed to be more barking of dogs than usual. The barking seemed to travel around the country from farm to farm. First one bunch of dogs and then another would set up a mournful howling as if they sensed the calamity that had come upon them. Occasionally, a shot or two would ring out as one farmer or another fired at something moving in the bushes.

When morning came, it was a day like any other hot summer morning, except that the people all ventured from their homes carrying either a gun or a club or a pitchfork — something to fight off the mad dog should they come upon him suddenly. Men gathered early at the school to plan the day's hunt and compare stories on what had happened during the night. If the dog had been in a small fraction of the places people were sure he had been, he was one busy dog. If the dog had escaped harm from the great volleys of shots aimed at him by men who could shoot the eye out of a squirrel at a hundred yards, he was one lucky dog.

The dog could be any place. He could be in the next clump of bushes. He could be under the porch, the house, in the haybarn, the road ditch, or under the next culvert. Or he could be gone altogether or maybe dead. Another problem was that there were some dogs in the community which looked something like Old Red and most dogs were beginning to act strange, what with people running all over the countryside with guns and clubs.

By mid-morning there had been two authentic reports of the dog. As if to add insult to injury, the dog showed up at the Collins place. Mrs. Collins heard a commotion down near the chicken house. She grabbed up a soap paddle from the black kettle in the backyard and went down

8

to see what was bothering the chickens. When she saw the dog it was already between her and the house. The menfolk were all gone looking for the dog but the children were watching from the porch. They began to scream at their mother when they saw her going toward the chicken house door. The children remembered something that she in her fear of the moment had forgotten. Lately, someone had been stealing the Collins's chickens and so Mr. Collins had rigged up a shotgun which he had loaded and cocked and mounted back in the hen house pointed right at that door. There was a cord tied to the door and strung up over a joist and back to the trigger of the gun.

The blast cut Mrs. Collins almost in two, killing her instantly.

"I should of knowed it," Mr. Collins said when he got there. "Trouble always comes in threes. I wonder what will be next?"

"One possible trouble could be avoided maybe if you would get a doctor for that boy," the teacher said.

"What's gonna be's gonna be," the old man reflected.

Some of the women of the community came in to lay out Mrs. Collins. They patched her up as best they could, washed her, closed up the wounds and body openings with cloth, draped her Sunday clothes over her as best possible, combed her hair and balled it back, tied a dish rag around her head and under her chin, put a copper penny on each eye, stretched her out on a buntling board awaiting the coffin.

The men divided themselves into three groups. A small group went down to the blacksmith shop to make a cedar box for the burying. Another group went up to the graveyard and began digging the grave. The remaining men continued to hunt for the dog.

Brother Ashby went down in the Collins pasture, down on the pond bank to pray. "God in Heaven, these is dog days," he reminded the Lord. ". . . days when even snakes is blind as they sheds they skins, days when waters are troubled and muddied as they turns over, days when big fish lay back in they holes and are afraid of neither man nor beast, days when wounds won't hardly heal, days when dogs goes mad . . ."

It was then that Brother Ashby heard the peculiar noise in the heavens. It was a sound which he had heard before. Come to think of it, it was that very sound which had changed his life, causing him to become a preacher. The first time he had heard that sound was when he was a mere lad. He had been a barefoot bashful boy on his way to observe a brush arbor revival where on previous nights he had hid among the trees and watched the foot-washings, the shouting, the praying, singing and preaching. But as he made his way across the countryside on that night years ago he had heard a bell in the heavens, just like the one he now heard. On that occasion, so many years ago now, he had taken the sounding of the bell as a sign from God — a call to preach! Rushing in to the meeting, he had fallen there before his God and given his life to Christ. He had gotten up from that tear-stained altar a new man and had gone back to his old mother's cabin down on India Creek and announced, "Don't get scared Ma, I'm gonna pray!" And from that day to this he had not only prayed, but he had stirred and moved hundreds to Christ with his preaching, telling always of the bell he had heard in the heavens and calling out to people all over the Ozarks and elsewhere, "Don't get scared Ma, I'm gonna pray!" But that was all in the distant past and it was the present which Brother Ashby now had to face . . . .

So he opened his eyes, looking expectantly toward heaven for the sign he needed on this troubled day. There was something hovering over him, not more than fifty feet away. "It is like one of them winged creatures out of the Bible," the preacher cried, trying desperately to maintain his faith. Doubt flooded his very soul, as he continued to focus his eyes on the creature. His very call to preach the gospel was being brought into question by what he saw. It was a trick of the devil. It **was** the devil! He would cast it out, exorcise it. The preacher scrinched his eyes closed and rebuked the repulsive creature: "In the name of the Father, the Son, and the Holy Ghost I cast thee from me," he commanded. "Thou foul demon on wings of an earthly buzzard, be gone. Be removed from me as far as the East is from the West!"

Mustering all his faith, believing with all his heart, certain that the awful creature would be lying dead at his feet, the preacher opened his eyes and looked about. The creature had changed its form. It no longer had the wings of a buzzard and was no longer airborne. A four-footed red demon took shape before his very eyes, chasing its tail, circle upon circle, faster and faster, a green froth dripping from an extended bloody tongue.

The preacher stood up, transfixed, as these images changed before his very eyes. Demons seemed to hover all about, amidst a beating of wings and ringing of bells. The preacher knew enough about demon possession to realize that he must keep his mind on the Lord or there was a good chance that he would become possessed himself.

The big red four-footed demon now lay at his feet, twitching and jerking, while the winged demons hovered about. Some alighted nearby. Gradually the red demon became a dog, a big red hound — the **mad dog!** The preacher's faith faltered and he fell backwards into the pond.

At just about that moment, Old Red recovered his balance and staggered off across the field and the buzzards again ascended into the heavens to hover over the dying dog. The wet and troubled preacher struggled out of the pond and walked up to the graveyard to tell the men what had happened. The men in the grave stopped their digging and leaned on shovels and picks. The men up top rested on the relatively cool mound of fresh dirt as they heard Brother Ashby's troubled tale.

Suddenly, as if in confirmation of Brother Ashby's story, they all became aware of a bell ringing. Looking up, they saw the buzzard. Just as suddenly, seeming to know what to expect next, they saw the dog. He had stumbled to the edge of the grave, swaying back and forth, clumsily deciding whether to try crossing over it or go around. Two men were down in the grave and the other three men, including the preacher, were across the grave from the dog. The guns were all leaning against a tree near the dog, out of reach.

The preacher fell down straightway before his God and begged for deliverance from this evil thing. The only answer he got was a gun sounding somewhere in the distance and another dog yelping in death.

One of the gravediggers took up a shovel and was slipping around the end of the grave toward the mad dog. The only sound that could be heard now was the heavy breathing of Old Red. A buzzard was again overhead. The gravedigger came down hard on the back of Old Red's head. The dog fell down like he had been dropped with a bullet. Then he began to quiver and kick around in a circle on his side, finally falling over the bank into the nearly-finished grave with the two men inside.

Old Red was still burning on a brush pile down the hill a piece as people began gathering at the schoolhouse for the Collins funeral. The buzzards continued to circle over the area as the congregation sang,

"Oh they tell me of a home
Far beyond the skies
Oh they tell me of a home
Far away . . .

Oh they tell me of a home
Where no storm clouds rise
Oh they tell me
Of an unclouded day . . ."

A subdued Brother Ashby spoke of a God who sometimes spoke to people through dumb animals in mysterious ways, warning them of the wrath to come. Then the preacher talked for a short while about a New Heaven and a New Earth and a bright day coming, just like the song says. The people marched by and showed their respect and whispered about how natural and at peace Sister Collins looked. "Just like she was asleep." Then the people followed the body to the graveside where Brother Ashby sprinkled dust on the casket and said, "Dust thou art and to dust thou shalt return." And then the people all went home to look for madness in **their** dogs and wait and worry.

The Collins children now had two games to play. The empty corncrib lent itself very well to both games. Playing church had long been a favorite pastime. They would get inside the corncrib and pretend they were grownups — singing, shouting, washing feet, testifying, preaching and praying. Recently they had been playing a new game called "Mad Dog." They would all get in the corncrib and one of them would go mad and act like a dog slashing out at everyone. Then the others would try to rush out the door and fasten the door on the one inside who was acting mad.

Exactly two weeks after Teddy Collins had been bitten by the mad dog the Collins children were all down in the corncrib playing church. Teddy was playing Brother Ashby and had already told about hearing the bell and had just said, "Don't get scared Ma, I'm gonna pray," when suddenly he stopped, grabbed his head and throat and fell down on the floor and began to thrash about. After a while he got up on his hands and knees and began looking about queerly, eyes glazed. He began to chew his tongue. Blood and saliva dripped from his chin.

The other children immediately changed games, from "church" to "mad dog," and quickly scrambled out of the building, locking the door behind them. But this was not the way the game was supposed to be played. They had never gone directly from one game to another before. Furthermore, no one had ever chewed his tongue until it bled before. So the other children watched Teddy through the cracks in the corncrib to see what he was going to do next. Teddy continued chewing his tongue there on all fours. The children tried pushing sticks through the cracks of the crib, teasing him as they had before to get him to bite at them, but they got no response, just glazed, vacant stares. Finally, they left Teddy in the crib and went down in the field to tell their dad.

"Teddy's been playing mad dog, and he won't stop so we left him locked up in the corncrib!" they told their father.

"I thought I told you children to stop playing that mad dog game," the tired and worried man said as he looked toward the corncrib.

As they went on to the end of the field where Mr. Collins could tie up his mules they noticed that the teacher, Mr. Bates, had gotten off his horse in front of the house. Mr. Bates had called on the Collins most every day lately.

"Where is Teddy?" Mr. Bates asked as they approached him.

"We was playing church and then Teddy started to playing mad dog and then he wouldn't quit so we left him locked up in the crib and went to get dad," Thersia explained.

The men looked at each other, neither saying a word as they approached the crib. They could see Teddy through the cracks. He was on his feet now, walking about in a circle amongst the corn shucks.

"Teddy, what are you doing in there?" the father asked as he started to unlatch the door.

"Don't unlock that door!" the teacher shouted from where he was standing.

"Why not?" the father asked.

"Come here and look!" the teacher answered.

They were all peeking at Teddy through the cracks. Except for the fact that he was now standing, he was just as he had been when the children had left to get their father. He stood there, totally oblivious to their presence, eyes dilated and glazed, blood and saliva oozing from his mouth.

"The boy is mad," the teacher said.

The father started to unbar the door. The teacher stood in his way and said, "No! He must stay locked in there. We will fix it as comfortable for him as we can."

Teddy Collins lived in hell for the next nine days. He did not eat or drink or sleep. People gathered as word spread of his madness and there were always some folks at the corncrib until it was over, watching, waiting.

"It is hard to get a mad stone to stick good to something like your ear," they said.

Karl Kopp

Buster Berryhill

He doesn't show his age yet
still bad-assing in his chevvy pick-up
.22 in the gun-rack
cooler full of Old Milwaukee in back
with his horseshoes and bar-bells
Billy Don beside him on the long front seat

His wife's got a new hairdo
comes to the party with a gal-friend
kicks off her high heel shoes
sinks to a lawn-chair with a bottle of wine
and a cigarette   Billy Don (on his knees)
strokes her belly

Buster does push-ups
his blue eyes clear as a child's
"Shoot, they's cousins ain't they?"
his bare arms thick as a grown man's thighs

The Judge

Let me tell you about your land:
four junk cars on it   blackberries
instead of motors   but parts a-plenty
for my lawnmower   and a rear-view mirror
for my truck   the best persimmons
grow here   and three big pear trees
that blossom white and fragrant
near an old shack I've stripped for boards
(I left one wall intact for the fieldmouse
and her babies)   best blackberry thicket
in these parts   sweet hay where J.D. Yarbrough
used to graze his cattle   a stream

Your land in November looks like
a Chinese print   all those stark trees
in the mist   blackjack oak and hickory
south of the stream   a pine grove
where I'd plan my mornings
I've seen deer   squirrels   quail
the remains of campfires   a small
junk heap of cans stoves refrigerators
that gave me a bookcase and shelves
for my potatoes   an old cart-road
where I ran my truck for the pleasure
of my son

and the place where Charlie Short grew marijuana
until the sheriff caught him   (you got him off
for the price of his land   a few weeks
before his suicide)   Clarence tells me
you came up here once in March   but thought
not to go with him to see your boundaries
huckleberries galore across the county road
where the mountain falls to the Mulberry
full of bream and cottonmouths   a spring
that even in August doesn't quit running
may-apples   walnuts   gin-seng   big trees
you sold for cabinets and tables

It's damned good land   Judge   you
got a bargain

Deer

How they fade   dissolve
into deeper woods than these I own
and clatter in

        (not quite true
for I go slowly slowly   a stick for snakes
through the leaf-mold   down the old logging-road
to the spring)

        Ah but they   how they move
into mystery

        My neighbors always share
their venison   cooked in rooms thick
with unwashed men   tobacco-spit
and soft Southern boasting

        Like jonquils set by some
woman's hands   deep in my woods
among old fallen stones by the spring
unmentioned in the title-deed

they return   with a flirt of their tails
they are gone

Chris Ellery

Mountain Lights

The tall lean pines on Whippoorwill Hill
across the road from Joe's place
The ever-present melody of water
from the beavers' dam on Mountain Fork   fish jumping
river falling   creek entering   below it
The wide green channel where perch and bass bite best
good goggle-eye fishing later this summer
when melon seeds lie for chicken scratch
    Chester Joe and me
on the big front porch   Hank and Babe
two orphan redbones
found the day Henry Aaron clubbed history
over the outfield wall   tussling
in the rain-rutted yard among wild iris leaves
bedded with Hazel's bottles   painted rocks   she loves
and honeysuckle vines that bring the deer this way

Peggy inside with Hazel   Mat Murphy
the baby   not five weeks old   nursing
at her breast

Chester looks up   a broad ridge of clouds
spilled down from Rich Mountain   rimming the sky
like a bowl   edged with the falling sun
stars quiet   invisible   beyond it

I believe it's gonna rain   he says
before a sudden gust
brings the smell of it
                    then I can't resist   say
Joe   that's a pretty baby you got
and he: Should be   Look what he come out of

Peggy inside   tucking Matt away
Peggy leaning forward above him   above the kiss of night
Hazel   an old shaking shadow
in the kitchen doorway   through the window
putting coffee on to perk
and joining us for dominoes

16

night in full darkness   across the old log bridge
where the woods are thick
and armadillos run

look what he come out of Joe said
with Chester rocking
stroking softly the wild calico

above us beneath us suns are blazing
stars dot this mountain sky   points of light
uncountable

The Hunt

The Hatfield City Council meeting
and most of them gathered early
in hunting coats and caps
to talk about last Sunday's bagging
way over on Rattlesnake Mountain
(I was there myself once,
pools so pure that the hand-sized fish
five feet down are clearly seen.
I tossed bread to the fish, then
dove with them in the cold,
rose to find a doe
lapping at my waves . . .)

The stony one with the beard
said he'd got the biggest buck
he'd ever seen (twelve points
and a nice head for that stained wood wall
above the fire) as it stood
watching near the woods —
dropped the canteen he was filling,
raised and fired his .20 gauge;
the empty shells leaped into the pool,
caught the fresh sunlight
all the way down

Home Repair

Pickled onions on the counter —
vinegar milk-white
from the root
               and sundry spices
Cucumbers, too,
waiting to be pickled
Fried apples on the stove
and biscuits in a pan

     Hazel, then,
opening the oven door (the broiler)
to see if it will work
                (Joe
was supposed to fix it yesterday)
and contemplating cobbler

Turns it on and stoops
but can't see in
Backs away and stoops
Backs some more, her old bones
crackling
as she does,
and keeps backing
till eight feet from the oven
she can SEE

Then it lights
in a blast
throwing fire (orange and blue)
nine feet
          and around her legs
and she jumps
screaming (half between her joy and fear)

"HE MUST UV FIXED IT
HE MUST UV FIXED IT"

Her ankles singed,
her old black shoes
buffed
        by the sparks

Resistance

You try to forget but you remember
how it happened that summer —the river low
so our canoe scraped the rocks
                                    How
we almost turned back   but passed Arrow Point
against the current (canvas shoes
cut on stones   like flesh   when we
had to walk the boat) to where mosquitoes
grew more thick and the trees more dense
against the sky like witches' hair
just east of the mounds

We back-watered   and turned the boat
into Dead Creek—we knew the Skeeter boys
swam there (dove from the tall twisted oaks
to the deep brown pools below) and carved
their stolen beef   poached doe—water slow
as a bayou and so low we had to stop and walk
from there
                        and the weeds grow
like something in a swamp   and a gator's back
and the swift white mouth
of a cotton snake

                        How we thought again
it wasn't worth it   and decided to go back
but waded one more turn
in the creek   day falling from our eyes
then saw it   what we didn't think to find—
the battered blue canoe we'd missed
and the split wood paddle   trapped in the brush
by high water
(so the sheriff said)
and above that   the brown hemp rope
weather-frayed and tied to an oak
and the bunch of bloody sticks

We've never seen the like   John   never should
look back

John Kerr

From: <u>Encounters in Arkansas</u>

I

Things is purty *modern* down here
    in Arkansas now.
All our rooms is got television sets.
    All *color!*
A motel couldn't stay in business
Without it was modern and up with the times.
Tell you the truth,
    though,
I don't much enjoy seeing some feller
    off up yonder in New York
Makin' a fool of hisself.
And in between times,
Hearin' what to do about breath that stinks
    and sweaty arms and bellyaches.
Hearin' all about women's underwear.
I'd rather set on the front porch
    and talk.
But tourists is all gone modern
    and give up talkin'.
They wanta strip off and go swimmin'
And then watch people cut up and prank
    on television.
And if they ain't nuthin' on
But what they done seen before,
They want a bucket o' ice so they can
    get drunk.
The only people that knows how to talk,
    any more,
Is these here long-haired hitchhikers —
And they ain't got no money.
I give 'em a room sometimes when I ain't full,
Just so's I'll have someone to talk to.
But a feller is got to stay in business.
So we got us a pool put in,
And we got that ice maker out yonder
    grindin' away,
And we got color television stuck in
    all the rooms.
You folks want me to bring you some ice?

from Notes to Joanne, LXIX

One damp February day
When I was too young to go to school,
I sat cross-legged on the kitchen floor
    beside the big wood cookstove.
I could hear the sounds of the hammer outside.
My daddy was out in his plaid mackinaw
    and his black felt hat,
Fixing the fences.
My mother was baking.
She moved about the kitchen with flour
    on her apron,
Singing the old hymns.
She kept a syrup bucket hanging on a nail
    on the kitchen wall
To save twine strings in,
And she let me keep my pennies hidden in the bottom.
They were safe in their secret place
    beneath the scraps of twine.
And then my daddy came in to sit by the cookstove
    and wipe the mist from his glasses.
His hair was turning grey and his face showed wrinkles.
I looked at his ruddy face and suddenly knew
    that death was somewhere waiting.
I'd buried my cats that died
And stood scrap shingles on their graves,
But I didn't know that people died.
My heart pounded with terror.
I wanted to put my daddy in the syrup bucket
    beneath the twine.
And now, sweet love,
When you lie sleeping by my side,
I clutch the covers tightly over us
And remember that syrup bucket full of twine,
    hanging on the kitchen wall.

THE SNOW-GEESE

I was five years old when I first noticed
    the snow-geese flying south.
Frost had killed the goldenrods along the fence,
And chilly winds ripped and tore the brown leaves
    from the cotton stalks,
And I played in the half-full cotton wagon —
Warm in my tight jacket and toboggan cap.
Mom and Dad dragged their picksacks along the rows
    for the last time that year,
Picking the few scattered bolls of white cotton.
The skies were dark with low clouds,
And I heard the strange cries off to the north.
I saw the distant specks coming south.
They were flying low under the clouds.
I watched them grow larger
As their cries grew louder.
And suddenly they were over the wagon,
Their wings beating the air,
Their leader dropping back,
Their red feet tucked up behind,
Their white, white, snow-white feathers
    below the dark clouds.
They swept on over the field,
And Mom and Dad stood up straight and looked.
For many nights, I snuggled deep into the feather bed,
And pulled the homemade quilts snug against my chin,
And listened to the cries of the snow-geese flying south.

It was a cold winter in Arkansas,
And the snows were deep,
And many people were poor because of the great depression.
Two days before Christmas,
Mr. Otto came walking up our lane in his ragged mackinaw
    and worn-out shoes.
He was carrying two big lard buckets.
My daddy was chopping firewood in the front yard.
He drove the axe into the chopping block and left it,
The wooden handle pointing upward in the bright sunlight.
Mr. Otto set his lard buckets on the chopping block,
And took the lid off one,
And pulled a limp snow-goose into the air.

He gripped it by the neck,
Its limp head over his wrist,
Its red feet dangling below the snow-white feathers.
He wanted to sell it for a quarter.
I watched the pained expression in his face
While my daddy scolded him for selling game birds.
He looked down at his worn-out shoes,
And in a meek voice, he said,
"Except I sell these here geese,
My younguns don't get no Santa Claus."
It was the great depression,
And I watched him lower the snow-goose
    into the bucket
And press the lid on tight.

Santa Claus brought me a cap pistol that year,
And one bright Sunday in the spring
When I was out shooting fence posts,
I saw the snow-geese going north.
They were flying high in a ragged "V,"
Their leader dropping back,
Their cries distant from the earth.
I watched them fade into the northern sky
    and disappear,
And my heart went with them.

Francis Irby Gwaltney

Tangle-Eyes

Her real name was almost lost in those mists that arose in the early years of the Depression. She was born in 1911, so by the time the Crash came she was already a grown woman, expected to have been married and a mother by the time the Bank of South Franklin failed, which was how Charleston measured the beginning of that peculiar decade that preceded World War II. We called her Tangle-Eyes.

She was kin to several people in town. Somehow or other, she was a cousin to such people as Windy Spears, Topwater Mulligan, and Melmer Dunmore. She was Spread Benefield's niece. She also shared a common ancestor with Miss Hettie McIntosh. None of them denied her, because Tangle-Eyes didn't make it a practice to talk about her kinfolks, but sometimes she passed them on the Street and called them by their family nicknames. It is to the everlasting credit of her kinfolks that none of them ever snubbed her.

Her mother was the agent of the family connections. She had been a collateral Benefield, the family founding Charleston, but she had had bad luck with the flu epidemic of 1918, so Tangle-Eyes was a half-orphan when she was seven. Almost everybody in Charleston agreed that the death was more than a tragedy; her father was Ransom Olds. He was neither Methodist nor Baptist. He wasn't even a Presbyterian. He was a Holy Roller, even if he was never holy and didn't even roll except on those occasions when he went to church drunk.

Ransom owned a farm but he wasn't a farmer. He rented it to Mr. Slim and lived on the rental. That meant, of course, that he could sneak onto his land in the dead of night and gather vegetables enough that he could take home, and, sure enough, Tangle-Eyes canned them in those Mason fruit jars Ransom stole in one way or another. So even if he had an income of no more than two hundred dollars a year, Ransom could spend all of it on drink because there was always plenty to eat.

He looked like a pirate because he was small, wore a patch to cover that place where his right eye should have been, and because, damnit, he was a pirate. Our iceman, Amil Curzon, once offered Ransom a ride to Fort Smith to pick up the regular load of ice, and, sure enough, Amil found himself making trips to such places as Lavaca and Greenwood before he finally found his way to the Ward Ice Cream Company in Fort Smith, where he was an hour late. He explained that Ransom didn't actually highjack him; it's just that Ransom had pressing business that had nothing to do with Amil's destination.

24

So we weren't surprised when Tangle-Eyes didn't turn out well. She was not, however, Charleston's Belle Watling; she was generous to the point that there was no price, but she was selective enough that there were no strangers either. A kept woman, certainly, and kept by several, but unkept by strangers.

Tangle-Eyes worked hard; she took in washing and ironing, she did practical nursing, and she baked and decorated cakes. Her work was absolute perfection. Those collars she starched were carefully trimmed of frays before she ironed them so that there would be no saw-tooth edge cutting at the neck. Her nursing was accompanied by a supply of broths, beef or chicken or pork — and she had one that we suspected too. But Doc Bollinger was the one who went after her at the onset of a sickness that might proceed unto death, so we knew that Tangle-Eyes knew some of Doc's magic elixers. There isn't a middle-aged woman of any social pretense at all who doesn't look back upon at least one of her teenage parties without remembering those cakes, huge, covered with candles as large as those seen at Christmas services now, basically white but decorated with a multiple whimsey of colors that somehow always became soft and nice and feminine and festive when the candles were lighted.

There wasn't a married woman in town who hadn't damned her, and more than just a few had even called her "that cross-eyed bitch." But there were others who, in their own ways, recognized her as an angel of one kind or another; besides her nursing, Tangle-Eyes had softened the tempers of husbands when women needed a soft-eyed man.

She liked me. She wore high-button shoes, and every other Friday she brought them to me for shining. They were old things with fancifully shaped heels but she took good care of them. She wore them once a week. To church. Perched on that ancient bay mule Ransom used as a facade for his farm, facing backward so she could lean against Ransom's shoulders for support, she rode to church every Sunday morning, those high-button shoes held daintily aside, and not until her feet were assuredly planted on solid ground did she slip into them, work the buttons, and, her left eye looking right and her right eye looking left, enter the church of her choice.

Ransom fished a pint bottle of home-made out of his pocket and, his back against the wall, waited behind the ice house until her worship was complete. She was in charge of the bay mule on the way home because Ransom was slung, face down, behind her: a pint of the stuff he drank was good enough for a full twenty-four hours of oblivion.

We all admitted that Tangle-Eyes might be special because she never got the Holy Ghost. Those Holy Rollers took the Holy Ghost seriously. They were regularly afflicted by it. One of their preachers, who enjoyed an unprecedented tenure of three years in their pulpit, regularly brought off a miracle of such duration that we finally accepted it for what it really was, a miracle. Wearing black-and-white wing-tip shoes with taps on heels and toes, he did a dance on that red-hot wood-burning heater the Holy Rollers used to heat their sanctuary. He sometimes stayed up on that thing, an iron monster three feet wide and seven feet long, for as much as thirty minutes, tapping out a little Fred Astaire dance and speaking in tongues.

As he danced, Tangle-Eyes clapped her hands in time to the hymn, a thing called "Glory Take Our Hands and Tongues," but this was a show to her, not a hysterical indulgence. And that's the man she married.

The congregation promptly fired him.

His name was Henry Goforth, and not a one of us ever found out where he came from. He had just appeared in Charleston one morning, hitchhiking and wearing those black-and-whites he was so fond of. He asked around and found out the names of the deacons in charge of holy rolling in Charleston.

They tried him out two nights later. Because Henry hadn't eaten a bite since his appearance in Charleston, he had become somewhat hysterical, so his first sermon was a thing nobody, not even a Holy Roller, really expected. He quoted, accurately, the thirty-fourth chapters of New Testament books that had only thirty-three chapters. He was as glib in tongues as most of us were in English.

Brother King married them. "I'll marry any couple with a legal license," Brother King told us, one time after another, "and if that foolish little man and that woman want to bind themselves in holy matrimony, I'll not only marry them, I'll ask the Trinity to bestow blessings on them."

Ransom promptly made a criminal of him. Henry was not one of those people instinctively a thief. He was caught by Mr. Slim, of all the people in Charleston. Jack Winters, our constable, caught him trying to devise a way to fetch pennies out of that lone gum machine in front of the Creasant Drug Store that had been there so long that none of us dared put its contents in our mouths. Miss Hettie regularly chided him about the eggs he brought to her produce company; like Topwater, Henry delivered those eggs in his pockets. On a special Saturday night, such as once every summer when Brunk's Comedians came to Charleston, Henry appeared at the produce company with a chicken. Miss Hettie paid him his price, fifty cents, and put the chicken in a special coop so it could await the claims of its rightful owner.

Tangle-Eyes was ashamed of him; she was a Christian woman. But she was amused by him too. When he was caught, she joined Ransom in that wild paroxysm that totally baffled Henry. He wanted them to take him seriously; countless congregations had. But perhaps the only time she ever took him seriously was when he decided to sign up for our National Guard regiment.

In 1939 a private could drill once a month and at the end of each quarter he could draw an unencumbered eleven dollars. That was more money than might be imagined. There were families eating rather well because as many as three or four sons were drawing that money.

Tangle-Eyes was proud of him. "You orta see the look on that funny little old face of his when he comes home with that eleven dollars, boy." She paused to push my cowlick out of my eyes. "Oh, I know. Nobody in Charleston thinks much of him, but he's more than nothing."

I told her the truth. "I kind of like him."

And she kissed me. Tangle-Eyes was that kind of woman, sentimental, affectionate, kind of soft and good. "Why, sure you do! Topwater does too, don't he?"

"I guess so."

"Top must have some kind of feeling for 'im: he's drew a thousand pitchers of Henry's face."

"Yes, he has."

"Are they good pitchers?"

I shrugged. "I guess so," I said. "Yes, they're good pictures."

"Did you show any of 'em to Miss Doll?"

"A couple."

"What'd she have to say?"

"She liked 'em."

"Miss Doll's a good woman, ain't she?"

And I said something I had no authority to say, because I had never heard Miss Doll even so much as mention Tangle-Eyes. "She likes you too, Tangle-Eyes."

Tangle-Eyes glowed, then she giggled, as if her name were a monumental joke. "She's the only one that wouldn't call me anything but by my right name."

"Is she?"

"Civility."

"Is that your name?"

"Civility Motherwell Olds," Tangle-Eyes said. "That's what my mother named me. She didn't figger I turned out — with eyes each looking the wrong way."

I never called her by another name. Civility was right. It was the way some people are called Jasper but finally become Windy. Or Francis and become Boy. Or Leon and become Dale. She did have eyes that were a terrible tangle, but she was Civility.

And that was when I began looking at Civility as a real person. Her father died that winter. Ransom. There was no money to bury him, but Will Bumpers put him into the ground and Brother King read over him. Topwater and I, not yet out of our middle teens, were pallbearers. We both called her Civility after that. We never took up for her when those jokes were told, but we made it a point not to laugh. And neither did we see anything funny about the fact that an ancient Methodist preacher had buried a one-eyed Holy Roller pirate; after all, his own church refused to bury him, and Top, Brother King, and I reasoned that any man had a right to a formal passage back to the earth.

But Civility never looked at Henry as a real person. "Oh now, y'all know old Henry. He ain't much, but that's all right; he don't want to be much. He preached because that'uz all he could imagine, and when a man's hungry, he got an imagination on 'im like a cat trying to mouse an elephant. Y'all jist don't worry about Henry; he'll be all right long after most y'all're buried out there at Nixon."

Meanwhile, she took in washing and ironing and surplus lust. Men laughed at her crazy eyes but they didn't laugh loud. And as World War II approached, because they were accustomed to her, various wives had begun to accept her in much the same spirit they accepted that cow in the back yard, needful of attention but kind of a necessity.

Civility was one of the few people who could make my mother take her medicine. Momma had problems in her head, and in 1939 there was not a really effective medicine that would do much for those bursting blood vessels. It was a green stuff, sticky with sugar to hide its hideous taste, and it had to be administered at least four times a day or my mother would become a vegetable, and soon enough she would die.

It was Miss Hettie who raised the money for me to attend the University of Arkansas, but it was Civility who gave Momma her medicine four times a day, daylight and dark. Somehow, Civility found daylight time from her washing and ironing, and darkness time from Henry and those other men who called upon her, to make her way to that little house on North Greenwood Street. Twice during the daylight hours, twice at night.

Brother King was explicit. "Angel, first class, boy. She's made a joke out of adultry, but I'll just bet there might be more than one angel in Heaven with a past history of adultry. There're a few people in Charleston you'd be nothing without, boy, and that includes Miss Doll and Miss Hettie, but without Tangle-Eyes, you wouldn't even have a chance to be nothing."

"Yes sir," I said. "Did anyone ever tell you her real name, Brother King?"

"Now, boy, do you figger I'd call a lady Tangle-Eyes if I knew her name?"

"Civility Motherwell Olds Goforth."

"Civility!"

"Yes sir."

"That was Martha's first name." Brother King's wife had been dead less than a year, and his eyes still clouded when he mentioned her name. "Come to think of it, Martha was a little crosseyed when she was a belle." He put his hands on my head. "Now how'd you find out her

28

real name?"

"She told me."

"I see." Brother King nodded a couple of times. "Seems to me a woman'd not tell you a name like that unless that's what she aims for you to call 'er."

"Yes sir."

"Does Topwater call 'er Civility?"

"Yes sir."

"What does your mother call 'er, boy?"

"When her mind's clear enough, Momma calls 'er Mrs. Goforth," I said. "When Momma was a girl, she knew a great lady named Goforth."

Brother King nodded several times, his craggy old face illuminated with a kind of satisfaction that not many people in Charleston will remember him for. "So do you, boy." He took my head in both his huge old hands and shook it gently and then he was gone.

When our regiment was mobilized in 1941, there were officers in Headquarters-and-Headquarters-Company who didn't want Henry Goforth to go to federal duty. Nobody knew why. Perhaps one of us, a somebody not likely to ever identify himself or herself, wanted to reject Henry. We were still patriots then, and there were people who drew the line before others they didn't deem morally worthy of serving our country. Everybody understood that.

Everybody also understood that a man rejected could be represented by somebody willing to testify in behalf of his character. Without too much trouble, Civility rounded up Brother King, Will Bumpers, Spread Benefield, and Scrooge Wilkins. Windy Spears, concerned with the military image in his background, found out about it and insisted on going along. They all presented themselves to Colonel McAllister, who commanded our regiment, and when the regiment actually departed for federal duty Henry was in ranks.

Civility bloomed with pride. She was quick to assure any and all of Charleston that he was worthless but she was proud. "Think of the fun that fool's having!"

I was gone when the regiment went to Alaska. I was in the South Pacific, and by then Charleston had begun to devote itself to that exercise of passion called patriotism. They pretended that Alaska was a dangerous theater, even when they knew nothing was going to happen up there. And when the Japanese gave up on our fortress there and when our regiment was brought back for retraining before shipment elsewhere on the globe, Charleston even pretended that our boys had been retrieved from horror by a miracle.

Nobody will ever know who that genius was who saw to it that our regiment was routed through Arkansas on its way to those various training camps in Texas, but that man did more for civilian morale (and the sale of war bonds) than any functionary in our country's history.

There were several trainloads of them, all carefully routed through those dozen-upon-dozen of tiny little towns that had produced the willing boys who had sprung forward so eagerly when the regiment was federalized.

When G Company came through Charleston, our people had been told that our boys "might" happen along that day if anybody just happened to be at the depot around two o'clock in the afternoon. Sure enough, proceeding at great speed, as if to assure Charleston that the railroads were serious about getting our boys to one fighting front or another, our train approached from Doctors Ford Creek with its whistle wailing mournfully.

The train slowed to a speed too fast for some hysterical woman to jump on and slow enough for every parent and wife in town to catch a glimpse of those broadly grinning faces.

On the station platform was Windy in charge of a rigidly saluting detachment of Legionnaires in their World War I leggings and gooseneck collars and Smokey-the-Bear hats. Not far away from him was Miss Doll, because there wasn't a man among them who hadn't studied in her classroom. And then, of course, nearest the train, because she was our queen, was Miss Hettie.

But as our train approached, something prompted Miss Doll to turn, find Civility's face in the crowd, fetch her forward, and stand there holding Civility's hand as our train paraded through our town.

Not many noticed, because Miss Hettie was so emotionally stricken by the passage of our boys, but on the platform of the last car, his feet clad in black-and-white wingtips, pecking out his little tap dance, was Henry Goforth. Without hesitation Civility put a finger to each corner of her mouth, and there was an ear-splitting whistle. Henry promptly stopped his dance. As the train disappeared toward east-southeast, picking up speed, its whistle still wailing with that music that was somehow a part of our decade, most of the Charlestonians there that day will remember the last they saw of the train carrying the last they saw of a son or a husband or a sweetheart — it was tiny little Henry Goforth standing there waving.

Henry died in no battle. He never rose above the rank of private. Nor was he decorated for bravery. The regiment knew what to do with him. He spent most of the war on KP until Colonel Mack happened across him, then Henry became a cook's helper.

Civility received him as a hero. "He wudn't nothing when he left and he ain't much else now, but he given all he had when the country needed it."

They flourish still. Henry so regularly appeared at the Veterans Administration Hospital on Roosevelt Road in Little Rock that physicians there sent him to the hospital in Fayetteville. A bearded pathologist there, quick to recognize the talents of a genuine goldbrick, recommended Henry for a pension of something like fifty dollars a month. Henry hasn't seen the inside of a hospital since then.

Civility, her eyes still so hopelessly crossed that moderns are beginning to wonder how she sees anything at all, takes in washing and ironing. People like me — and there are some several dozen of us — remember that she nursed our parents when we were away, and because some of us have prospered, so has Civility's washing and ironing business. Indeed, it is really a laundry now.

According to Windy, Civility made the gown in which Momma was buried. She also nursed Momma through that last wild bout of insanity. When she is questioned about it, she is faintly amused. "That momma of yours jist couldn't git it in her head that you were really fighting a war."

Perhaps Charleston's real understanding of Civility came in 1956. The country had begun to wonder about the Legion because there were Legionnaires who burned books, not because they had read them but because they had looked at the titles, which they called "The Captions." Not the Post at Charleston. During that year Windy, an old man now and really not long for this world, saw to it that Civility was elected head of the Ladies Auxiliary.

Nobody ever found anything to honor Henry. He wasn't much, anyhow.

besmilr brigham

Riding at Night on the Country Roads

and that people say here 'life
must go, goes on', watching the old at
the Nursing Home

waiting for one's own to die

it is good
to think of cars going along this road, past
the cemetery
Millwee,
a curve at Walnut Springs, the big
clump of crepe myrtle
clusters red with fall

where the white crisp bells of the
century plant come up volunteer each
spring,
and a roadside of roses

the uncut woods. still at night with
sleeping eyes, folded wings:
men sitting at edge of the tall pine
grove till the sun goes down
talking,
                a circle before a campfire

and the bright ponds. where rattle snakes
crawl into the yard, and the fire-
black moccasin
sheds his skin like a burned coal

where the big black hawks come down
·on cinder wings. turtles
crawl in their tight-fist shells and
birds hover
near evening

going to town
going home —
we watch the life of the woods pass, first
dog wood
spotted on bare limbs like freshly fallen
late flakes of snow, their blanched
clover shapes

that come before leaves, before the thick-grape
drops of redbud
                    as lovely
turning scant and lean in fall, all
still in violent change

the change sleeping. as the change in us
sleeps. and something that does not
change
blowing into the car

<u>you want a piece o' the country</u>

you drive right down that little road
or the one
turning the other way, or past the
church
you hit the black top, turn off
any direction. it's hot, a hot day or

it's cold
the temperature
it's all the same, nothing makes a
difference — up there an old virgin lives
her long white hair

uncle clay poon read the bible, if
a member
(member of the church, member of the
congregation) offends
he read, cut it off, and with a butcher
knife he did
this is a strict world man, clean
as old car valves. they had to pass a law
to get the old cars off the road

thrown by the wayside. you can still
find what ya want though

Winston Weathers

animals along the highway in arkansas & louisiana

After fog
burns from the valleys
in Southern

mountains/ highways
emerge like naked
veins, petrified

veins in
the Southern body/
& small

animals — dogs,
rats, muskrats,
foxes,

opossums,
cats, raccoons — sleep
with broken

ribs & frozen
jaws on the dark
shoulders

of these state
& national monuments/
they dream

of blind
mechanical blood/ they
stiffen into

highway
signs/ directions/ brief
warnings

/ & we are
reflected (light & motion
through the Southern

night) in
the mirror of their
dead eyes.

Jane Kopp

Farm Wife

the earth so hard
no nail could be driven in
above whitened grass
air dims

too hot to weep
and no use
but her cheekbones ache
lying across the bed

through rusty screen wire
blackberries die
okra and
the very trees
drop leaves

two days ago
in the afternoon
a light rain
fell
minutes on end

all that wealth of dust
was briefly fragrant

Looper Motel

Emerson Electric of St. Louis
(air conditioner muzzed with dusty grease)
wambling the windows.   (View of the motel
turnaround.   Crabgrass, fat
man and woman in thirties chairs, sick
trees, ring of whitewashed stones.)
Refrigerator screaking.   Somebody's
skillet of dead grease.   Thin-thread towels
in the john, and a faint stink.   Plastic
curtains (green, pink, and flesh-colored
bananas and orange wedges, hearts and flowers.)
Plastic plaque, awry, lettered "Cocktail Time!"
Linoleum skinned brown. Hot
water heater vent pipe shoved
off center through a hole sawed in
raw plywood:
                    yes, the true mystery of the world
is the visible.   Useless
to think about anything but God,
and heat, and the heat, and heat, and the heat,
    and heat.

Gearld Hobson

GOING TO THE WATER

This morning I come to the water again.
It has been a long time.
It has been too long.
      Having the need to pray
I come to the water's edge
where dawn light spreads out
                    over the riverbank
like a blessing of hands.
             The water is cold.
Sunlight on the river's surface
diffuses into peacefulness
and adds luster
to the currents of my soul.
      An undertow of grief
lost in fragments of dreams
              broken on rocks
carries me calmly
         into the eddy.
      I face the east
and breathe gently to the sun.
I am praying softly:
      I turn southward
and talk to the wind.
      I turn northward;
and last to west.
        I bathe my body,
touching my face
        and the coolness of water
prays with me.
      I am reluctant to leave the cold stream
but my prayer
at least this part of it
is nearly finished
        and I go shoreward
to burn red tobacco
for the earth's new morning
for the river's new earth.

from THE ROAD WHERE THE PEOPLE CRIED (a long poem in progress)

1.

Sge! Listen!
A spavined horse stands beside the rutted road.
Wagons with busted axles
                          are hub-deep in the frozen mud.
Morning campfires that give no warmth.
People huddle against the winter wind,
a constant gale of it, blowing on and on,
and there is no surcease of pain and cold.
And off to the side of the frozen road
in a stand of leafless hackberries
the five who died the night before
lie in stiffened attitudes
beside open graves (mouth of Mother Earth —
                    black and pitiless, cold
                    and waiting — end for all
                    our pains.)
And three who died not even three years old.

            Raincrow speaks:
                "Somebody said that seven children
                were down this morning with whooping cough.
                That makes eighteen now — not counting the
                ones that died."
People in blankets stand waiting,
Praying for the comfort that cannot be found,
waiting for the word to move on,
in another day of westward walking.
Wind howls like a wounded bear
filled with outrage. Icicles
fall from naked branches
breaking into brittle slivers.
Over all the mantle of whiteness,
dotted with blackened forms
of naked trees,
the expanse — and the way west —
is illimitable.

            Did you hear the wolves last night?
            If only the wind would stop.

Listen!
      Susie Wickham speaks:
            "It's hardest on the children
            and the old folks."
Her son lies buried
back at Gunter's Landing,
she still has five more mouths
to feed and care for.
She stirs the kettle with a long stick
and dredges up the turnip greens,
picked frost-mauled two days ago
out of the unhospitable Arkansas ground.
            "I can't ever stop thinking about it.
             Them little faces all drawed up
             in hunger and cold.
             Some don't have shoes to wear, even."
The greens are ready
she calls her family,
a poor breakfast,
but better than some folks will have.
            "It's a pure-true trial on a body.
             All our people ain't going to
             make it. You know, a dead child
             is a sure-hard fact to face."

In mortars of hewn log,
lives — like corn kernels —
are ground into a grain
of misery.

Only the buzzard knows
the watermark of our Evil Days.
Only the buzzard can claim
an ultimate authority.

Listen!
Asádihi had dreamt of green things,
Of unwinterlike things:
Tall green corn, and muskmelons,
lying fat above the warm soil,
hidden in crisp weeds.
Scuppernongs on the vines,
trailing up hickories and sycamores.
Jaybirds and woodpeckers
making loud noise
in rhododendron thickets,

and whippoorwills calling softly
in the evening shade
of red-haw and dogwood.
It was Green Corn Dance time in eastern Tennessee.
Cherokee men played the little war
on the ball-play field,
using racquets like war-clubs,
and bets were wildly made.
Then the young women played ball,
no less violently than the men.
Oconuluftee people had come over
to join the people of Chota town
for the summer holiday.
An outsider, a half-white Chickasaw,
had won the footrace
and his wife's people were happy.
   The dogs had jumped a fat buck
out of the tall corn;
the young men began the chase,
and the deer ran fast.
The people laughed and shouted,
cries echoed in the piney hollows
of the high hills.
the older men laughed softly, wisely,
as though to say:
    You can't catch the wind.
The chase was not long:
   When the buck reached the creek-bank
and swam across,
the young people gave it up
and stopped,
and caught their breath,
and played in the water.
Drops of splashing water
glistened in the sun and shade,
reticulate as a rattlesnake's back,
and the long hot August sun
sank behind a hog-back ridge.

    A melting icicle awakens Asádihi.
Groaning, he remembers where he is.
His ninety years burdensome,
like old unmelting snow,
the years lay heavily
upon the earth of his flesh.

Listen!
Old, determined Going Snake,
Rides his horse at eighty-two,
looking straight ahead and never back,
straight into the face of death,
straight to the west.
The young warriors follow him,
riding straight and proud,
tall as old-time Indians,
behind the Keeper of the Old Ways.

The crack of ice in trees
fills the air
like *unega* rifles on a massacre morning.
The wail of torture ascends
the frozen waste. People,
animals, covered wagons —
entire wagon trains —
stop at the Mississippi crossing-point:
The river is frozen solid.

Many two-voiced prayers aspire above the misery:
  — Rock of Ages
    Cleft for me,
    Let me hide
    Myself in thee . . . .

    O Lord God Jehovah in Heaven on High,
    Grant solace to your children.
    Help us through this day
    As you have helped us
    In so many days gone by,
    In Jesus' Name, Father,
    We ask thy blessing. Amen.

    Listen! Ancient Red One,
    Great Spirit,
    Sun of other mornings,
    Make these bad times bearable.
    Have a kindness on our little ones
    and on all our old folks.
    We suffer and we die
    Unless you melt this river's ice
    And let us go forth,

We Cherokees will be no more.
So, listen, Ancient Red One,
Great Spirit,
Have a kindness on your children,
We are all your good Cherokees.
Wadan.
Sge.

Leon Stokesbury

To All Those Considering Coming to Fayetteville

Often these days, when my mind holds splinters
like the pieces of the shampoo bottle
I dropped and shattered yesterday, I think
of other places. It is wintertime now,
and the Ozarks are hushed up with snow
everywhere. They are small mountains, almost
not mountains at all, but rather, with trees
sticking up, they seem more like
the white hairy bellies of fat old men
who have lain down here. What has this to do
with anything? I don't know. Except
it makes me think of snow elsewhere, and what
it would be like to be there. I might drive
across Oklahoma, then on into
New Mexico. I could be there tonight.
The land would be flat, the snow over
everything. The highway straight, and forever
the snow like blue cheese in the moonlight,
for as far as there is, and air, cold air
crisp as lettuce, wet lettuce in the store,
and I would keep driving, on and on.

The Trees in the Middle of the Field

> A word has power in and of
> itself. It comes from nothing
> into sound and meaning; it
> gives origin to all things.
>
> —N. Scott Momaday,
> **The Way to Rainy Mountain**

A lone clump of gnarled sassatras and oaks rises out of a great meadow a short mile northeast of Summerfield, in the hill country of eastern Oklahoma, where the land was once heavy with wood and game. Nobody knows why the clump of trees was not cut down when the land was first cleared for the plow. Dim memories hint that the spot is a sacred burial ground, but nobody will say for sure.

Once there was a house a few feet east of the trees. The broken tile of a well long since filled still rises a few inches above the earth. But you have to look long, for the tall grass hides it like the night. I cannot remember a time when the house stood there. My mother says that, as a child, she lived there for a short while at the turn of the century when her parents first moved up from Texas. But she does not recall the house, nor why it ceased to be.

Maybe the maker of the house knew why the trees were left in the middle of the field. At any rate, the trees are still there, and are not threatened. Local legend has it that the trees once guarded a rich burial mound, but now no mound rises among the trees. Instead, a musky sink in the middle of the clump shows the scars of many a shovel and many a fire-lit night. The story of one night in particular sticks in my mind, though I was much too young at the time to know of the night at all. But like bedtime ghost stories, some things told again and again when you are young and lying with your brothers and sisters on a pallet before the hearth of the fireplace later illuminate the dim, unremembered years. It is the story of how my brother outran a horse.

Before I could stand alone, we lived on the lane that borders the east edge of the field where the trees still stand. My brother was nearing manhood and owned a horse and was a night-rider. He learned that three men, neighbors and good-for-nothings, planned to dig in the trees. He asked to join them. He longed to prove himself a man. They had visions of gold and told him there was money buried there.

So when the October moon was dark, they gathered in the clump of trees and hung a lantern over the chosen spot. There was frost on the limbs of the sassafras and oaks. My brother broke first ground, and a hushed moan moved through the still trees. He dropped the shovel;

strange pieces of bone-red matter began to show up in the dirt at the edge of the pit. While all were gathered about, another moan, much louder than the first, moved through the night — and my brother leaped out of the dark pit. But the good-for-nothings held him fast and howled with laughter as one of their cronies strode into the circle of the lantern's light, drunk on erupting mirth and bootleg whiskey. Everyone had a good laugh at my brother's expense. And he laughed too.

But the laughter was short-lived. A deep, low moan, ghostly but unmistakably human, rolled up from the bowels of the black earth. There was for a moment, my brother recalls, a stillness like doom upon all of them. Then everybody was running, running: the good-for-nothings were running, the original moaner was running, my brother was running and all the beasts of the field. A great shadow passed beside my brother. It was a horse. The moan persisted, even over the sound of thumping boots and racing hoofs. Now my brother passed the horse, and burst through the barbed wire fence at the edge of the field with one wild bound. He flung himself down the lane and plunged through the doorway of our house and hugged himself close to the dying coals in the fireplace. An hour passed before he began to cry.

Several days later my father filled in the pit and brought home the lantern, dry of kerosene, the wick burned to a crisp.

The clump of trees in the middle of the field was the hub of the universe of my childhood and my adolescence. We always lived within sight of the field. And after the field became a great meadow, I found several days of bone-breaking work each summer helping a cousin bale the tall and fragrant lespedeza which had been urged to grow there. But never did I seek the shade of those trees for my noonday rest. For me, they were too ghostly, foreboding, scared. In my mind's eye I could see beyond all doubt that here was the final resting place of the broken bones of some great Choctaw chief. He had made it just this far west. He had come within sight of the blue Kiamichi Range to the south, which was to become the last home for his dispossessed people, and had fallen dead on the spot from a homesickness of the soul. Among the sassafras and the oaks he had been buried with all the pomp and honor that there was left to his migrating children. For me, the spot was inviolate.

And thus it has remained. Only recently have I had the courage, and the reverence, to penetrate the gnarled clump of trees in the middle of the meadow. I went there in mid-afternoon and sat as motionless as I could while the sun dropped well below a long, low line of trees far to the west. Sitting there, I tried to grasp something I could not name, something I knew was gone forever. I could not invoke it. I did not know its name. Once, just as the sun went down, I heard a hawk cry out high above the clump of leafless trees. Perhaps there was a moan. But I did not hear it.

H.L. Van Brunt

DEATH OF THE INDIAN CARPENTER

the timber rattler's head
swung heavy as a plumb
into your log thigh

. . . .

the buck you didn't kill
beds down on a rise

warm breath, and belly full
as the harvest moon
that's red on the window

of the tahlequah funeral home
& shines in his eyes

GODS

the buck recoiled
more than the rubber
butt against your shoulder
the time he took to list
the way his knees touched the ground
the quiet manner in which he slid
down among the leaves
the vacuum stillness after that
the coolness of what had been hot
my hand upon his neck
we felt that things were not quite right
as though a spirit had been removed
something so huge and wise and gentle
it could have made sense of what we'd done
all we had was a stiff-legged creature
bleeding on the leaves
we felt abandoned by a god

THE HUNTERS

We saw a wolf
that saw us first.
Wind dipped from
trees to snow.
We had a way to go.

My stepfather's .22
looked like an elephant
gun. My rifle shot a cork.
He walked as sure as an Indian,
avoiding the drifts and thinner ice.

I floundered on behind.
Stumbling out of those blackjack woods
I was first to my uncle's house.
We had a fight. I shot him twice
before we had to go.

The night was mostly moon and snow.
He was cross: not a thing to shoot
at but that wolf all day.
And he had missed.
I howled the long way home.

Frank Parman

BUFFALO STATION

[for Kathy, 22, in E

1)   prelude: July 21, 1851-1878.

"In less than a year
he had blazed his name
across the front pages
as one of the most
audacious
of train robbers

46

                              and had laid the foundation
                              for legends
                              that would give his name
                              a lasting place
                              in America   's folk-
                              lore."
                                      (Wayne Gard, SAM BASS)

Sam Bass
died
on his 27th
birth-
day.
              of the 9,
              maybe 10,
              stage holdups
              his biggest take
              was $400
                    & 4 gold watches
                                  once
              near Deadwood   all they got:
                                      fresh peaches.

        he never robbed a bank
        but was planning to
                              &
                      of all the Texas trains
                      the Rewards offered
                      were greater
                      than the sum
                      total
                              of the loot.
his one big haul: the Union Pacific train
at Big Springs, in the state of Nebraska
when Trail boss, Joel Collins
taught him how:
                  the gang of 6
              split $60,000
              in $20 gold pieces:
                          mint fresh: 1877.

2)   September 26, 1877
                              "On their way back to Texas,
                                      they robbed the U.P. train,
                              And then split up in couples
                                      and started out again.
                              Joe Collins and his partner
                                      were overtaken soon;

                                                          47

                                                With all their stolen money,
                                                        they had to meet their door
                                                            (Ballad of Sam Bass)

camped in a ravine, 60 miles west of Hays City
sheriff Bardsley of Ellis county, Kansas
with a de - tect - ive   from Denver
& 10 U.S. cavalrymen
                            Collins & Bill Heffridge stopped
                            to get some grub
                            inquired of the station agent:
                                                "What place is this?
        "Buffalo Station."   then   "Who are those people? "
        "Soldiers from Fort Hays.
         They're here . . .
         to protect us from the Indians,
         though I don't suppose
         there's an Indian
         within 200 miles."
                        &, on an envelope
                        the agent saw the name: Joel Collins
                        &, went to tell the sheriff
                        he'd found the robbers of the train
                            while Collins bought supplies
                            &   then, with Heffridge,

                                                slowly rode away

the sheriff & the soldiers came riding up behind
                        the desperadoes were still calm
as sheriff Bardsley informed them:
            "I have a description of some train robbers
            which answers well to your appearance.
            I want you and your partner
            to return with me to the station.
            You need fear nothing
            if you are innocent; but
            if you are the men I want,
            then I am $10,000 better off."
                        "You are mistaken in your men,"
                        Collins laughed, and said: "but,
                        of course, there is no use to object.
                        We will go back and have the mistake explained.
                        We are Texas boys
                                    going home,
                                                that's all."

they rode back toward the station
a hundred yards or so
then Collins said: "Pard,
                    if we have to die
                we might as well die game."
&   the outlaws
           reached for their 6shooters
but   never fired a shot
the soldiers filled them both with lead.

                              the sheriff found $20,000
                              (double-eagle shares for 2)
                              & actually started dancing
                              & shouting:
                                    "I've got the gold,
                                    I've got the gold!"

the soldiers searched the bodies
& found in Joel's pocket:
                    a poem
          addressed to him
          & written by a woman's hand

                         it was easy to determine
                         Joel Collins' identity:
                              5 times he'd trailed
                              Texas cattle north
                                   & he had friends
          but no one recognized the man
          he knew as Bill Heffridge
          until a woman came to say
          she knew him as William Pitts
          she'd made the mistake of marrying him
          then learned he'd left a wife back home
          in Pennsylvania
                         to travel in Indian Territory
                         & Texas
                         & he stole horses & cattle
          in her identification she was positive:
          she knew it was him
          by his tatoo:
                    a girl
                         dancing
                    on his right arm.

David Ray

A HILL IN OKLAHOMA

A cellar would keep jars cool.
You promised to dig one.
You could dig one with a mule
And a piece of iron.
But first you had to break the mule
And that was a mean business.
But you kept your vow
And later the mule
Ran away, flipping the iron
End over end
Frightening me like everything
Else you and the mule did.

And she bore jars into the damp earth
Like a Cretan girl.
She placed the jars
Upon shelves that are fallen
Here, all broken in this
Agamemnon's tomb.
And I have come to dig the shards
Out of the wet leaves
And find what you left.
Here are the rusty cans
Our mother fed us from
When she denied the breast,
Small dugs that I remember,
With nipples like figs.
Here are the rusty springs
Of our bed, both brother
And sister.
And here is a rusty ring
Like a half-moon,
The basin she washed us in.

You were indeed the most cursed
Of parents.
The deep rains hurt at your house
And at last washed it down
The hill.
The open fire in the middle
Of your dirt floor

Burned at your poor bed
Like a rich man's eyes.
In the day you went out and broke
Stones.
The mule learned to turn away
From the ruins
And salt stains on the earth.
And stunned by your own failure
When you left, Christ's life
Ago, you left the gates
Wide open. Iron gate.

Norman H. Russell

your circle

the headless owl flies into the oak
which swallows him whole
i have circled this small tree
the owl is not there
or he has turned behind my circle
or he has turned behind the tree's circle

a star falls in the night sky
he dies brightly
he has broken his circle

stay in your circle
for your circle is a circle within circles
you live long and well
if you do this

the arrow circles the sky
the deer circles the meadow
the sun circles the heaven
only that which breaks its circle
and touches the circle of another
only that one dies.

oklahoma april

the wild wet south wind
is no barrier to the mockingbird
who sings long before the dawn
when low clouds wash by
when the new tulips dark ghosts
lie on the ground looking north
eyes of flowers
and dawn finally is so painful
and day is a distant mist of sun
and suddenly
the new grass is waisthigh
the windows rattle with wind
and the mockingbird
grows as great as a storm cloud
and sings and sings beyond the wind.

voices of mosses

this is a secret place
behind the fern above the waterfall
there is moss here a good place for my fire
but first i dig below the moss with a stick
for such a fine camp may have been found before

there are stones and sand
below the stones and sand the earth is black
old ashes lie below the moss
another friend was here many fathers before
his sticks have turned to dirt

my father taught me to look in such a place
the moss with the small white eye
the moss with the twisted stem
the moss with the tilted rattle
all speak the campfires which they hide.

Francine Ringold

Passage

will they set a scar on his stomach
the mark that is to brand him man?
so says the shaman
so says the wise one

spirit-woman knows the man in the boy
knows he is whole now
that slim lines may rend boy or man

so she steals him away in the night
so she wraps him in sheep wool and fern
so she bathes him in the salt sea seven time
and seven time again
once for each year of his life

over the thunder of the bull roarers
over the wail of the wives
the men come
the men come
deftly they mix pigment and proud blood
slyly they chant the cry of the bird
the twill of the loon

the loam crawling between her toes
Llano, mother, roosts with spider-woman
crooning and sighing
straining to move circles into silence
forgetting there is no power past the womb
forgetting that
the thing will be done
the boy will go off to the hunt
the dove will wrestle with his eagle

the mother will turn
to see a grey feather
marching in his hair

James Whitehead

VISIONARY OKLAHOMA SUNDAY BEER
for Clarence Hall and Jane Cooper

The small window opened. I asked for the six-pack
I paid for, then saw the women playing pool
In the loud and common light where ball and stick
Have always met.
                        The oldest on a high stool

Was big as a mound but wasn't simply fat.
She glistened and shouted — she was having fun
With all the other Indians — each one great
With child in a way to make that bulb a sun.

All fancy with no men around, they played.
Hey, let me in is what I think I said.
I meant of course to ask where are your men
And what of pageantry and life and death?

Her break shook me and a brown arm closed down
A show I would have stayed a season with.

Carl Mayfield

A Few Lives

The red clay of Oklahoma:
feeding cattle in the bitter cold
wild turkeys picking their way
down the slope —
following them
we stumbled onto the carcass

yes the earth was frozen
my uncle and I set
the steel traps
with picks and axes
to catch the wild dogs

before they pulled down
another 900 pound heifer

and then:

a crazed German Shepherd bitch
leaping at us
on a moonlit night
her two hind legs
broken in the trap

my uncle finished
with one shot
the gray and black
streak of wildness

in the trees
the turkeys woke up
gathered their young
and moved to an oak
further away

Deno Trakas

BRAVE BLOOD

My friend is the grandson of a grandfather.
He stretches that name, that tanned pride
of skin and tight bone.

The name thunders, thunders
like time's hoof — his image raises dust
in a far curl, in a horned plain.

The name skips, skips
like a flat star across the lick
of salt reflections.

The name puffs, puffs
like a desperate war cry smothered in the pipe
though he is the muscle of fire.

The name — but what of his mother's mother,
the white feather of her
age touching ground —
no one knew her name.

Under The Clock

Mary Lou would be twelve the next week. I met her at the fence separating the girls' playground from the boys' and we talked through the steel net. "I'm leaving next week," she told me, sticking her fingers through. "I'll be too old for the Children's Home."

I just looked at her face. I was in love with her, with her frightened eyes, with her straw-colored hair clipped evenly all around the same way my sister's was. She and my sister stayed in the same dormitory together, in the other wing of the big yellow brick building.

"Mrs. Spessard told me," she said. "Saturday I'll go."

"I don't want you to go," I said. Saturday was our movie day.

"I don't want to go," she said. "I'm scared. I don't want to leave you." She put her fingers through the wires as far as she could. The square openings were just wide enough for us to hold hands if we twisted them. I looked toward the yellow brick of the main building to make sure Old Lady Norton or one of the other matrons wasn't watching us. We weren't supposed to be by the fence. Then I looked over at the boys' playground behind me; boys were playing in the sandy hollows kicked out of the grass. Donald was the only one looking at Mary Lou and me. I wanted to run over and kick him. He could go to hell. He was probably still mad at me for the fight we'd had the week before. We'd run at each other like billygoats, lowering our heads and charging. Old Lady Norton had spanked him twice as hard as me because he was bigger. He had hair on his body; he was the only boy in the dorm that did and he was always showing off when we took the shower. Once Old Lady Spessard brought some rich people through, showing them how everything got run in the Children's Home and they all stopped at the door and watched us taking a shower. We dropped some soap it made us so nervous. All of us were taking a shower right before bed. There was a rich girl about my age with her mother and father and she was just gawking at us because we were all naked. Then they walked on like rich people do. We all got mad but Donald liked it because he said the girl saw his hair. Donald was mean as hell and he only had a Gramma. Christmas they finally called him down to the visitors hall and she gave him an apple. That's all he got for Christmas. His fat old Gramma brought it. Of course he got some Crackerjacks from Bob Wills and his Texas Playboys just like the rest of us did. If anybody deserved not to get anything it was Donald. I would have beat him if the matrons hadn't made us stop fighting. Old Lady Norton really gave it to him hard. If he didn't stop looking at Mary Lou and me I'd run over and knock him down even if he was bigger than me.

Behind Mary Lou the girls were playing their sissy games, jumping rope and playing tag. None of them was paying any attention to us. Mary Lou was the only one with a boyfriend and the others didn't even want any. We were as alone as we could be, that was for sure. If I was ever going to kiss her it might as well be now. It might be years before I'd get the chance again. We could sit in a movie and hold hands, then. Who cared about Donald? My voice got soft and I said, "I don't want you to go either. I'll miss you. We have to meet when we grow up." I already had it worked out.

"What do you mean?" she said. She looked like she was going to cry, but she always looked that way, even in the dining hall when I'd look past everybody and see her sitting over there with the other girls, just glaring ahead and looking all sad and choked up. Sometimes we both got to set the table together. That's when I'd got to talk to her more. In the playtimes, in the evenings, we only got to talk to our own sisters, not to any other girls. Mary Lou and I had become lovers while we were setting the table.

Hilda didn't mind at all. She was busy with the steamy old dishwasher. Besides I think she liked the idea of us getting along and maybe getting married when we grew up and got out of the old Children's Home. She was Hanson's wife. They made her wear a uniform and an apron all the time. She had fat legs and fat titties. Hanson worked in town running the elevator. When Mrs. Spessard told him to, he had to drive the station-wagon. He took us to get haircuts and to movies. Once he took us into town to get our arms vaccinated. We had to go up in the elevator. I was afraid of elevators. Hanson didn't run it though. But guess who the nurse was that punched us? I still can't figure out why. It was my own Mother, sticking needles in our arms.

When we were in town Hanson and Mrs. Spessard and Old Lady Norton and the rest of them always said to meet in the lobby of the Philtower. So that's where we always met. We'd wait and everybody'd look for Mrs. Spessard's purple dress with white polkadots. She never wore anything else. She'd be leading a bunch of girls along while they tried to stay in line and not stop and look in any of the department store windows and not run into anybody walking by. But I always looked around Mrs. Spessard, looking for Mary Lou every time. I never even noticed the other girls.

That's why I thought of the Philtower now. It would be the best place. Everybody knew where it was. At night we could watch it too, and think about meeting each other. At night they lit it up with spotlights, with different colors so it was always changing from blue to orange or from orange to green. It wasn't far from the Criterion Theatre, either, in case we wanted to see a movie. The last one we'd seen there was **Wings of an Eagle.** I forgot all about Mary Lou sitting in the row in front, it was so good. They had a lot of airplanes in it getting ready to fight the war. Everybody wore the right kind of hats and saluted all the time. They had to build a lot of planes to fight the Japs. It was a more important movie than the Shirley Temple stuff they liked to take us to, and the Walt Disney stuff. I knew it was important later, too, when I saw the M.G.M. lion column in the **Liberty** magazine. They had a picture of the lion roaring and underneath that they talked about the **Wings of an Eagle** movie being so good, and patriotic too.

By the time Mary Lou and I met I'd probably be wearing a uniform and a nice hat too. The war wasn't ever going to be over. They were going to bomb the Douglas plant a few miles away. Some of us listened at night to hear if the bombs were falling yet. They might knock the Philtower building right over, so we kept watching that too. Sometimes I cried when I watched that because I thought if I was there I could slide down to the street and go find my mother. She was there somewhere in town. If I had to go to war Mary Lou'd worry about me. I'd promise her to come back after shooting down a few Jap Zeros. That would be in the sky like all the fighting should be. It'd be a hell of a long way from the Children's Home too. No more matrons making us fold our bed covers right all the time or yelling at us to shut up and not cuss. I'd write them a letter from China where I'd be in the Flying Tigers telling them to go to hell.

When Mary Lou and I met, they wouldn't know about it. They'd be real old by then. When we got married they'd read it in the paper. We couldn't help that. She'd walk up to me there in the lobby. She'd be all grown-up, though not very tall. We'd meet under those chandeliers that had the gold chains. I wouldn't be bashful at all. We'd hold hands right there in front of everybody. We wouldn't kiss till we got alone. We'd get married right away and if it all worked out right she'd put on a nightgown and then meet me in the bathroom. By that time we'd know all there was to know about everything. We could take a bath together if we wanted to. She'd be all filled out like Charlene Bowen by then, too, and wear brassieres.

"I just want to stay here now," she said. "You'll forget all about me."

"I never will." I squeezed her fingers again.

"Promise?"

"You have to meet me at one o'clock in the Philtower Building the day you're twenty-one years old. We'll get married." Mary Lou was older than me so I wouldn't be twenty-one yet.

"Yes," she kept saying, "yes." She took a crayon from her packet and wrote down her birthday and we figured out what year it would be. The Philtower Building at one o'clock, she wrote that down to remind me. She wrote the same words on a paper for herself too and then handed me the one through the fence. The crayon was red like lipstick then. "We'll never forget our promise," she said. "I love you." She said that too.

58

The rest of the week was agony. I kept looking for Mary Lou all the time, in the dining hall and on our way to school, but it was like they'd told her to hide from me. I couldn't hardly ever find her. Only once, when we had cooked turnips and she was serving. She laughed when I told her what I thought of the cooked turnips. She looked at me a lot of times when she went around the table. I knew she was wondering if I really was going to marry her. I was going to write her a note telling her I really was. At night I lay in my bed and if I got a chance when everything was quiet I'd go to the window and look across to the girls' side. Mary Lou and my sister were over there inside those windows with all the other girls. When we got married I'd get to watch Mary Lou undress and everything.

I wondered if she was thinking of me. Sure she was, I said. Maybe she was looking at the Philtower Building just like I was, saying Green when it changed to green. One time I woke up real early in the morning when it was getting daylight and there weren't any colors at all. There was just a real dull white light shining on it till the sun came up. They'd already taken Mary Lou to the Francis Emmons home. She'd turned twelve, and when she was eighteen they'd let her out. And she'd start walking up that dusty road toward me.

Jim Barnes

Postcard to Brian Bedard from Somewhere on the Illinois,

Near Tahlequah, Oklahoma

Dear B, you wouldn't think these cliffs hold bones
that knew the earth was mother and the river below
food for more than thought. Burials abound
that put most mummies to real shame. The skin
is too tight across the teeth, though, to sing
again of white-water runs and black bass,
the ears too cracked to catch the sound of solemn
wind, the echoes of ghost arrows ricocheting
cliff to cliff. It's too bad, B, we lift them up
from a lap they knew from birth, from a dignity
so deep we can learn only they knew how
to die. I've looked for the bear we heard about
roaming these woods. The closest I've come is
a birch scored a hundred years ago. Peace, Jim.

FOUR CHOCTAW SONGS

1. Choctaw Death Song i

When I pass,
this prairie
will hold
my tracks
as long
as the wind
sleeps.

2. Choctaw Death Song ii

I ride
the wind
to another corner
of the sky.

3. Choctaw Hunting Song

Wolf eats
the wind:
his skin
will keep
me warm.

4. Choctaw Eagle Dance Song

Eagle feathers
talk to me:
they say,
touch us to your lips
and know the way
we knew the wind.

A Season of Loss

We left the horses in the draw
and climbed the painted ledge to see
the blue and distance home but saw
an autumn sun set fire to trees

on ridges we had yet to pass:
gnarled trees that burned and stood
more than a shifting phoenix, cast
in colors other than mild moods.

Our blood was now too thin to know
the half-moon brother, our skin too pale;
yet we, hands out, tried again to sow
our spirit in the stars. A frail

effort: our fathers' blood pulsed slow.
At our back a glyph grew perfect:
hard in stone a hand drew back to throw,
a sun stood still, a moon arced, sticks

grew into bones. Only human,
we touched thoughts, hands, eyes,
assured ourselves of the moment,
and leaned together hard against the sky.

Arn Henderson

Purgatory's Mouth

Jacob:

We Seen a Branch Which We Sopose to be
Pikes first forke

      We Stoped Heare

Some Ware Hunting and others Cooking
Some Picking grapes
      and the Cry of a White Bare Was Raised

61

1)   We Ware all armed in an Instent
       and Each man
       Run His own Cors to look for the desperet anemel

2)   the Brush in Which We Camped
       Into Which the Bare Head Run

       and Surrounded on all sides
       the Bare
       Sprung up and Caught Lewis doson:

            Pulled Him down In an Instent

3)   I Was my Self down the Crick
       below the brush
            and Heard the dredfull Screems
       of man
       in the Clutches of the Bare

       the yelping of the Slut and the Hollowing
       of the men to Run in Run in the man
       Will be killed

4)   His Head Was In the Bares mouth at least twice
       and that
       When the monster give the Crush
            that
       Was to mash the mans Head
            it
            being two large for the Span of His mouth
       the Head Sliped out
            only the teeth
            cutting
            the skin to the bone

5)   I am killed that I Heard my Skull Brake:
            but We Ware Willing
            to beleve He Was mistaken
       as He Spoke Chearfully on the Subgect
       till In the after noon of the second day

       and on examening a Hole
       in
       the upper part of His Wright temple
       Which We
       beleved only Skin deep
       We
       found the Brains Workeing out

Purgatory:

i look back with this compulsion to confess
as i
waist-deep in your waters stand
at the mouth, Jacob

i am a thief and
i have stolen from even you

> 6)   the unfortnet
>   man died at day Brake
>   and Was Berred
>   near the Bank With a Strong Pen of logs
>   over Him
>   to prevent the Bares or Wolves
>   from
>   Scraching Him up
>
>   this Is the (first)
>   anemel of the kind We Have met With

from Document For An Anonymous Indian

ASHER, OKLAHOMA   could i see
                                   a menu

                                   all
                                   we got is hamburgers

ASHER   177 CAFE

          at the right: a long counter with dozens
          of flies swarming in December

          in the center: 3 tables, 4 teenage girls
          in levis sit around a table knitting
          & talking, oblivious to the 4 teenage
          boys at their left playing pool

          behind the counter: an old Westinghouse
          refrigerator with a hairbrush on top
          & a large handlettered sign:

                              ABSOLUTELY
                              NO CREDIT

on the opposite wall, by the pool table:
a row of calendars advertising RC, Coke,
Colvert Dairy Products, Tom's Peanuts
& another handlettered sign:

NO PROFANITY
NO GAMBLING

on the back wall: a pair of pencil
drawings. distorted faces the shape of
a pressing iron with human features
& tubular fat worm-like bodies without
arms & legs & with handlettered titles:

DREAM
GIRL OF 177 CAFE

DREAM
BOY OF 177 CAFE

at another center table: a teenage
white girl & an indian boy perhaps 20,
sit listlessly, occasionally glance at the
pool players

the boy has a red devil tattooed on his
left forearm, underneath the inscription

BORN TO RAISE HELL

the girl walks to the cash register,
speaks to an elderly fat woman who opens
the drawer, gives her change. the girl
limps to the juke-box, the silver button
at the knee-joint of her artificial leg
bulging under opaque flesh colored hose

are you a song-
writer

huh

are you copying
down that song
on
the jukebox   the
elderly woman
smiling

. . . .

reno street

                saturday
afternoon in the autumn
                warm enough for the
                bar/grill bar/hotel
                            to
leave their doors open for the indian ladies
                            of
                            all ages
                perched on green leatherette
                                    stools
                popping chewing gum
                smiling
        to   young blonde hair cow/poke types

                strolling casually (pausing
                        in groups of 2 & 3
                        looking
                        in open doors

                (perched on green leatherette
                                    stools
                        one
                        bird-like & thin

                knee length pants
                with too many teeth & gold
                        yells at an indian youth
                passing in the sunlight

                YOU DUMB FUCKIN INJUN

                        all yell whoop & laugh
                bird-like cackles   spills her beer
                                smiles/teeth/gold

Susan Schmidt

Vacationing on Route 66

I have been driving on Route 66
for thirty-one years
on vacation.
There have been stopovers,
nice places to eat,
greasy spoons.
I have measured distances by the
radio stations, their broadcasting ranges,
and the hisses between them.
I have judged the territories by the sea
levels, by the size of the rocks
and their placement on the hills,
roadside,
by the height of trees,
by the hawk's wingspan,
and the number of cows
grazing.

And I have packed.
The cold chicken,
the thermosed coffee,
the bread and butter sandwiches,
and salt for the hard-boiled eggs.
the blanket for sudden cold,
the tapes for sudden quiet,
the pills,
the remedies,
the medicines,
the kids,
the dogs, the cats, the plants, the weeds,
the bird. Their food, their bones, their toys.
I have swept out the car
and filled it up.

I have followed the green Porsche
till it left.
I have tracked the orange van
till it broke down.
I have raced the silver Mercedes
till the police came.

I have been driving on Route 66,
knowing no one sees
or if they do
they won't remember
to write me down or even take
mental notes.

dave nichols

casings

the lilacs

whisper

forgotten prayers

cold

like december limbs

still

as the doe

rifle frozen

in

crimson

ice

Joy Harjo

White Sands

my sister is getting married
in a white dress in Tulsa
the way my mother knew it would be
with her daughters
                    (a December wedding
                      under a pure sky)
but i am the one
who lives alone with two children
in the desert of a place
                    in New Mexico
and she never saw me in a white gown

when i drive to Oklahoma for the wedding
i will be dressed in
the clear blue sky
that burns the silvery white sand
near Alamogordo
and my mother won't see this
my eyes burning
                    behind my darkened glasses

the last song

how can you stand it
he said
the hot oklahoma summers
where you were born
this humid thick air
is choking me
and i want to go back
to new mexico

it is the only way
i know how to breathe
an ancient chant
that my mother knew
came out of a history
woven from wet tall grass
in her womb
and i know no other way
than to surround my voice
with the summer songs of crickets
in this moist south night air

oklahoma will be the last song
i'll ever sing

As much as size, the variety — of landscapes, cultures, hopes and regrets encompassed by the State — has undermined the conscious and unconscious lives of Texas writers. Most every literary artist who has sought to evoke or probe the nature of the place — its people, its heritage, its language (all in the plural) — has met with overwhelming demands, made on him or her by diffusiveness (in terms both of territory and of the grandiose treatment required), as well as by the necessity of creating with no audience or with a hostile one at most. Tied to these demands is a tendency among the natives of the land to belittle anything homegrown, except beef and barrels of crude. This is even reflected in a drawing from the early fifties meant to encourage investment in the State's insurance companies, which pictured a cow with her head in Texas, grazing, while New Yorkers milked the tits.

The result of this situation is that many a Texas writer has settled elsewhere, or for a limited view of subject and style in hopes of achieving even the off-and-on respectable label of "regionalist." In addition to a reluctance of many Texas writers to produce "rooted" material, a haughty challenge is inherent in the heart of Texas itself — that it will, by God, take more from an artist than it will ever grant. Recently, despite the odds, Texas writers have begun to return, in spirit and in person, to a well which seemed eternally dry, and have found even to their own surprise a thirst-quenching source left long untapped. The new writing derives basically from an acceptance of limitations, of the small gains for inordinate pains, from a desire to plumb the depths rather than just to scratch the surface with cliched drill-bits, and from a dedication to make do on what is seen at last as suitably native: the stubby subject that is yet durable as a common post oak; the cedar-chopper's furry, rusting, sweet-scented stake which, as he would say, may be crooked as a dog's hind leg but can stand a hundred years.

Likened throughout its history to hell, by both the visitor and the settler, Texas, with famed heat and monotonous plains, has been looked upon as not even fit for the devil himself. This attitude, along with the typical western image and its wearying burden, has deprived her artists of the ability to come to grips with the truly diverse and deeply fertile character of the region. For the land has proved a magnet of torment attracting peoples as distinct as Scotch-Irish, Mexican, Comanche, Italian, Negro, German, Swede, and Jew — and would seem to call for no less than a Dante, a Milton, or a Whitman to tally it. But it may be that Texas will produce, instead, a throng of minor voices of every race raised not in praise of any one vision but to an expression of thanks for each and especially for the very least.

In the make-or-break Texas crucible the new writer faces the same fearful yet inspiring prospects on the literary score as his forebears knew on that of oil patch or cactus range. The healthiest signs are that native writers are taking Texas seriously, are also seeing the humor in many sides of the State taken too soberly in the past. As to any place offering to the artist a ready-made pattern for theme and form, it remains true as ever that these the artist must make for himself, inventing in a sense even the place itself. To answer her haughtiest challenges, even knowing that in the end the writing may turn out to be a mere tight-fisted testament to a place which has ever insisted on the impossible of her inhabitants (while somehow in return promising and supplying a measure heaped rare as real) offers an undertaking unequalled in potential at present by any other region of the nation.

Thus travelling from Fort Worth in the north (Amon Carter's comeuppance reply to dandified Dallas), through Waco (home of Baptists and of Brann the iconoclast), Austin (city whose industry is "non-polluting" paper — Capital and seat of the sprawling University system), San Antonio (welcome-mat for the chicano-mexican migration), swinging near but missing sight & sound of killdee & Gulf at Corpus Christi, passing on to the orange orchards of Harlingen and finally arriving at palm-treed Brownsville on the border, the changing sameness, the dry and then humid heat, altered styles of year-long lightweight dress, drawling modes of address, all seem too much for any one author to handle. If he knows those areas lying beyond this narrow strip down the middle of the state, he will feel even more humbled, or rather pulled apart on this procrustean bed, incapacitated in the face of what will strike him as great stretches of the imagination, a beckoning like Scylla and Charybdis on either side threatening to wreck even an enlarged sense of place on the vast reaches of piney woods to the east (where men have lost their ways and never come out alive) or the brush country endless and exhausting to the west.

Looking to the skies near Kingsville, one takes in the long wavering lines of geese written against the billowing clouds above alternating marsh & prickly pear, but how to get them down, how to imitate such alexandrines escaping the coastal page, with that same sweep & grandeur of their going? In fields extending flat to the horizon, bundled hay lies like pungent, compact quatrains the Texas poet can barely dream of penning before the image of mesquite or oil slick breaks in upon his romantic reveries. Just as he has registered his impressions, so many prize-winning herefords of words, the blatant city lights & accents put them down as out of date, cornball, tied too closely to a tradition no town boy in his right mind could ever accept. Yet he must feel that to record alone the hotrod racket of metropolitan streets is to remain too silent upon the ingenuous twang of his country cousin's guitar. Listening to the Mexican-looking, native-born Texan at the chain store register making change in two languages at once, the writer wants to blend his images, his words, his rhythms, but wouldn't that be copying what is natural to the chicano, cutting in, riding around on a fad? How does one man find it in himself to incorporate such diversity? Where in himself can he honestly discover the right to so much land, so many tongues, at a time when corporate holdings present such a singularly evil aspect?

Indeed, it is this very paradoxical and unsettling state of things that comprises the stuff of his richest writing. And we are back to variety and the question of whether one writer can contain it all, whether he should even worry if he has managed but a meager hold on a minor part of the whole. Today there is no one figure we look to in Texas as laureate or leader, and why should we, when the landscape demands more than a single voice can ever hope to sing, urges its artists to try their hands at every available form, denying none, just as the land would have not a thorn nor a devil's-claw less in its array of satanic plants. What is needed, then, and what we are beginning to get, is a harkening (here & back) to the many stories & poems, old & new, those of the folk & those of the refined, an encouraging of each in what it would say of a place we can only know once it has been sounded by those who love its ways, those begrudging fields that yield less than we foolishly want, yet more than any man or woman will ever need to make it on.

Faced by the vastness of the task, Texas writers may in the long run come to create a smaller art, one more in keeping with their sense of the worth of each man's contribution in a land where the mythical individualist is seen at last as not so heroic in himself as he is in relation to the grander scheme of true regional representation. The Texas writers of our day indicate they are on that road by their modest carriage and the genuine message they are learning to bear.

— Dave Oliphant

73

Robert Bonazzi

HOUSTON'S ADOLESCENCE WAS MY ADOLESCENCE

I

murder capital of the world
when i was fifteen
bobby clay's mom shot at a prowler
his dad swallowed fumes in a locked garage
howard stabbed a girl because she wouldn't
she was fourteen
he was a quiet kid
terrific jumpshot

II

i have stitches in the arms i didn't break
& stitches in all the other arms too
my brother stuck a dart in my head
at forty paces
he said he took a knife away from me once
i don't remember that
he could catch a football with one hand
better than anyone with two

III

best view was the rooftop sunset
twenty years ago these backyards were neat
now they're cluttered with dog houses
chicken coops toolsheds & old truck tires
hanging from the lowest limbs

snake bayou's filled in
hills are leveled
clump of trees we called
a jungle's a parking lot
plaza's fun show was all day for a dime
now it's skin flicks
three bucks a head

IV

i came home from california baldheaded
it was 102 degrees
i was the only one off the santa fe
which is gone
& my dad didn't recognize me
i recognized him
he's the one who walked
ten miles to school in the snow

Paul Foreman

IMPRESSIONIST

Paint outdoors?
    In the summer . . .?
        In Texas?!

No, I would rather
sit in the shade
    of this chinaberry tree,
smell the smell of milkweed,
    let my tongue
fall asleep on leaves
    of prickly ash,

And watch the sun,
    A welt of bright Reason,
burn each thing to its core.

PECANS

We walk down a red clay road in Texas
towards the pecan bottom, totin' a towsack,
two gallon buckets, and a cane pole.
Gonna frail some pirate pecans.
We come to a halt and listen
to squirrels barkin' up the creek, and crows
cawin' further along the orchard;
I wonder, who owns these pecans.
Is it the man in town selling insurance,
with paper deeds locked in a steel vault?
Or do they belong to Earth, herself,
who keeps pushing up pecan sap
through the veins that root the tree,
then lets the ripe nuts fall to her chest,
or fill the craws of coons and possums.
Certain these two hobos
whose four worn-out shoes
are sticking to the clay dirt
don't own those pecans. No sir,
I make no bones about it, but I'm sure
they'll fill their pockets and towsack
and hull a few on the spot
before they mosey on.

    CAW!   CAW!   CAW!

Go on you old crows!
Swipe all these pecans
and leave old Insurance
to curse the sky when he comes
to gather his crop.
Here's clay mud in your eye,
old Insurance, and sweet native
Texas pecans in this old varmint's gut.

Joseph Colin Murphey

YIPPEE YI O TI YAY

The men in my county
who come to the Texan Cafe
each morning to drink coffee
and fight the world off
with fine old stories of how
it was, are getting older

They still wear Justin boots
fine creases in their faded khakis
and Stetson hats that curl just right
over their brows. They park their
pickups in front with the three
rifles in the back window

but now some walk in with a cane
and pale corded cheeks. They reach
for the sugar and say the grass
is greening up. They talk of Ranger
Hardy Purvis who shot that Negro
spat between the eyes fast draw

on the courthouse lawn for trying
to escape on the way to Huntsville
of Old Sam Scurlock who killed three
deer from the same stand with
one bullet, all of them in the head
fifty feet apart in the morning rain

They play the numbers
on their coffee checks to see
who pays, but on Fridays
when the Methodist minister
joins them, they take his ticket
and the loser pays all

Then they crawl slowly
back into their pickups
sitting tall and grim
and drive away easy and slim
by the bearded college boys
looking twenty years younger

TEXAS BOOMER

My father
was a graduate
of the second grade
a man who made
every strike
from Spindletop
to Eldorado
a jazz-hopping
rig-topping
bum!

You may gather
my dreams do not
equate my old spade
with grade A
bourbon- straight
He was diluted
a proud-booted
brassy sot
loud as a bass
drum!

In love he was
no man to be proud
of. His best deed
was the day his need
sowed me in a cloud
of blondness
Contrary to his wont
she was a woman
whose only evil omen
was he

Love to him was
a rabbit fit —
animal whose tail
is a white sail
over the hill! Split
his ears ever were
by a train whistle
thistle prick
of a cheap song
calling

His second-
best deed
was his going
*Christ pity his
lovers' eyes.*

TEXAS GOTHIC

This is a strong-chinned image
with a body heavy with beef
chili and beans, plus some barbecue
Whether with bourbon or some other brew
he's generally Southern Baptist with
perhaps, a touch of Methodist or Camelite:
for him always a Sunday religion

with week-day allowances
in cahoots with whatever is bent
to prosper. In a white hat, sheepskin
coat, tight pants and Australian snakeskin
boots, he can create a gasp of awe
in the fast draw of a cigar from
the pocket of his Continental

I once had no resistance
to this critter but now I know
that he grows with a meaningless chatter
of *machismo*. He coughs and wheezes
with no strength of soul
and dies with a busted heart
or the common cold

But whether he be
                        A Senator
                        A Governor
Or   A President

he definitely will be as pious
as a virgin in a cloistered convent
in the acceptance of campaign
contributions, as smooth as silk
in the pass of money
from the public till

Dave Oliphant

Palominos & Paradise

from "Cowtown Sketches"

Looking out from Brad Barrett's porch, the home on the right of his granny's housed the Rawls, mother, father, and three daughters. While not so unkempt as the Travelers' infamous weed lot, the Rawls' place presented a decidedly jungle aspect with its long uncut grass, the horses grazing it unevenly once a week, and with its wide assortment of trees, more exotic than those of any other house on the block, which shaded and loosed their inedible fruits and flowers on all sides and along the street. In the front, near the curbing, grew a chinaberry, its wrinkled yellow berries arming the neighborhood fights between bands of boys and girls, though more often pitting boys against girls. Near the Owens-Barrett side of the yard a large catalpa tree leaned its limbs along the roofs of both houses, providing the same warring bands with its long green pods, good for sword fighting, guns, whatever game required a lethal weapon.

While the chinaberry and catalpa trees served for hostilities erupting at regular intervals, on the Braun side, a solemn family in a white two-story with immaculate manicured lawn, the latticed garage of the Rawls, overgrown with muscadine and honeysuckle vines, supplied the sisters and their visiting friends with a shady and fragrant seclusion when the boys elected to hold their hands instead of throwing berries or stabbing with pods. In the Rawls' backyard, grass deeper there from no horses ever violating the greensward, were trees made for climbing — redbuds and vitex with low-hanging limbs of smooth skins and luscious-looking blooms — into which the younger couples found their way in between the battles.

Of the three daughters, Gloria was oldest, too old to take much part in her sisters' games played in garage or redbud tree. Her teenage boyfriend would accompany her on his own palomino when she herself would ride hers in of a Saturday morning from the stable where he was kept during the rest of the week. Living on the very edge of the city, it was easy to enjoy having a horse without the neighbors complaining, though even riding them in one day a week bothered the Brauns, who stared from their porch, just daring the mounts to let one dropping fall on their spotless lawn. The Rawls' grass was allowed to grow, partly to give the horses something to feed on while their riders sat showing off for the neighborhood kids and trading horsetalk as a substitute for necking, but grew tall as well because Mr. Rawls found a bottle after office hours and on weekends more stimulating than sweating at the bar of the pushmower. Mr. Rawls was rarely if ever to be seen outside the house except on leaving for and returning from work. Mrs. Rawls could be heard from as Mr. Rawls waxed tighter, but otherwise neither interfered with the daughters' lives. The father never interested himself in what the girls were doing and the mother never meddled, except to call them in a little after dark if they had not come in on their own.

Granny Owens did not like her neighbors the Rawls, knowing as she did of the father's drinking problem. She felt the whole family was immoral and tried to discourage her daughter's boy from playing next door in that den of iniquity. Yet she did not forbid her grandson from going there, except when she caught him throwing things at the girls, when she would not allow him to leave his own well-trimmed yard. Granny did not like it either when the boys and girls sneaked off to the garage or to the fenced backyard where she could not keep an eye on Bradley. She knew he was sweet on the youngest sister, and though she never kept him from seeing her, she did not trust any of those Rawls girls. The best proof of a sinful nature to Granny was a girl riding around bareback and barefoot on a big old horse.

Gloria's fetish for horses had begun when she was the age of her primary school sisters. At her urging the parents had finally broken down and bought her the palomino pony, which had grown with her, its varied shades of brown hair a match for Gloria's long, wavy blonde and cream-colored blend. From her own all-absorbing interest in horses and the men who rode them had come the younger sisters' enthusiasm for western movies, and in particular those starring Gene Autry. Rather than being fascinated by horse flesh, Betsy and Ruth Ann were attracted more by the film hero himself, but they too could praise the idol's horse Champ and admire their sister's riding style. A favorite pastime for the younger sisters, when they felt like disagreeing with the neighborhood boys, who one and all preferred the hard-riding Roy Rogers, was to argue how much smarter Champ was than the rival horse Trigger. The boys countered by pointing out that Trigger could do better tricks any day, like rearing up or running to Roy when he whistled, and that besides, Roy could sing, Dale was pretty, and Bullet was quite a dog. Yet Betsy and Ruth Ann were indomitable when it came to Gene Autry and his easy-going way of winning in the end. Anyone they said could tell his voice was the real thing. But then their examples went beyond the obvious and touched on areas the boys could not so easily appreciate, such as his handsome smile and his comfortable look in the saddle. The arguments would go on and on until the girls clearly had the better of the boys, at which time the latter chose chinaberries and catalpa pods to prove their superiority to any line of reasoning.

The youngest, Betsy, was in the same grade as Brad Barrett, though more mature as is commonly the case with girls. Like the other boys,

Brad sided with Roy against Gene Autry, though it often hurt him to do so in front of Betsy, just as it never seemed right to throw berries at her, though he felt he had to when the other boys did so. Betsy, for her part, pulled no punches when she took on Brad in the battle over which cowboy star was tops. Brad did not really care that much but found that he just naturally preferred Roy and that somehow it was incumbent upon him to defend the actor against Betsy's impassioned attack. His defense was never very good, for what he liked about the Rogers movie was more the action than the man. He would see in his mind's eye the unreal color of the picture, of faded or overdeep tints, the blood always too orangey, yet all of this appealing to him in a way he could not explain, and of course he knew it had nothing to do with a horse and rider or how the one looked on the other. Above all it was the action of the Rogers film that he favored, like the one he remembered most, where the bad guys were smuggling in Chinese in empty oil cans, one can rolling off the truck and giving away the outlaws' black market business. These were the memorable parts of the cowboy's picture shows, but how could he expect to convince Betsy using such episodes when she was only concerned with the way Gene Autry dressed.

When the girls and boys talked horse-opera stars they sat on the two concrete slabs high as the foundation of the Rawls' house, set beside cement steps leading steeply to the porch, swing, and front door. Their legs dangling, boys on one side and girls on the other, the arguments led inevitably to name-calling, chunking of chinaberries, and jabbing of catalpa pods, the boys having jumped down from the slabs, leaving the girls to return with their tongues the best they could or to retreat inside the house. But on other days, laying aside the cowboy question, Ruth Ann and Randy would seek the garage arbor while Betsy and Brad crawled into redbud or vitex leaves.

On such an occasion Betsy had already beaten him into the boughs of the vitex, Brad's heavy brogans slipping on the slick bark and making it hard for him to climb. Reaching at last to where Betsy sat plucking a twig with its rich purple flowers to stick in her dark brown hair, doing something wonderful to her olive skin, so unlike that of her lighter-complected sisters, Brad wanted to kiss her quickly before he lost his courage. He had thought of the kiss time and again, had almost managed it at a Halloween party when the lights were off, but as usual his fear of her unknown response had restrained him from nearing her face.

Now the problem was how to get up close enough without falling out of the tree. His shoes kept sliding when he tried to move around behind, so as to catch her when she would least expect it and he would not have to look into her face until he was already pressing his lips to hers, those soft, bluish-red lips. He thought of Tarzan and envied his agile acrobatics among the branches. Struggling to get to the limb above and behind his Jane, Brad suddenly felt Betsy's hand on his sock, pulling it down, then moving further down, pulling at the bowknot, loosing the string of his shoe. He froze and then carefully turned about to sit down on the limb above hers, when Betsy began with the other shoe, loosing the knot, loosing the string where it criss-crossed, then pulling the oxford off by the heel and letting it drop to the ground. Having done the same with the other, she pulled off his socks by the toes, uncovering two milky-white feet. She stroked the foot nearest, Brad's heart pounding and his lips trembling for hers.

You should go barefoot so your feet won't be so white, she said, looking up at Brad with a disapproving squint of her hazel eyes. And why do you wear those funny socks with so many colors? I'll bet Gene Autry wouldn't be caught dead with that kind of sock. She continued to stroke his foot. He wanted to bend over and kiss her but no limb was available to lower himself down by. He slid down from his limb onto hers in hopes she would turn her face to his but instead she turned the other way and grabbed the branch by both hands, letting her legs down and swinging there below him for a few moments before dropping on to the ground. Bye, she yelled, running off through the high grass and on to the back of the open-ended garage, tearing off a sprig of honeysuckle as she entered the arbor. Sucking on one of the flowers, she turned and waved before leaving Brad all alone in the vitex tree.

Tasting her mouth sweeter than honeysuckle, and as if pledging allegiance to the flag, willing to swear to her on a stack of Bibles, Brad sat on for a time feeling with his right hand the heart beats subside, then eased himself slowly down to earth. Picking up his shoes and socks he started through the grass, but finding it cold and tickly, stopped, and, standing, pulled on socks and shoes, tying and balancing himself on one foot at a time.

He could not believe he had failed to kiss Betsy. He despised his argyle socks, the pair his granny had bought him at his request. The orange and brown diamonds now recalled to his mind the Roy Rogers picture show, the blood on the Chinaman's cheek when they opened the can and found him dead. He would always prefer Roy to that fatty Gene Autry, but he would never wear those ugly socks again. He went back to the vitex, leaned against it, and removed his shoes, ripping off the socks, stretching their elastic tops.

With his shoes back on, he let himself out the back gate, into the alley, where the trash cans stood. He opened one and threw the dead Chinaman's orangey blood-stain-colored argyle socks into the smelly barrel, closed the lid on the evidence, and walked with feet feeling as naked in shoes as the knowledge was of that corpse left lying in the garbage can.

Naomi Shihab

THE PALACE CAFE, SHINER, TEXAS

i walk into old places / something clicks
i'm in love with heavy china cups
stacked upside down on a clean towel

it's hard to order
COFFEE i blurt
because the lady is frowning at me

she pours
i sip
but that's not it, that's not what i want

i want this room, the sense of this room,
rooted in a million lunches,
the fat pies cooling on the wire racks

i'll take the sweaty backs of the old men
leaning over beer at 10 a.m.
discussing parades they didn't attend

i've been following this world all over Texas,
opening screens to find it waiting
in places called Shiner, Buffalo Gap, Quitman

every time we meet it's real
it has a smell and a taste
okra, butter beans

every time i eat here
i can't get enough

THINKING ABOUT COWS AT TEN O'CLOCK IN THE MORNING, ABILENE

The marker reads : "Western Cattle Trail"
for a second you remember Western movies,
dust rising up around hooves,
the wild driven look of their faces

Now it's tires
Sky Hawk, Gremlin,
a stampede of Rabbits and Pintos
in appropriate lanes

Lately my favorite absolute involves cows —
wherever you go, cows are eating

Across Texas, their slow bodies punctuate fields
You can depend on their bowed heads,
the little ones close by the mothers

When I didn't eat meat
I could look a cow in the eye
Now I say
Forgive us
for using you
to drive ourselves
where we think we need to go

SITE OF THE INDIAN FIGHTS OF 1871, ABILENE

little purple flowers under our feet

it's hard to imagine
the Indians finding one another
in this huge space
and having something to fight about

Robert Joe Stout

NATIVE TEXAN

Arm in the window, hat bent back exposing lack of hair,
workshirt (the same khaki he's worn for years)
fitting like iguana fins
where the laundry starch pinches the sleeves,
he knocks his pipe apart
and laughs, hoarsely,
"I oughta know! I bin here all m'life. . . ."
It's true: fifty-seven now, bone hard,
he gave the earth his boyhood
(". . . s'poor we even et the mule. . !")
and lived on squirrels and turnips
until Roosevelt——still his square-jawed saviour——
pumped the country full of C.C.C.
"Gotta git—ol' lady's waitin!" Hand's cracked leather
dips inside the window, gadgets at the pickup's frozen air.
The Wallace sticker on the bumper winks.

If he were just one man—a mixed-up farmer—
I could shrug and let the image fade.
But he's a part of every town in Texas
—definition, history and hate.
Brick streets, pre-depression houses,
shoppingcenters, factories, the lakes
circle out past shacks of servant Negroes
to the hills where Nike missiles gleam.

Jon Bracker

Yard Sale

Slamming the screendoor and slopping down the steps,
a wraith with teen-aged head haloed by curlers like an iron-knuckled fist
informs the mountain in shorts chairing the backyard sale,
"Grammaw said them Avon bottles is fifty cents apiece."

Awaiting the decision, the two
malevolently eye customers
heavily hovering over bottles and babyclothes
set on doors on saw-horses above the dirty earth.

Two kittens are also for sale.
In and out of a tumped-over box
they pat at each other, lively
in the drowsy summer sun.

"Ain't they *cute*?" a mother-in-law demands.

"We had more but my husband run over two of them
last week," the mountain, shifting, smiles,
neighborly and ready to be nice.

FLOWERS

Flowers are
                    the grandmothers I never knew,
The aunts I was moved away from as a child.

They are the porches,
                        and the swings depending from thick hooks
Secured into wooden roofs lofted by unfluted spool-like columns
Joined at the base by slats, on top of which an unfragile ledge
Was there for your heels
Whether you sat in slightly jiggling dark-green metal chairs
Or in gray or white or dark-green woven thrones light to be moved
From sun to shade or back into the sun.

Flowers are many things: grandmothers, aunts,
Porches, swings and things to be revealed,
But only bachelor's buttons and nasturtiums
Are male, to me.

Hydrangeas,
Hydrangeas summon up the days.
Hydrangeas sum up the years, their heads
Like the head of Miss Mary Ellen Oatman (elderly Southern female
Educator, placid as a sheep behind her desk)
Dipping a little on their stems, as though above the leaves
Reading Keats out loud, nodding to our quiet words . . .
There would be lemonade.

Flowers—perhaps honeysuckle, perhaps not—on boughs brushed by the wind
Are the thwacking tails of flattened dogs
Porch-raised above the heated cement walk
Where white alyssum's honied breath's exhaled
And ageratum, purple-blue, deepens in another dusk.

And roses when there were roses
Were all the gardened women of that world.
Ladies, ladies.

Susan Bright

texas lady, leotard and blue jeans
            bouffant blond tint
            blue eye-shadow
            mascara, lipstick
            (at 8 a.m.)
            have another cigarette
            while your clothes dry
            you grace that
            est/10,8396 chevy pickup
            you look like
            a cowboy's woman
            with your yellow belt
            svelte hips
            thin lips
            you're
            mean
            you have spunk

David Rafael Wang

THE BATH

Squatting on his haunches
he soaps methodically
his chest and neck
then pouring a bucket of water
over his head, the suds
streaking down his back,
he seems oblivious
of the world with the lambs
maahing and nudging around his legs
as the barn door opens
and a shaft of light
catches the luminescence
of his face.

Big Damon's Quilt

For John R. Humphreys, **always**

Old brown trunk, lock all tarnished: to fit a key inside takes a lot of working. Big Damon hammers at the rusty lock: yellow hands pounding time's weir.

Vestal watches: *he'll get it open soon and scoop out pecans. They'll be papershells grown in brown sap.* But it isn't just knowing this, but rather watching him that makes her skin feel tingly. It's really the way he covers those pecans, like they were hidden gold wrapped in his grandmother's quilt. *Her name . . . the one that made that quilt . . . it was Mourning Water, and she's my great-great grandmother: a real Indian too. She sewed that quilt with blue threads, and it's all blue. Big Damon says she made it for a good luck sign.*

"Good 'ole papershells," Big Damon calls, bending over the chest. "Catch 'em, kid; they got brittle shells. Yeah, you kin crack 'em. They ain't too hard for even a li'l mouse."

Big Damon pads to the cowhide chair. Sound: lone and heavy like a big dog's feet with no place to go. He winks his eye at Vestal: "I suppose everyone around here knows that it takes a feller like me, Big Damon as they say, to graft these papershell pecans."

Yes. Everybody calls him Big Damon and I call him Big Damon too. But he's my Grandpa just like Grandma's my Grandma. Reckon I couldn't say Grandpa to Big Damon if I wanted. 'Cause it's like puttin' him side by side with Grandma, and that ain't right even if they wuz married a long time ago.

"I tell you, Vestal, it's the way you graft the tree that makes the shell. Got to git a branch at just the right time. That's when the sap's runnin'. 'An it ain't jus' any branch will do. Gotta git a stout one from the Guadalupe River bottomland for these pecans if you want 'em to be the grandkids of real kings."

"Papershell pecans," Vestal thinks some ageless water has washed them white while they hung on the weighted branches, even, crouching in green pods. She has watched them growing in Grandma's backyard on the old pecan tree Big Damon grafted before he left. Watched until her head got dizzy looking up the tree and down again to the grave at the base. And spinning around and around, she saw the first brown clusters hazy under the webs where spiders lived in the spring. Grandma would stop her watching: "There you, Vestal, you stop that gapin' there like a li'l ninny." A miracle dream of spider's webs and pecan papershells broken because her Grandma had to stop it: "Gotta watch you all the time, young'un, or you'll be runnin' on poor Ollie's grave . . . My poor boy in that ole wooden box, like we couldn't afford him a decent buryin' . . . It was his idea of a-buryin', an' shameful I call it."

Big Damon's fingers snap, cracking pecans. He digs out little bronze sections of meat, tight-fitting in tan-fading-to-white shells. Two or three pecans fall on the floor, sap-filled marbles leaking through shriveling grandfather branches.

"The kernel ain't hard to find if you know jus' where to crack 'em." Massive and gaunt-faced, Big Damon sits looking at the long naked core inside, grandchild of a rich river bottom, progenitor of a king-sized pecan. And while his sharp eyes inspect hard, his ancient nose sits still — that nose which came from his grandmother, the Comanche girl who married Lucien Callamades — a Spaniard-Frenchman.

Vestal is thinking: *and she . . . Mourning Water . . . was just fifteen and ran off from milking a cow to marry: and with no shoes on and a hole in her apron.* But Vestal is saying: "Big Damon, didn't you plant the tree in Grandma's backyard?" Cotton print panties squirming on the rug in front of Big Damon, Vestal remembers almost what she saw in a dream she had once about him.

"Yeah, an' I grafted 'em the spring you were born . . . and your mother, my own Vestie, held you there watching. You wuz a tiny babe. I never thought your mother would be gone so soon. She wuz a strong girl and happy, my Vestie, an' it wuzn't right to me, d'yuh hear? I mean them a-prayin' over her an' lettin' her die . . . Ollie an' your Grandma . . . . . . like it wuz prayin' she needed an' not a doctor. She died, my strong girl, an' Ollie, well, he lived on."

Ollie had it first an' Mother caught it while tendin' him and Ollie got well and Mother died. I wuz just a baby. She wuz strong and Ollie wuz always weak, Grandma said, an' she says too: 'Sinful I call it, buryin' my poor Ollie later on under that pecan tree in a wooden box. It wuz his idea.

Once Vestal dreamed Big Damon was a pecan, and watching his leather-yellow skin in the weak light of his lonely hotel room, she thinks she sees his skin fading into a cracking white shell. In the dream it was like a big pecan was cracking open and each crack was cutting through a current of time until the wrinkled kernel inside was laid naked for an instant, and Vestal peeped.

"What you been studyin' in school, Child?" Big Damon never talks long about the summer his daughter died. "Been makin' the grade in history; is it still your mark?"

And she wuz just fifteen and Callamades asked her to go when she wuz milkin' a cow. And they run off: her standin' there marryin' 'an holdin' a bouquet of bluebonnets like she sewed on the quilt — an

Indian girl with no shoes on and a hole in her apron.

"Well, I been studyin' 'bout Bowie an' Fannin an' how they fought 'ole Santy Anna at Goliad. You ever been there — to Goliad?"

"Yeah . . . Goliad's a town near Cuero and Gonzales, not too far from where the Callamades first settled . . . Hey, what yuh doin', Child, sittin' on the floor?"

An' before it wuz a republic, there was four flags flyin' over Texas . . . the Indians they came first, then it wuz the Spaniards, the French, and then came the Mexicans.

Big Damon waves his arms at Vestal. He looks part ghost, she thinks.

I guess it's because he wears white overalls all the time and look at the black streaks on 'em. He gits 'em black paintin' houses, an' they're brown an' green streaks from paintin' brown an' green roofs. He smells like a tree in resin time . . . an' lookin' at him with those streaks is like that dream . . . only what was it like now . . . in that dream . . . once there inside?

"I said, what yuh doin' sittin on the floor, Child? Don't yuh know a chair's for lay-dees, an' say you won't be the first one to sit in my leather chair neither."

Cotton print-panties against flaking leather, she wishes she could move back to the floor and look at Big Damon's chair.

Grandma says don't sit in the seat of sinners. Says Jesus said so. Says it wuz sinful buryin' him under the tree an' him so sweet an' prayerful layin' there in a little wooden box.

"There, that's better. A chair befits any lay-dee who comes visitin' Big Damon. I'll swear if you ain't some squirmer, though. Just like my Vestie . . . No, she never could stay still neither, always hoppin' around an' laughin' just like you. A strong girl too . . . an' yur Grandma always after her, her an' Ollie both with them prayin' sprees."

Named him Oliver but called him Ollie, Grandma says, because he wuzn't strong from a baby on . . . he'd stand around all quiet an' prayin' an' talkin' about eternal peace.

"So you're makin' it fine with your history, are yuh? Reckon you couldn't tell me whuts the state flower?"

"Bluebonnets. My teacher says they grow all over hillsides, and I'm always seein' them on graves."

"Thet's true . . . say, lemme tell yuh how they got their name. A long time ago the Indians wuz very sad. It was the Comanche folks out on the plains that wuz all downcast. Yuh see they'd been havin' lotsa trouble. Couldn't grow no corn an' berries because of a drought an' they wuz a cold an' hungry bunch. The chiefs and the medicine men called a council fire and asked the Great Spirit to help 'em. An' the Great Spirit tole 'em that afore their sufferin' ended to make a burnt offerin', somethin' dear to the whole tribe.

"Now the chiefs and medicine men didn't know it, but while they wuz prayin' an' invokin' the Great Spirit the high chief's little daughter wuz listenin' an' takin' in all they wuz sayin'. Now it happened too she wuz holdin' a li'l doll close to her heart . . . This li'lo doll was made of doeskin an' had long black braids of horsehair, an' on its head was a head-dress of bright blue feathers.

"Well, this little Indian princess tole herself: 'I know the dearest possession of the tribe. I know what I gotta do.' So when all the tribe wuz asleep she hugged her doll close an' slipped out of the tepee where her father was sleepin'. Her moccasins didn't make a sound as she was takin' a red coal from them that had been the council fire but wuz now all covered with ashes. She went to a hill close by an' built a little fire. On the fire she laid her precious doll, prayin' to the Great Spirit for her people to have food an' happiness again.

"But all at once the wind caught up the ashes an' scattered 'em all over the hillside. The little princess patted the ground where the fire had been to make sure they wuzn't a spark left, an' under her hands she felt somethin' soft, but she couldn't pick it up on accounta it wuz fastened to the ground. An' next mornin' that whole hillside wuz a beautiful sight, for Child, do you know what? Why, thet hillside wuz covered with bright blue flowers — jes' the color of the doll's head-dress.

"But this ain't all. There's more. When the chief heard what his li'l girl had done, he called all the Comanches together an' told 'em: 'The Great Spirit has taken our offerin' an' evil passed from us. These here blue flowers are sent us as a sign of peace an' plenty.' "

An' there's bluebonnets standin' on Ollie's grave, wavin' in the wind an' sometimes gettin' beat against the ground when the pecans fall down . . . it's sad . . . that grave.

Big Damon is his happiest when telling Vestal stories, but he loves talking to her about their region almost as much: "Can you tell me the bird for this state?"

"Sure. It's a mockin' bird, that's what."

Once I heard one singin' over Ollie's grave, first like one bird, then like another. Sittin' there so lonesome an' makin' a wild crazy chatter.

"You're sure makin' your mark today . . . Say, when I wuz a boy I used to whistle at them birds, an' they'd always whistle back like they wuz laughin' at me with their mockin'. Well, you tole me what the state flower an' bird is. Now whut about the tree?"

"Miss Gammon says it's a pecan tree. She's my art teacher, an' she has us make all kinds of things in class. She says the tree stands for friendship, so we oughta use it to make sumthin' for our friends. An' so that's how come I made somethin' for you, an' here it is.. I got A in her class for doin' it too."

Vestal hands her grandfather the tiny image of himself that she has made in school. On a pecan, she has painted a gaunt face with an

Indian nose. Two black eyes made of tiny black beads stare out from the shell while a sharp sliver of rock placed in the position of a nose sticks straight out over a body unbowed.

Vestal has set the head on a cardboard cut-out body with painted white overalls. There are black streaks running up and down the overalls, and brown and green ones too.

"Well, Lordy, if that ain't the beatinest'," Big Damon laughs. He lifts Vestal up, tosses her gently in the air, and then puts her down again. And all the time he rocks hard with laughter in this unexpected gift. Vestal titters too, pleased with his thankfulness.

They have just stopped laughing when the door opens, and Grandma runs into the room, her minister following her, but stopping at the door. "You take yore filthy hands off that child, you 'ole devil," Grandma screams out running straight toward Big Damon with an umbrella thrust out at him as though it were a sword.

"Now Sister, let me handle this, please," pleads the Minister as he rushes up behind her and takes her by the arm. "Kidnappin' ain't nuthin' for a righteous God-fearing Christian like you to have to be a-copin' with."

All this time Big Damon has just been standing there, the lines of his recent laughter freezing now into the stone ridges of mockery, now appearing in the wide, hard line, which is his mouth. All he can do is watch wildly and with disbelief as Grandma struggles loose from the Preacher to shake her umbrella under his own sharply-chiseled Indian nose.

"For a long time I been prayin' for your soul," Grandma screams on . . . "I been prayin' your wickedness 'ud end, an' you'd be ready to meet your Savior, and here you been makin' mischief right on top of my prayers. Thought you'd get away with it, then, did you? Kidnappin' this child an' bringin' her here to your sinful 'ole hotel room . . . But the Lord called me tonight at prayer meetin' and' led me here."

"That is to say, Mr. Damon, sir," said the minister again, thrusting himself between the two of them: "The Lord led Deacon Cryer through Kosanky's alley tonight and the Deacon saw you leadin' this innocent child . . ."

But Vestal interrupts: "That's not so . . . I wanted to come here . . . I begged him to bring me over here, an' I'll keep comin' back."

"You, Vestal," scolds Grandma. "You hush lettin' him put words in your mouth. We know what he's up to and we won't let him hurt you. He can't be trusted ever again. He killed my Ollie . . . just as sure as if he'd pushed him outa that tree."

At last Big Damon speaks; his words come roaring out: "She lies. It's blasphemy, that's what. The kid was weak an' sickly an' after he got up from that bed of typhoid he went half-wild, prayin' all the time, jus' pushin' my sick Vestie into her grave when what she needed wuz a doctor, not a coffin. An' after she was gone . . . I couldn't help it. I lost my temper one day an' started to whip him. I wuz doin' it jus' so's I could straighten him out. But he ran off from me an' climbed that tree. He did it, weak as he wuz, before I could get to him. I tell you that boy was losin' his mind an' it was all because of **her** continual Bible talkin'. He climbed up that tree I had just grafted an' the limb broke under him."

"You drove him crazy tellin' him he killed Vestie, like he oughta died instead of her. But I knowed God had spared him to be a preacher," shouts Grandma.

Big Damon trembles. Standing up straight, he shakes his yellowed fists above Grandma's and the minister's heads. He cries: "Now get outta here. Out, damn you. Yeah, you kin take the kid home with yuh . . . I ain't sayin' it's any place for her to be here with an old coot like me. But don't start thinkin' I ain't gonna see her ever . . . an' whut's more: jus' you satisfy yourselves that I'm not about to let you kill her either with yu're prayin' sprees an' crazy palaverin', the way you killed my Vestie. Nawh sir, as long as she's a little girl, Big Damon will be around to keep an eye on Vestal here."

Grandma grabs Vestal by the hand, and as she starts toward the door screams again: "We'll run you outa town . . ."

And the minister pleads all the while: "Please folks. Let's stop this and have a word of prayer and then take the child home quietly."

But Big Damon reaches him in two angry steps; picks him up by the coat and pushes him through the door: "Ain't no prayin' an cavortin' an' jabberin' a-goin on under my roof."

Vestal can see one of his hands as she moves along the hallway past him with her grandmother. And she knows she can never forget what she has glimpsed there quickly — that little pecan doll, now cracked and torn inside his palm.

And looking, she remembers: it was a tree in that storm and its branches were shaking pecans off on a little grave underneath. Then it thundered and one great pecan — a whitish-colored one which had black stripes — crashed off and cracked open. It was just lying there cracked naked onto the grave below.

And then it was so quiet in that place, with blue flowers covering up its kernel . . . its seed . . . like an ancient quilt waving in the wind.

Ray Gonzalez

intruder

I stand
beneath mountains,
jealous of their
darkening stones.
the cottonwoods
around them
are grey, rusted cans
at their roots.
I watch a cloud
part above this
old, spanish mission.
I climb steps,
smell ghosts
of holy water
at the doors.
in search of a
miracle, I stand
beneath the arch,
jealous of its
cracking stones.

paso del norte

in the bar,
I float in tecate.
the whore belongs outside.
I grow old and fat
in the desert
without desire to die.

summer is an illegal alien
clinging to my arms.
thinking of comfort,
I see the rio grande
cares for its mud.

Jan Seale

Pearl Bell Pittman
1888-1976

She lies 1000 miles away,
all life-support tubes removed.
She breathes in and out, day after day.
I think of her great pendulous breasts
like warm loaves of bread
on which I rested my head in the back seat
through Arkansas and Tennessee one summer —
now shrivelled, crawling under her arms
like little shamed dogs as she lies there.
I see her thighs, hairless,
one bound in a brace since it snapped
one day as she merely stood:
seven babies came through these posts
(the seventh she told me of
one rainy afternoon sitting in
a certain gray armchair —
I horribly fascinated over the dead baby's
perfect curls, the prettiness of his face,
Grandfather wrapping him up and taking him out back.)

Her hands twist open jars
of pickles, tomatoes, okra, black-eyed peas;
they skin onions, pluck feathers
from steaming headless chickens,
flick pinches of baking powder into biscuit dough.
They pick about in the turnip greens
for her favorite piece of hog jowl.
Delicate now, the tough, stiff fingers
lift the canaries' cage door,
set in the lid of crumbled egg yolk.
She has me come to see the two eggs
in the corner nest, "quietly so as not
to disturb the motherbird."

I see her great astounding Victorian body —
six-foot-tall bride with a sober hand
resting on Grandfather's sitting-down shoulder.
The wedding — a Sunday night after revival meeting,
a trip 3 miles in a buggy home to her house,
a sister going upstairs with her

to help with a white nightgown,
wide pink satin ribbon woven down the front,
how she trembled when her sister left her
at the top of the stairs,
how she righted herself with a small smile
when Grandpa, ascending, said,
"Why Pearl, you look so pretty!"
(She wouldn't tell me more.
He had been dead fifteen years that afternoon.)

I think of her as a seven year old
on a train three days and nights
from Mississippi to Texas,
women and children in the passenger car,
men two cars back with the cattle
and household goods.

Another trip later, much later,
her first-born dying in her arms
for want of milk. She rode two
summer days in a wagon to exchange
David Lee for his cousin.
Home again with a strange baby,
fat and ready for weaning to the cup.

Now my Amazon grandmother
lies a great broken continent,
a land over-grazed;
breast tumor removed, colon unobstructed,
cataracts frozen, skin cancers erased,
bladder dilated — all the unnecessary,
acting-up parts long since removed:
womb, tonsils, appendix, gall bladder.

I want to get in bed beside her,
warm myself against her massiveness,
hear the punctuating sucks and clicks
her tongue makes cleaning her teeth
of chicken bits as she thinks of the next part
to the story she is telling.

I want to line up like a paper doll with her,
staring straight ahead on a genealogy chart —
my mother between us holding our hands.

I want to pick through the homestead
in the Indian Territory
for corset stays, sachet bags,
her churn lid, next year's dahlia bulbs.

I want to tell her it is all right
to have lived thinking mainly about
turnips and egg custard, the neighbor's child
with polio, whether the road out front
will be oiled down today or tomorrow.

A part of me lies in her eighty-eight-year-old
death-ridden body.
A part of her walks in my thirty-six-year-old
death-ridden body.

Goodnight, my Amazon lady.
Thank you for my bones.

Carolyn Maisel

The land of the much loved
and unwise is a yellow target

in a yellow desert. Ma said
if she lived to be a hundred, she'd

always be in the poorhouse. Her good heart
blasts away at everything,
like a passionate shotgun.

Witnessing

(In Three Voices)

Aviaries, bee-hives, beasts of evangelism
out of our childhood, the sin in animals,
the raw genitals of Grandfather Monkey.

Baptism of water and fire, no angel tongues, the humpbacked
black devil hangs like a baby at my tits. The hump touched
by every hopeful peasant is my baby, my darling,
how I will not give him up, no . . .

                *   *   *

Bobby Hearne shot Bobby Woodruff by accident,
he said, in the swamp, carried him a ways
and left him propped against a cypress knee
in five inches of water to run the last mile
for help. The pellets pierced his throat, arm and side.
From the shattered larynx came high-pitched
frothing whistles that would have been words or screams.

In summer boys went to Red Clay Ditch
to swim. Two drowned, no one told
exactly how. My cousin Billie Douglas lost his right
eye from the infectious clay
beaten into him during a fight.

Day and night the shift men labor in refineries.
Uncountable lights and flares and filmy poisons
decorate the river edges. By the catalytic crackers
and along the pipelines huge vats of water tremble,
when the acid exploded on my father the crew
got him in fast. His eyes are uncountable faceted scars,
a brilliance along the dark margins.

Instead of the river we had a green-tiled
baptistry. The church darkened, the distant
light above the choir loft revealed
Brother Gayer's head and hands sticking out
of his black suit and the newly-born
emerged dripping.

That high-placed pool was small
and deep. The pastor put his white handkerchief

over your mouth and nose and laid you under.
Your leg jerked. How long would he keep you there,
your lungs were not prepared, they hurt.
Clumsily he brought you up again.

The girl with the ugliest name in Sunday School
was baptized before me. The old Brother
said her name for mine and the blessing
was lost. Perhaps it dissolved in the green
unsteady water.

We sang Bringing in the Sheaves and drove
to Louisiana honky-tonks in the woods, into
liquor, cars sliced on drawbridges, the
newly dead sunk into bayous. Their bodies
did not rise. The sheriff and skilled divers
brought them up.

*　*　*

there are hands in the solitary flowers of the sheets
and water circles in the pool around a flower as around a hand

there are hands in the solitary flowers of the sheets
it is your own hand at the wrist

of the doctor, the poor man, the gentle thief in you
moves cells and eggs

the silvery circuitry of your eye encodes it
in a clear air so liquid it might be

water rising like voices over your head
and shoulders like your best-fitting

dress or the strong hands of your husband
holding within you a breath

connected to the air,
even your feet and hands shine,

the dark beds, sex and event,
acquire a case, hands and voices,

sea, shore, geography, the sun emerges
you emerge, a small shining eye into each day

besmilr brigham

THEY GOT WET, MOJADA

*two Otomi friends
from Zimapan*

crossing at Del Rio the river
washed
up deep as their hearts

their hearts in the river

they walked
nine days and nine nights
picked nuts like the squirrels
hid with the animals

following the *monte*
indians
camped on rabbit hunts
indians and coyotes

bows and arrows held above the water

arms extended the border patrol
didn't see them
they walked into, through the
country
still as the animals
(moved strange deer hunting water holes)

wearing
a hide of surplus clothes, and it was easy
they looked
a part of the earth

they walked on

Betsy Colquitt

Honor Card

Five by seven, aged brown,
it confers in fine penmanship
privileges on Miss Eddie Young
for her good scholarship,
Spring 1902, McElhaney's Academy,
the academy a note now
in someone's history
of Major Erath's county.

She was bright and had good bones,
now gone to earth, and heavy hair
that lasted almost long enough,
and in 1902, too poor to stay,
left the academy
with contempt for her father
who couldn't pay
couldn't manage hen and chickens,
squandered the little he made
on books, the only things he owned
or wanted to, and read
driving a borrowed plow
on a rented farm.

And from the womb was angry
with her mother, passive ninety years,
a cow birthing in season,
who widowed dragged
her stairstep progeny pillar-
to-post to bed in unwelcoming houses,
and spent her last twenty years
in spare rooms waiting death
to come like a dark bridegroom
and he did and found her sleeping.

And fifteen, their firstborn,
she my mother left
whichever rundown farm
where cotton never made
    furrows what they were
    and weevils rampant
to work for money

selling in a general store
and buying there almost her wages
    the gold bracelet delicately chased;
    apricot mull for dress so lovely
    it stayed sixty years unfading
    in her mind; and tortoise comb
    to become the lavish hair.

This of course is long ago
and finding honor card
of her abandoned school
in her death-abandoned house,
I conjure by this relic
this once girl
most recent to me old woman
who, wheelchaired, counted hour by hour
'one two three ten,' beginning again
a hundred times, knowing such numbers
get no honor cards
nor starting the alphabet with k;
who screamed at thoughts
meandering like a buried river
through terrain of dying brain;
and cried at her one good hand
gauzed like a boxer's against her jerking
from her flesh
unwanted intensive cares.

Contemptuous of her pooring
    rich beside her father's
and of passiveness
    mighty beside her mother's
and angrier at herself
than she ever was at anyone,
she tried again and again
to escape her paralyzed world,
restore brain to order, body to use,
but numbers were random
letters lost
and motion only dearest fiction.

And frustrated
she raged at this old woman
unable to please the ghost
of Mr. McElhaney or God
and certainly not herself.

I like to think her now
beyond rage terror tears
beyond forgiveness and forgiving,
turning young light
in raiment bright as apricots
soft as mull, her hair splendid
beside Bernice's, her wrists
supple and gauzed only by gold,

and in honor and God's grace
moving sure as star
radiant as constellations
easy in Zion
and easy too in self.

Stephen Shu Ning Liu

TORMENTA DE ARENA

When August wind in
the Texas panhandle
begins to roll and
voluptuously tears
apart a schoolgirl's
skirt and takes off
a cowboy's hat and
brings you and me
yellow sand that is
enough to cover up
the cattle
and fields
and rooftops
and the sky,
you may call the sun
an illusive moon and
the world a boiling sea
which is too rough to
travel even
for a Texan.

Fish or Cut Bait

The uncle, home on shore leave, wore his regulation khaki trousers, tee shirt, and canvas shoes. He carried a hoe. His nephew wore bib overalls, no shirt, and no shoes, and around his neck hung a bead chain with his uncle's dogtags, which he could keep for another week. He carried a moss-filled syrup can. He had a folding knife in one pocket and a box of .22 shells in another.

They moved gracefully through the bottoms searching out chunks of stranded driftwood, which the uncle rolled with his hoe, alert for snakes. He then tilled the damp humus for salamanders. When he found a salamander, or "puppydog," he put it under the moss in the can to be used to bait the line, alternately with the large crawfish.

During the past week the man and the boy had spent most of their time in the bottoms. They got up early each morning and quietly ate the enormous breakfasts of biscuits, gravy, and fried game which the man's sister-in-law cooked for them. Meat was rationed. Then they went about their business of hunting and fishing, telling the boy's mother, "Don't look for us till you see us coming — but keep the grease hot!"

She had been in a good mood all week.

"Ten," the boy said, adding another "puppydog" to his can.

"Enough," the man said.

They returned to the Blue Hole in a sweeping, waist-deep bend of the river, where the uncle had decided to set line. The Hole had always been there in the belly of the bend where the river swept it out. The opposite bank above the Hole was green with moss, and the dry sandbar where they stood was white. The wet sand and gravel slanting into the water were golden. It was late spring. Light filtered through fresh, green beech leaves.

"It **looks** like a good place," the boy said.

"I money-back guarantee it." He gave the boy the free end and unrolled the line carefully, because at every three-foot stage there was a drop line with a new, sharp hook. He'd made the line while at sea. Once the line was unwound it had to be kept tight, or the hooks would tangle. "Through the middle of the bend — so we get the channel, see?"

"Yeah."

"How deep is the Hole this year?"

"Neck deep — on me," the boy said.

"A crawdaddy, a puppydog, a crawdaddy, a puppydog, just like that."

"Okay."

They stood facing on the sandbar, and as each new hook was

exposed they backed farther apart, slowly, until the whole line was stretched tight between them, thirty yards with twenty dangling hooks. There were five free yards on either end for tying off. The man remembered making the line. He remembered that while he had tied it the sailor above him was tapping a silver quarter into a ring, using a tablespoon, tap, tap, tap, tap, mercilessly tap-ety tap-ing thousands of tiny taps until he'd shaped it into a perfect ring, and then he'd made a cribbage board of ivory.

"Just keep it tight," the uncle said. "Always tie the upstream end first." Because he was upstream he waded into the water above the Blue Hole. He had already selected a snag on the opposite bank to tie to. As an afterthought he said, "Whenever you set it by yourself, tie the upstream end first and then wade down, unwinding."

The boy nodded.

The uncle liked the press of the current which was alive and steady. The water was cold and clear. At crotch-deep he shuddered. It didn't get quite waist deep as he crossed and tied to the snag with four wraps and a slip knot. "Hold a bull," he muttered, testing the knot. Then he joined the boy and they pulled it tight, tying the downstream end to an exposed root on the bank. Most of the line was under water, and because of the way it was placed in the bend it crossed the current at an angle. Then they found a weight rock for use after baiting, when they would tie it in the middle to sink the line, holding it fast in the channel.

They were both half wet when they flopped in the patch of sun on the tail of the sandbar. The boy looked upstream and said, "Well — it's set."

"Yes it is. Ready to bait."

"It's a good 'un."

"Now remember, stay on the downstream side when you fool with it. Those hooks'll get you. And always keep a knife with you so you can cut yourself loose — if you have need to."

"Yeah."

"I mean cut the line."

"I know."

"You know. Do you know how to take a hook out of your hand?"

"Yeah."

"Push it through till the barb comes out, bend the barb down or snip it off with some pliers, and then back the hook out."

"Sure."

Mourning doves called downstream.

"Think we'll get anything?"

"I guaran-damn-tee it." The man nodded. "Wish I had a Lucky Strike." He'd smoked his last cigarette the day before. They were nine miles from town, and because there were no tires the car stood on wooden blocks.

The boy said, "Wish I had a million dollars. Tell me some more things about the Saratoga—yeeeaaaanggg—" he flew his hand low over the sandbar, its engine screaming, and set it down perfectly on the carrier deck.

"Oh — I'll teach you some knots," the man said, taking a length of cord from his pocket and working it with his fingers into a bowline. The boy wasn't interested in learning knots. He wanted to hear about torpedoes, submarines, and fires at sea, but the man tied knots.

Soon the boy thought about food. His mind took him to the town cafe, ripe with hamburgers. He asked, "Wonder why we got worms in our meat?"

"Was it wormy?"

"We couldn't eat a bite of that shoat Daddy bought last summer, when he was home on leave. All wasted."

"I guess your mother didn't do it right."

"We salted it and smoked it and everything."

"Who killed it?"

"Momma. I couldn't shoot it. I been feedin' it all winter, scratchin' it with a stick. It had little-bitty eyes, but it was smart."

"Yeah. It's hard to kill stuff you've raised. I guess you didn't cure it right. It's not her fault. She just doesn't know how to cure pork."

"You want to hear something funny?"

"Yeah."

"Ambrose caught four possums with his old dog. He knocked 'em in the head and skinned 'em and went in the house for supper. When he got back to the yard three of 'em was just playing dead. They'd climbed up the peach tree and was lookin' down at him — grinning — all pink and blue and shiny!"

"God **damn!**"

"Yeah," the boy giggled, "Ambrose took his .410 and shot 'em. Just left 'em there. Said he never would eat no more damn possums, after seeing that. Said they looked just like big old rats!"

"I couldn't eat a **rat**."

"I couldn't eat one neither."

"A squirrel is a tree rat."

"Do you get a lot of beans in the navy, or is that just a lot of bull?"

"We get a right smart. Why do you think they call them navy beans?"

Quickly, with a new idea, the boy asked, "Did you ever see any whales?"

"Never saw a whale, not yet."

"Daddy saw one."

The uncle nodded thoughtfully.

"Do you know Moby Dick?" the boy asked.

"Well, Moby Dick was a famous whale, I believe."

The boy recited: "Here's to Moby Dick, the only man alive with a corkscrew prick! They say he traveled on a world-wide hunt to find a woman with a corkscrew cunt — But when he found her, he fell down dead. The sorry old bitch had a left-hand thread!"

The uncle looked across the river, embarrassed. Then he said, "Where did you hear that?"

"Town. Some men were drinking beer. Ever time one would open a can of beer he would hold it up and say Moby Dick."

"I don't like to hear it."

The boy was hurt. He flexed his toes in the sand. After awhile he said, "I know about all that dick stuff —" He blushed, tempted to say, "I seen them rubbers in your suitcase. In the zipper bag." He'd made a sneak inventory of all his uncle's things, counting each tinfoil wafer. Moreover, he had observed their number diminish.

"Knowing and saying are two different things," the uncle said, avoiding his eyes.

"When we gonna bait the line?"

"Sundown. Always. That's when you bait up." He patted his tee shirt for the cigarettes that weren't there. "You better check the baits. Put fresh water in both buckets. A crawdad will drown in old water — you know that?"

"Sure."

"Good boy."

As the boy got up to check the bait he kicked the sand and asked, "Do you think they'll find Daddy?"

The man said, "I don't know." His eyes blurred. He looked away from the boy. "I certainly hope so," he said, staring at the trotline where it entered the water and split, going off into two lines, one into the water, one reflected on the surface. In his mind he saw each submerged hook bare and sharp at the end of its drop, swept out horizontal from the line like an arm in the wind, open, hooking the current. The tight line vibrated.

The boy returned from checking their bait and sat down.

"All alive?"

The boy nodded.

"What we've done —" the man stopped, then began again, "If your daddy does get found — it's gonna be hard."

The boy didn't reply.

"We both hope he gets home safe. You believe me?"

The boy nodded.

"You don't have a brother. Your daddy is **my** brother. A brother is like your best friend — only better. If he gets found, we'll just tell him all about it. He'll understand."

The boy stood up. He said, "Let's go ahead and bait up the goddamn trotline."

"No. It's not time. We'll bait it at sundown, after supper, and then we'll check it every hour. We'll build a good fire here on the sandbar. Your mama can come help us wait."

"You think he's dead, don't you?"

"There's no way of knowing."

The boy's eyes closed, squeezing out large tears. He turned away from the man and said, "I don't care what happens now. She's not my mother. She's a whore. I'm not gonna stay here and hunt and fish to keep her alive!"

"She is your mother. And you will stay here with her and help her, because next week she won't have anybody else but you. I believe you will stay and help her, and I believe you will do a good job of it. And I believe the next time I see you I'll see a man."

The mourning doves called again, closer.

"Don't do it anymore," the boy said. "Don't do it anymore, and I'll stay and help her. Missing ain't dead. We kill all these things, the hog, the squirrels, the crawdads and puppydogs, and they're dead. But missing ain't dead, and you ought to have enough sense to know **that**."

Then the gray birds landed on squeaky wings not twenty yards from where the uncle and nephew sat. The birds walked to the water to drink, jerking their skinny little heads with each step they took. The man smiled to see them, and the boy took them as an omen, vowing secretly that he might trap the little chicken quail or even smoke the soft-eyed swamp rabbits from their hollow gums, but he would never again shoot a mourning dove for the two bites of meat on its dark breast.

Ramona Weeks

SMOKY SMOLIK

When the rice fields blew down
in Texas, Smoky Smolik,
and one could see the rice birds

feasting where you'd played football,
we said it was too bad
you were a Catholic.

I had high girlish plans for you
in Protestant beds.
You walked in boots that shone
to gates that squeaked
and let me in.
You offered milky joy in an arcade
downstream where green winged flies
were snapped up by turtles
and gar were rumored to swim.

Your escape was managed.
Slick as a cucumber
after a long fever

you went away. A cassock's
got you now, Smoky,
holier than a football

that spirals with grace
on God's football field
where you rambled, a smoky Cadillac

of a boy with rich tail lights
in the Texas grass.
A winner

in the licorice history
of the priesthood, a loser
in the poems

where I roast you slowly
over a fire on a spit,
Smoky Smolik,

old piranha fish swimming to safety
in summer,
you rosy bum of a father,
you good old boy.

Charles Behlen

TO THE RETARDED JANITOR OF A PHOTOGRAPHY
STUDIO IN LUBBOCK, TEXAS

On straddled legs
of wooden easels,
glistening daughters
of bankers, professors,
grin through glass at the
long bright cars of
their future husbands.

Since tossing your hoe
into a cotton field
in 'fifty-seven,
you have rehearsed
a silent broom dance
in a city where
dusty sidewalks
make mailmen slip.

Pushing ahead a
grinning rim of
daily sawdust
that has become
a lipstick smear
flecked with dirt,
with hayloft straw,

you climb rough hewn
angled rungs in the
barn of your skull,
and mount from behind
a brittle bridesmaid —
wooden bodies
flesh for a moment,
smiling in stillness.

BASTARDS

Dwarfed by the bed
cradle up attic
the child's first storm
pierces walls
shakes him like
his parents' words
but a truckful of
Mexican wetbacks
roars past his window
in from a day of
chopping cotton in
fields that quiver
with West Texas sun
singing   laughing thru
black rain   lightning
back to the owner's
tarpaper shacks
accepting a gift
going to sleep

Jane P. Moreland

Christine Mouton: Cook

Mornings, she is gray chambray and sunshine,
Barefooted, with fists of wood hyacinths,
Hair pulled to one tight knot,
Searing sausages, hot cakes, brewing stiff coffee,
Gutting fresh water catfish for frying at noon.

Afternoons, she is a quick shadow
Down the swimming path, resting
Ancient Creole bones on a creek-pitched willow,
Soaping, rinsing fully clothed, chanting
Her soft, nasal patois back to some Atchafalaya swamp.

Spindletop

Ride a mud-rut road to 1945.
The boom is long over. Wooden derricks
Are down, except one. There are no tin-roofed shacks,
Except one, where men wait
For pumps to fill tanks, slide
Fallow dominoes under one naked bulb
In a mix of rawhide seats, stale cigars,
And crude, delicious crude.

"Bring lunch and the kids,
Well's comin' in today."
Spread quilts on sparkles
Of salty sand crust. Watch leathered hands,
Rusty tractor send down bits that bore rock strata.
Climb ladders on creosoted tanks, waiting hollows.
Mimic artists at the road
With easels, boards, sketching.

Stand where they stood.
There's nothing left to sketch here.

Bert Almon

Fishing on the Sea Wall.   Sabine Pass 1950

I still see dead-end bridges in my dreams
long chutes to nowhere (you find them over bayous
the picked and broken bones of abandoned trestles)

the sea wall was a bridge with only one bank
a curved hook of concrete to catch the Gulf Stream
so much like a trestle that my body trembled

but I let the brown water suck at my toes
and mottled my palms on the rough ledging
then worked awhile on the broken tacklebox

my sealed armory under a transparent lid
cat-gut lines, hooks with wicked barbs
jagged death lying jammed under my fingertips

(little luck I'd had with hooks — catching
my own dog once when he retrieved the lure
the dancing toy that bit back at him)

without my tackle I turned to crabbing
string double-knotted around salt pork
grasping creatures ambushed by their own greed

I dumped each one into the wicker basket
clatter of plated flesh brawling in the cage
and remembered the turtle at the reservoir

lying on its back, pinned by its armor
a gift for my grandfather, who made a rich soup
and got himself sick on the greasy liquid

I left the jetty on the landward end
seven crabs dueling in their dark prison
(you count them while the salted water boils)

and felt nothing in common with my victims
but now I see us all in hand-woven baskets
caught by our armor, illusions and greed

and how we all cling to that baited line

Wives

We sat at the roadside park off highway 80 that led to the neighboring towns we well knew: Stamford, Haskell, Seymour. My grandmother had parked her car just off the road and although we could reach home in an hour, we stopped late midday to relish the picnic lunch we'd brought. My grandmother brought a baked ham encrusted with pineapple and cherries, while my great aunt had specially prepared her salty recipe for black-eyed peas. The peas grew in her own garden, just behind the house that was shouting distance to my grandmother's. My aunt Nell had poured the peas into fruit jars.

Neither had known Ella over a year. Anyone who noted how fat Ella was, then wondered what my grandmother and great aunt were doing with her, for she was years younger than they. This Sunday we had come from a singing at Cloverville. Sung our hearts out under a tent. Ella let Nell and my grandmother correct her two children, Manny and Dorie Lou.

Ella unwrapped cellophane-covered deviled eggs.

"You kids sit down a minute," Nell said. "You'll drive a person crazy."

Ella didn't mind. She was occupied undoing the tinfoil from the ham.

We each secretly hoped for a piece of the pineapple or possibly a cherry, although the cherries lost flavor in the baking.

In fact we were in quite a stir, including Manny and Dorie Lou, until we had eaten dinner and were satisfied with the tasty food. Then we sat at the table, talked about the singing, and drank iced tea kept in a thermos. We poured the tea into the multi-sized cans we carried to drink from. The chilly cans improved the taste of the sweet tea, and each of us had a favorite. Most cans my grandmother would throw away, but occasionally she would say, "That'd make a good drinking can; I'll save it" — and it did, and I never knew how she told. Just any can didn't work; a peach can was my personal favorite. When we travelled to singings we brought a block of ice and picked off chunks for tea.

We sat under the sparse shade of an oak. Nell fanned first; in a minute all the women would stir the air with the paper fans that closed up like birdwings. Ella managed to eat more potato chips.

Grandmother commented on the passing cars that, just as they passed, made a noise and rushed by too fast to see. She waved at the passengers.

"I don't know that Sister Lawton has such a good voice," Nell said. "It's nothing to brag about."

"I never did like all that warbling myself," Grandmother said. "She sounds like she's dying." Usually you could hear my grandmother above anyone, clear and on the note.

Ella chuckled. "I think she's stuck up."

Sister Lawton drove a Buick everyone looked at. She styled her hair into a French roll and wore her glasses attached to a shiny chain about her neck. She sang professionally on Sunday afternoons like this one, and she usually left early, not long after offering.

We cleared up the table, put the leftover food in great brown sacks in the car trunk and the trash into the rusty barrel provided by the state highway. Then we sat at the table a little longer because we were not ready to go home. We counted eight cars as they passed.

"You know, Nell," my grandmother said. "I bet you could catch a man if you left your name and address on this table."

They often teased each other about every man in the county. Any bachelor or widower was immediately claimed or given away on sight and for good. "He's yours, Nell," Grandmother would say. "He's got a hitch in his getalong, poor old thing. If you marry him you'll have to nurse him the rest of your life."

"He's not mine," Nell would say.

But he was. Whenever Grandmother referred to him, she'd say, "Your mister so-and-so," or "Your boyfriend." Nell resorted to giving men to Grandmother, too, and if a nice looking older man happened to pass their eye, they weren't above a tiff over who saw him first. They claimed the best for themselves.

Both were widows and dolled up for singings or Saturdays downtown. They had life-size busts and wore dresses that tightly wrapped them up. I can swear that, on a cold night, either was warm and comfortable as the other and could heat layers of cold quilts. They didn't believe in much make-up. Each wore some powder and some lipstick and, for jewelry, hanging thin moon earrings given them half a century ago. They wore their wedding rings. They smelled of cologne and of scented stick deodorant and sweet bath powder. Really Grandmother was prettiest — eyes like blackeyed susans and cheeks the color of pink roses. Nell was less pretty. She had little vertical wrinkles on her top lip.

"Why you could, too, Ella," Grandmother said, "you could get a man."

Ella weighed as much as both of them combined. Two pounds under a cow. Her short brown hair strung about her face. Her stomach spread across her dresses and she could rest her elbows on it, laughing. "Do you think so?"

"It's possible. You're always saying you want a man."

"Why I wouldn't do it," Nell said. "You can't tell who'd read that."

"That's just what I mean. Some man might come along and see it."

"Do you have a pencil?" Ella asked.

Nell looked the other way. Ella wrote her name and address on the white painted table top. All of us had to wait a quarter hour for her to spell it pretty. She looked hopeful when she finished. We took turns reading it, then Nell said she'd smudge it off with her hand, but Grandmother said to leave it up to Ella. Ella left it, and drew a heart to make it noticeable. We left, then, with a memory on the picnic table, and on the drive finished the bag of potato chips.

The next day when Nell visited — she spent much of each day with us — Grandmother told her first thing that they had to buy some different stationery at the five and dime.

"Why, she'll know you wrote it," Nell said. They had a thousand tricks up their sleeves. You understood it as they did when you spent the summer with them. Grandmother herself had tricked Nell with love letters from men she'd given her and Nell had fallen for it, never to admit the truth, even when confronted with the evidence. Frequently they cut out Bible verses they thought fitting to one person or another, and Nell would leave the verse on the doorscreen or in the mailbox because Grandmother drove the getaway car. Mostly, when Nell visited, they talked about themselves and about people in the town. Everyone knew everyone else and anyone who didn't know that Grandmother was a character soon found out. But she and Nell in the heat of the day were usually at their homes alone; they languished afternoons taking naps in front of electric fans, and spent nights in a lonely succession in their beds by the screened-in windows. I loved Grandmother and she was at home, in the town where she had met her boyfriends at the cemetery wall fifty years before, yet she still knew anyone from a glance. I often entertained myself by traveling with them afternoons on long visits from house to house where Grandmother told the same story in a hundred ways until by nightfall she herself didn't know what to believe.

"No, she won't know," Grandmother said. We went straight downtown. I bought the stationery — cheap plain paper with oblong envelopes.

"That's fine," Grandmother said.

When we got home, she took the salt and pepper shakers off the kitchen table. Her yard was profuse with an array of flowers from tiny purple mosses to towering hollyhocks, but she never cut them.

"Nell," she said, "You come write this down. Ella would never be able to read my writing." It was true — Grandmother wrote in humps and slants she'd taught herself. For instance, she wrote "before" as B4. Didn't waste time.

Nell wrote with a knife-sharpened pencil, but the blunt script was flurried.

"Dear Ella,

I read your name on the table and wish you'd write me a letter telling about yourself. I'm 65 and live in Crowell. I am a widower farmer.

Sincerely,

Sam."

"Why, it's silly," Nell said. "Ella will never believe it."

Grandmother kept sheets of postage stamps in her sewing drawer. She tore one off, licked it, and placed it carefully on the corner of the envelope. "You wait and see," she said. "We'll get an answer." She made the return address to her cousin in Crowell.

"She sure does want a man bad," Nell said, as we drove to Crowell to mail the letter. Nell rested her elbow on the rolled-down window. The landscape was flat and dusty and the windows in the car fanned in hot air as we rode. In Crowell we visited my grandmother's cousin, Anna. Anna said she wasn't much taken with the idea of fooling a Christian widow, but that she wouldn't destroy government mail which belonged to my grandmother. When we left Anna's yard, her hound dog barked and Nell and Grandmother discussed what a shame it was Anna didn't plant grass and flowers and keep a garden, if she was so holy.

Three days later, we saw Ella and her kids coming down the road. Grandmother sliced us all watermelon. Nell and Ella sat on the iron swing. Grandmother and I sat in metal chairs with oval backs. They passed the shaker around to salt their juicy slices. I liked my watermelon sweet.

"I've gotten two letters already," Ella said. "You sure were right." She was tickled pink.

"I don't much believe you," Grandmother said. "How on earth could you have gotten **two**?" She looked curiously at us.

"I think because I outlined my name with a heart." Ella felt smart. She cut her kids another slice of melon and Grandmother told them not to spit the seeds in her flowerbeds where she'd have to pull up the shoots later. The kids scurried to the alley to play.

"Who are the letters from?" Nell said.

"They have the same name. One is from Sam Buford; the other is just Sam."

"Isn't that surprising?" Grandmother didn't like to be taken for a chump; she wasn't sure which of us wrote a second letter, if there was one. She had her curiosity whetted. "Have you answered them?"

"I have the answers," Ella said. "I'm going to the p.o."

"Why I'll take you," Grandmother said.

They cleaned the dishes, then the six of us piled into Grandmother's car. In town she drove twenty or under and as we crept along, we talked. "Where does Sam Buford live?" Grandmother asked.

"In Angleton."

119

"Oh, he does," Grandmother said.

At the p.o. I dropped the letters in the box without looking at the addresses. On purpose. It would cause a thousand questions.

The next day we waited for the next and finally Nell and Grandmother and I drove to Crowell to pick up the reply.

Cousin Anna handed over the letter but said she'd rather **not** hear the reply. "Well, darn your hide," Grandmother said and we drove off, stirring up dust in the worn out yard. We drove through town, then stopped off the highway to read the reply. "I guess Anna doesn't deserve any fun," Grandmother said. "Well, I wish you'd listen to what Ella wrote":

I'm a Christian woman and have two kids ages 5 and 3. I think I'd make you a good wife. I did my first husband. He died three years ago of a heart attack. I've got good furniture and can sew five shirts a day.

"Five shirts a day!"

"Can you beat that!" Nell laughed. "Do you think she wrote it?" It was Nell's tease of her own. As if she did it herself.

Grandmother looked at the letter with a smile.

"It looks like the writing on the table," I said.

"Bless patty, that girl probably means it." Grandmother wasn't convinced though. "Who is Sam Buford?" she asked. "Are you sure you didn't see where that postmark was from?"

He came by our door mid-afternoon five days later. Sam wasn't much of a looker himself. He wore clean overalls, but his face was a swollen plum. He didn't have a stitch of hair. He drove up in a bruised blue pickup and was at the front porch, behind the trellis, before anyone noticed him. Grandmother kept her beebee gun behind the front door. She shot stray dogs and once, ten feet away, had snipped a caterpillar. She was startled to see on her porch a man neither she nor Nell had seen.

"Can I help you?" she asked in a sweet voice.

"I think you can, Ma'm." He stood outside the screen politely; Grandmother came out. She invited everyone she knew in.

"I'd be glad to if I can."

"I'm a friend of Ella Munger, at least she and I are thinking of getting married."

"Just a minute, let me get my sister." Grandmother called Nell from her garden and waved her over. "Have a seat in the swing; I'll get tea." She didn't give Sam time to blink.

"Go on out and entertain him," she told me as she fixed tea in the kitchen. I hesitated, then went outside and looked at the cannas by the swing. He didn't speak to me. His eyes followed me, though.

Nell walked up, dust on her cheeks and her bonnet. She was embarrassed Grandmother wasn't there to introduce her, but

Grandmother came out at that moment. "This is Sam," she told Nell. She carried a trayful of sweet tea in tall jelly glasses. "Here," she said, "If you'd like more sugar just say so." Nell would have been insulted not to have been included. She looked peeved, however, when Grandmother motioned for me to take the other outdoor chair, making Nell sit in the swing by Sam Buford.

He tasted the tea. His thick shoes had bulging toes and were cracked about the shoelaces. His blue shirt under his overalls wasn't pressed, even if it was washed. He had shaved and he turned his head and spit tobacco juice in a nearby flowerbed. When he turned back, his lips were shiny. "I'm just asking about Ella," he said. "I saw her this morning and she told me I might."

"Ask about what?" Nell said.

"About Ella," Grandmother said.

He shot more tobacco.

"Well, you'll have to quit dirtying my yard with that nasty stuff if you want to visit me." He had, by the way, stained a shock of white petunias.

"Excuse me," he said, and swallowed.

We waited. "What did you want to know?" Grandmother asked. Normally she would have told anything about Ella, but if he **wanted** to know, she'd only tell him the bare minimum.

"I'm interested in a good Christian woman who doesn't run around. She says she's a widow. Did you know her husband?"

"No. And if she runs around with anyone," Grandmother said, "I hope she wouldn't be fool enough to let me know. As far as being a good Christian, I know many a woman at church every time the doors are open who wouldn't qualify in my book."

"I know just what you mean. I don't go to church myself."

"Well, I wouldn't brag about it. Ella's clean, neat as a pin. You couldn't find a better housekeeper than Ella."

"I appreciate that, ma'm."

Grandmother frowned. "I think you'd be lucky to catch her if you can. She's got a good personality. That's what a man should look for."

"I appreciate a strong woman," he said. "I burn pears."

"Lord," Nell said.

"It's honest," he said. "Prickly pears."

"There's nothing wrong with hard work," Grandmother said. "One thing about Ella, she's got a good personality."

He nodded.

"Would you like more tea?" Grandmother asked.

He shook his head.

"You saw her kids, didn't you? She's a good mother."

"I wish the boy were more the age of this one. Now he could be of some help."

"This one's not for sale; he's mine."

"I'd better go," he said. "I want to thank you two ladies." They got up with him and walked him to the truck. Nell straightened her bonnet.

"Are you two getting married?" Grandmother asked, over the roar of the truck when he started it. She liked to talk to people just about to go.

"I don't know," he said.

"Where did you say you met Ella?" Grandmother asked.

He waved before he hit the last rock in the driveway that gave the truck a bump.

"Can you beat that. I don't know what I'd do to a man that went about inquiring about me before we were getting married. He was as green as gourd guts, Nell."

"He sure was," Nell said.

"You'd better get the okra before it gets any tougher," Grandmother told me. It had needed picking several days. "Some of them are already big as your fist."

"It's too hot for me already," Nell said. She carried in the tray of glasses.

I got the knife to pick the sticky okra. Usually Grandmother cut up the okra and fried it crisp in flour, but sometimes she boiled it. She and Nell went inside.

Hardly fifteen minutes later, Grandmother came out and had her apron heavy with okra I'd cut off. She looked up and exclaimed, "There's Ella." She dropped the okra in a white dishpan with a red rim and went to meet her. Nell came out, too, and brought the beans she snapped.

"Mr. Buford just left," Ella said. She had more color in her face than I'd ever seen. Like she stood in a rainbow.

"He came by here." Grandmother offered Ella tea.

"Thank you." Ella sighed. "I left the kids with Mrs. Ford."

Nell brought and poured the tea. I sat beneath the arbor of honeysuckle thick with summer blooms.

"Wht did you think of him?" Ella asked.

"He didn't stay long." Grandmother wasn't sure what to say. "I've got something to tell you, Ella."

"We just agreed to get married," Ella said proudly. Sucking on her lip.

"Married!"

"Why do you want to marry?" Grandmother asked. "He's too old for you. You'll lose your pension. I wouldn't marry any man who spit that nasty tobacco juice around the house."

Ella smiled. "I don't mind."

"Well, why do you want to marry him? You couldn't love him."

Ella ran her fingers along her hair. "I don't know about you," she said, "but I miss a man. I don't want to live alone with my kids. I want a

122

man to take care of. I think I do already love him."

"He'll be too old to swallow grease in a year."

"I don't mind." She combed her hair with a new comb. "Why, today I feel like the happiest woman in the world."

No one spoke. When she went out that afternoon, she bobbed up and down in the street, carrying a pan of fresh okra. From the back you could tell she talked to herself. I watched her and thought to myself that she was wonderful.

Nell smiled. She sat in the swing and watched Ella, too.

"I guess you learn something every day," Grandmother said. "Would you have him, Nell?"

"I sure wouldn't at my age," Nell said.

Grandmother stopped. "I wouldn't have him at any age," she said. She glanced over and our eyes met. "At least I don't think so." She laughed.

"Do you miss a man?" Nell asked. Her husband had been dead ten years.

My grandmother had outlived two and she was sixty-three. She noted to a day each of their birthdays, their anniversaries . . .; she would sigh and tell us how many years she would have been married. And the photographs! Framed and hung on the walls. She lived every moment in sight of them. "Of course I do," she said . . . Why else did we go to the cemetery every day?

They smiled at each other. I could tell all was erased but gladness for Ella. Hope that it worked out for her. They were proud they had helped.

I remember them like that because they looked very pretty amid their flowers and their gardens and in their rare reminiscent smiles I could see how much their husbands still meant to them, and what wives they'd been.

Virginia Baltzell

Gindo to a Pecan Tree

Remembering childhood
I tasted salt as I saw
Pecans flung down

Naomi Clark

THE BREAKER

Maria we called you:
a Spanish mare, they said, up from Mexico —
born to the saddle, but unpredictable, skittish, liable to panic.
We were not, anymore, the kind of family to keep saddle horses.
Straddled bareback, past dry holes and dry grey slush pits, past the mound where
we buried the cows, I'd stolen time from field and chickens
to ride low, nag transformed, under the scrub oak branches,
through darkening johnson grass where puma screamed, out onto the Great Staked Pl
You sold cheaper than a nag,
kicked out the end of the trailer, the gate off the horselot.
All night I head you circling the barbed wire, stamping.
All night I rode through the sky.
You were a small, dark mare, Spanish, bought for a plowhorse.

    I remember you in chains, Maria, the day he broke you to plow-harness.
    Tied to a post, dragging the heavy iron beam, the heavy log chains,
    twisting and kicking, whipped and driven round
    and round. Foam flew, and blood, with the broken harness,
    with the tangled harness and the slipped chains. Your eyes turned white.
    Only when you both fell did it end. Next day
    you plowed ten rows before it started.

You come to me now, Maria,
in so many dreams: your mad eyes,
your flinches, your broken stance, the slouch in the heavy harness,
your bowed head blindered, the break into frenzy.
My hands burn to heal you, to gentle you, to gentle your eyes.
Maria, you lift strong black wings,
rise free over the mesquites and the prickly pear, over the Caprock,
over the untrampled high grass of the Llano into the age of Comanche, Apache.

    And the man who broke you?

How shall I heal him, how stretch out my hand
in healing, my cold hands in healing
and warmth, how gentle?
O father, how shall I heal you?
What wings from the fire where you burn, and I the breaker?

FOUND POEM: FIRST LETTER FROM AUNT CAT

I gess you'r surprise to get this letter.
Think of you often   where is your mama
you would not know me I way 137
yes this is yr big fat Ant Cat.
      if I cd tell you
But to get to that — is this something
      colors you never did see
have started loosing 10 lbs a week
      bluegill   sunfish
for no rime or reason
      swim   round thru in
I have some kind spell
      blossums
I just leave this world
      sandstorms ever day here but there — plum petals
come to in hospitle
      wind all plum petals snow
Been having one a month
      feedsack dress all turned to plum blooms
Dr says they got stop or
      breath all plum bloom smell
I'll be a vegetable for as long as I live
      and the water
so pray for me that they find out what
      whirlpool   still mirrer
it is   broke left arm   Hon   once
      scoop a drink
heart   back   last time
      moon in my hands
cant be by self or do nothen
      drink moon
take medcine that makes me drunk
      swim in moon
but Dr say its bettern being out
      cloud wind pool moon
Grady is on way to Big Spring Hospitle to see
      fly up
if he can get something don too for him
      I'm the sky
So pray for us
      bigger
I love you
      than big
Ant Cat

Dave Oliphant

HUSTLING SHUFFLEBOARD WITH HEARTS-&-FLOWERS HAROLD

Beeson
better known as the
Beast

from his acned face
& physique
like a bouncer's over cross

the Beaumont railroad tracks
at the College St. Flamingo Club
made all the county beer joints

just after classes
on Hemingway & Faulkner
ordering only Jax

that New Orleans
coonass brew
sprinkling the sandy stuff

on varnished boards
caressing long piano-player's
fingers round a metal puck

sliding it along the flesh-colored
wood   back & forth a bit
getting the feel & angle

to hang it off the edge
or give the sucker's a
click   would send it

sailing for the gutter
& take him for a 5 or 10
high-tailing it outa there

if & when the guy'd wise
up & decide alluva sudden
to go for a gun

or like the night
a dozen rough-necks
off the tower shift at Spindletop

went for him in sawdust
after he'd crunched a cheater's ribs
up against a washbowl

on the humid wall
of that house converted
to a cockroach bar

or shot thru the underarm
running from a sheriff's raid
out the backdoor to sweetgum & pine

what little he made
going for booze
& poetry books

in
of all places
Rose City, Texas

from MEMORIES OF TEXAS TOWNS AND CITIES

Driving down the viaduct,
descending to what was once a ritzy section,
given over now to Boys Clubs, Golden Gloves, Mexican
food-to-go, I come to Livestock

Exchange, a sand-colored structure,
still a stop for cattle buyers, its style
of Arabic arches & red Spanish tile,
housing sellers of hogs & sheep, the poster picture

of a champion steer, and out the back,
steps caked with half-digested hay,
raked off handmade boots, lead to charolais,
short horn, white face, or black

angus — an auction arena, an amphitheatre
with silver-painted ribbed fence,
a half octagon holding ephemeral prints
of hooves destined to patch dinnerware

with their mucus-colored glue,
the dirt on the stage-like floor trampled powder soft,
the performance attended by rows & rows of off-
white straws, hats stained by rain & sweat, not a shoe

on any foot. The show begins when the electric doors
swing to welcome them in, bunches of half-grown cows,
frightened as amateur actors, announced to the house
by the auctioneer singing a song of trills & figures:

"Gi'me a half gi'me
got 24 gi'me a quarter
25 need a quarter
29.75 now 3."

Outside among the pens, whips crack,
driving them in, long trucks backed up
to loading chutes, cattle cars coupled
beside the branding lots, then the pack-

ing house: its name in red & white,
though SWIFT has faded, crumbled now to *ift*,
a mass of wires & rods, twist-
ed, doubled, rusted pipe

reaching into rubble, the fire-
ravaged brick as if bombed out,
granted, no atom has fallen here, no Kraut
or Jap returned the favor to Convair,

today General Dynamics, whose plane, the B-29,
sprouted engulfing clouds, here first spread wings,
to fly not with seed but deadly droppings,
while up this wooden ramp longhorns waited in line,

moved slowly to the slaughter, the fire an "accident,"
burning for months, consuming blood & fat
that seeping down had soaked the wood, matted hides, the conflagration making but a dent

in the years of calf eyes crushed to bleed
sadly bright on flaying floors, the nightly flames
razing the ruins, emblazoning brands, oily brains,
swollen tongues sputtering until we heed

the meaning of this chapter, this hidden life,
the one we never have cared come upon,
not old-fashioned, written by an age gone
by, but that we find fingers fit the knife,

fashioned this sloping passage, spared by tribal spirits,
rising still to a gutted, a caved-in corporation,
reminding of even a risen sun's
decline, kinetics the seeming-innocent drive inherits,

in reconciling past & present a ramp
of remembrance, to render us down to what we are,
would yet ascend us higher than bigger spreads, a grand Lone Star,
set instead on our impoverishment an ancient, sanctioning stamp.

William D. Barney

To Be a Bull

He does not understand my obsession
but I wish to be that white-face bull.

Not for his heavy sex, and that look
half-stupid of sufficient lust in his eye,
nor for that stob nor the vast back, nor the
huge pyramid of leg; nor even
the harem-handy life and the unanxious acre.

It is his advantage
of being stupid without mankind taking
his mind to task. For he has no mind.
What pleasure, to stand beside the fence
heaving one's mighty belly and slobbering
delightsomely over a cud, quaking off flies
but never moving except with the shade.

To be for a time a bull
stolid and imperturbable, massive
and yet very gentle, hair hanging from my ears,
indisputably male and not a little moronic.

The Sleepers

Once I came on them suddenly
in yellow lingerie, in March,
embarrassed by the show of youth,

but mostly they sit in the sun
glazed with heat, older than the land,
lost in the drifts of afternoons,

and a curious thought possesses me:
the mesquite sink imperceptibly
into the earth. That, or the dust

is building up about their trunks
as ancient Mayan temples once
went swallowed down by jungle soil.

No jungle here. Only the remorseless
plain of short grass and the thin sky
open to dry infinity.

The ash of long dead stars it is
that falls, sifting through bent years
a humus of eternity.

The soft compost of space comes in
to bury crooked trees, that sleep
senile in the alluvium of time.

Dwight Fullingim

Vehemence of the Wind

I inherit the language of a windy plain
a swirling, gritty farm-land dust
the blinking eyes of cattle
and the sky in the North grown dark
with layers of air iced in the Rockies.

Words were strung like polished beads
in patterns of tradition handed down
father to son in the Sunday School class.
The sounds and the speakers were a nonsense chorus
that followed me with anthems and hymns
the litany of teacher, preacher, police.

The real language was a windmill's banging gears
ice broken in troughs for the herd
and workers howling for girls beneath
a sea of bobbing western hats.

At church on Sunday I read the New York Times:
interest rates, travel notes, and B. Altmann ads
and lost my voice to speak to the neighbors
cowboys in boots
and
wives in rhinestone bat-wing glasses.

The Communion of Saints

As is well-known, Reverend Jerome Black, the pastor of our poverty-ridden little church on the edge of our desert ghetto, was an odd-ball, a maverick, a chronic innovator. He would try anything once if he thought it would get his congregants to attend church services instead of playing golf or shooting jackrabbits.

And so, we had bassoon soloists from our local high school oompahing their way through Rock of Ages. We had an Easter oratorio by our choir. We had children's sermons, complete with puppets and organ accompaniment. Jerry walked around the pulpit; he walked up and down the center aisle. He wore open sportshirts, he wore pink shirts with purple neckties, he did everything that he could think of to gather his little flock unto the church on Sunday mornings. If he had thought to deliver the benediction or the doxology while standing on one forefinger in the middle of the baptismal fount, he would undoubtedly have attempted to do that.

Yet, for all of Jerry's strenuous efforts to bolster church attendance, nothing seemed to work. The church did not prosper and Jerry's salary was always a week or two overdue. The electric company made it a clerical routine to call the church office every five weeks to remind us that the utility bill for the past month had not been paid.

One Sunday evening we held our monthly meeting of the Administrative Board by candlelight, which we thought was most innovative and dramatic until we realized that our electricity had been shut off because we hadn't paid our bill.

It was the new communion service that really finished Jerry's tenure of office with us. Admittedly, it was not one of the best ideas that Jerry had ever put into practice, but certainly it was the most memorable. I mean, how could anyone foresee the consequences, or how certain people in the church would react? Certainly I, as the head usher for that month, had no faint inkling of the storm that this one event would cause.

The typical communion service in a Protestant church is a matter of set routine, a play in which roles are acted out according to strict rules of protocol. You go up to the railing; you kneel; you take a small piece of plain bread from a silver tray. The pastor prays a short prayer and you eat the bread. The process is then repeated with tiny glasses of grapejuice used instead of biblical wine. It is all very simple. And presumably has been practiced for hundreds of years.

Now, as the communion service is designed to celebrate the Last

Supper which Christ shared with his twelve disciples in the upper diningroom of a private home, it appeared to Jerry that we had been doing it all wrong for all these many years. Jerry would show us how it was meant to be done. In all humility, of course, and with the highest of Christian intentions.

It was, naturally, a physical and cultural impossibility for us to lounge on large pillows in front of the church in groups of thirteen while we partook of a last supper. But we could at least gather about a table in the church while we ate our bread and drank our grapejuice. Surely there was nothing that could possibly be wrong with this, and Jerry told me he believed that it would bring the spiritual lessons of the Last Supper, the lessons of sharing and giving and receiving, home to those who participated in the holy sacrament.

On the surface, the concept had validity. Except that our people were not accustomed to breaking off a little morsel of bread from a whole loaf and then passing the remaining bread along to a fellow communicant. And except that Jerry had forgotten that we had a black family in our congregation. Either he did not know the effect that the Tammers would have on the rest of the people in our church, or he hoped that they would not have any. In any case, Jerry was wrong.

Now, for a west Texas community, we are not especially prejudiced against our black citizens. They number only four per cent of our total population, and therefore constitute little or no threat to anyone. Besides, we have a large Mexican-American and chicano population (there is a difference which I shall not explain at this point) whom we can hate and fear with relative impunity and even a certain degree of practical legitimacy.

The Tammers were our token blacks, our shining symbol of racial unity under the banner of Jesus Christ. If every black family were like the Tammers, we said, there would never be any trouble with the race. The Tammers were very black, and seemed to have been ideally created for the roles that the members of the church expected them to play. Jobadiah Tammer was a retired army chaplain, a colonel complete with medals and scarred jumpboots. Marie Tammer baked fabulous cakes for bazaars and umpired little league baseball games. Terry Tammer was captain of his high school football team and that year would win seven scholastic scholarship offers. The Tammers were definitely an asset for our church. An asset, albeit a black asset. It is my private opinion that Jerry, in his enthusiasm for his concept of a genuine communion service, did not take this into account in his thinking. Or maybe he knew and did not care, thinking perhaps that we, as a congregation, had learned a few of the lessons in brotherly acceptance that he had tried to get across to us on Sunday after Sunday.

The front of the church was brilliantly resplendent that Sunday morning. Two of our long dining tables had been pushed together and covered with freshly washed white linen tablecloths. There were candlesticks at each end of the table, and the tiny communion glasses were prim and proper in their wooden racks. The focus of our attention, however, rested upon the three whole loaves of fresh baked bread that were strategically placed at the left end of the table. They were whole. They were not broken up into little cubes. And there were thirteen chairs at the table, one for each of the twelve disciples and one for Jerry, who was to sit at the chair nearest the altar for the simple reason that it was the one that was easiest for him to reach after the opening ceremonies.

The church was alive with subdued chatter. What in the wide world would Reverend Jerry think of next? It might all be very scriptural, but it certainly was **different**!

After the opening prayer and the first hymn, Jerry gave the instructions as to how the communion service was to be conducted. The people who wanted to receive communion would come down to the table in groups of twelve. They would sit at the table. There would be a short prayer. Then the people would take a loaf of bread, break off a small piece for themselves and then pass the loaf on to a neighbor on the right. The same conditions would be in effect for the wine. A congregant would take a glass and then pass the wooden tray to the person on the right. It was simple. And, when you get right down to it, this representation of the Last Supper was certainly more dramatic and scripturally accurate than our usual method.

The first twelve people straggled down the aisle. There was a slight mixup about the seating arrangements; should families sit together on one side of the long table or should they face each other. Just sit the way you come from your pews, said Jerry, and the problem was solved.

Jerry prayed. Then he took the first loaf of bread, broke off a piece, then gave it to Tom Bowers on his right. Then the bread was passed on down the row of people, each breaking off a piece. The prayer this time was by Mamie Scorpadis, the chairperson of our Stewards' Committee. Then came the grapejuice. Another short prayer. Communion was taken. The people folded their hands and walked slowly back to their pews.

Twelve more people straggled down the aisle. It was going all right. Jerry's idea of communion as people having supper together was valid, it was succeeding, the people were getting the message.

It was only when the third group of twelve communicants rose from their pews to participate in the service that there was even the slightest whisper of trouble. But then it came, and it was more like a bellow than a whisper. The Tammers were in this third group of Christians now sitting at the communion table waiting for Jerry's prayer. And the Tammers were black. Very black. Colonel and Mrs. Jobadiah Alexis Tammer and son Terence Adolphus Tammer. They were all there facing the congregation, waiting to take the Lord's Supper as they had done ever since Jobie's retirement six years ago when they had first come to El Paso.

The prayer ended, Jerry took a fresh loaf of bread from the center of the table and handed it to Jobie Tammer, who pinched off a piece and handed the loaf to Marie Tammer on his right. And then the whispers began. And grew louder, more insistent to be heard, not to be denied.

I don't know what I expected but I moved down the aisle from my post at the front door.

And the whispers became a tribal roar in the church, centered in one voice at the table, a voice that shouted, "He touched that bread! I'm not taking no bread that nigger's touched!" Three Christians, a whole family, rose from their pew and strode angrily up the aisle to the door of the church. And they did not look back.

Jerry put his hands on Jobie Tammer's shoulders as he gave the prayer that closed the service for that Sunday. It was just about all that he could do under the circumstances.

I knew that Jerry would have to move on to another church after this episode, and I was right. The Jobie Tammers remained active in the church; maybe they were accustomed to such incidents, or maybe they just knew that they would probably encounter similar hostility wherever they might go. I was not accustomed to such things, so I left when Jerry did, along with three or four others.

Robert Burlingame

NORTHWARD AT CHRISTMAS

The storm has passed over.
The road to Albuquerque is open again.
Around here our mountains shout the look
of light. I imagine high up in them
small animal faces. What do they think?
Have they caught the sounds of our city?
Do they wonder why so many trees suddenly,
strangely begin to swallow the stars?

137

EL PASO MORNING

On this morning, hedged about with green,
The light breeds and blossoms with the cries
Of small hidden birds.
Male trumpets blaze upon the vines,
Scarlet wakens at the roots of trees,
The earth turns slowly, drowsily,
Like a woman sunning her cascaded hair.
A river winds through the land.
Solitude is good and anything but lonely.
The gods converse nearby.

E.A. Mares

In the San Antonio Hotel

In the San Antonio Hotel
Juárez, Mexico, on a Sunday night
my only companion a bottle of wine
which I brought from the states
and therefore must drink tonight
because you can't take it back,
so the bartender told me. He is a man
to be listened to because he is old
and has survived the transformations
of Mexico, Díaz and the Positivists,
Villa and the Revolution.
He remembers wagon trains
moving north from Chihuahua to Juárez,
the breadline in Torreon
during the Revolution, standing all night
to buy bread at five in the morning.

138

By six all the bread was gone.
The Positivists gave way
to the Revolution which gave way
to PRI, which gave way to this night
in the bar of the San Antonio Hotel.
I drink my tequila straight
and ask the bartender about the old days.
He talks his way
back through decades into youth.
My mind's first photograph
shows the black hair, sharp cheekbones,
black fire opal eyes.
Then a series of changes
to softer features, grey and pudgy,
something like cauliflower
many folds and wrinkles, and the eyes
now those of an elderly widow
who has attended mass daily.
Half a century of rosaries,
of fervent tongue and fingers
beneath a black shawl.
Here there are only three of us.
The bartender, another mexicano, and myself.
Later, back in my third floor room
I throw open the window.
The green and red sign of the Intermezzo Bar
promises a garish interlude
between night and the new dawn.
There is a thick saracen moon above.
I peer across the river to El Paso, U.S.A.
In the space between two worlds
the Rio Grande makes its way alone.
There is a silence outside
and in the distance I hear
the moan of a moving train.

James Cody

THE NECHES RIVER

1970 we put into it.
1971 we left it.
We began at Dam "B",
    we have stopped at Silsbee
This river is an Eastern River.
Sixty miles we rowed.
Not much.
This East Texas.
Spending four days has not told me much.
We saw cypresses and Spanish moss.
We saw birch and willows and oak and pine.
It was sometimes hard to tell.   It's winter and
    most had not leaves.
We saw wooden houses for hunters, and river boats
    for hunters and places for fishermen.
We saw no snakes, but it is winter and snakes are not out.
We saw two cows and horses in some pens, but only two
    at a time.
We saw an eagle or two, Robin says he saw an Osprey
    and I know we saw some red-headed buzzards.
Because it is winter there was no foliage, except on
    evergreens and they were scarce.
The woods were full of hunters and shotgun blasts were
    abundant.
We saw no deer, no coons, no cats, only tracks, and one
    set for each.
Hiding out from hunters.
We saw the tracks for something.
Mike says they are bird tracks
And I insisted they were possum tracks, but
    I don't know.
In the winter the Neches is a lazy river.
At no time from Dam "B" to Silsbee are there any
    rapids and there is no danger.
The Neches River is a dull river.
At least in winter.

What has the Neches River taught me?
It has taught me that I do not enjoy the
    Neches in winter,

that I do not like more than one extra person on a
        canoe trip.
    that I am ready for more dangerous waters.
One night we read from Justice Douglas's *Farewell to Texas*
        on the Santa Elena Canyon.
Some day I'll run the Santa Elena rockpile.
I long for the Guadalupe first.
The Neches River has taught me that I cannot
    get away from Mary Ellen.
    that I cannot abandon canoeing
    more to make a book on canoeing

    more to say, write and understand about
        Texas, the world and myself.
Is there a history to the Neches River?
There is, but I don't know much about it.
I suspect that the Spaniards crossed it lots of times.
There may have been a post or two on it.
Cabeza de Vaca crossed it.
La Salle crossed it, at least twice.
Logging camps and paper mills are and have been on it.
Bonnie and Clyde crossed it.
They may have hidden in it and along it.
Trappers came down it to Beaumont.
And Beaumont uses it as a port.
Oil wells are here and there.
The federal government wants to make it a
    National River.
I used to see the Neches every morning when
    I was a teenager in Beaumont.
I smelled its creosote plant
I saw its shipyards
Its steel company
I have ridden the bridge over its swamps and
    seen alligators go "splash" into its murky waters.
I have seen the Neches River Festival in preparation
    but didn't have the stomach or the courage, or the
sickness to watch it.

I have seen the Neches many times.
And I expect to see it many more times.
What people live on the Neches?
They are Southerners, East Texans, Coon-asses.
They are town and country people.
They are hunters, genuine people.
They can be vicious-mean or wonder-kind.

THE HEART OF TEXAS

Texas, unlike the rest of the West
has a hole in its heart
Texas has no Indians
The heart of Texas
cut off its own blood stream and
sent it to Oklahoma
but there are signs/
where the artery was ripped out
an arrowhead on the Colorado
petroglyphs on the Pecos
a few torn strands of
ancient camping spots on the coast
along the Brazos, the Colorado
Comanche Peak is still there
No red-skins in Palo Duro Canyon
driven out in '39 by Mirabeau B. Lamar
in 1874 by Co. Nelson A. Miles
That is better than in the East, they say
There is not even a heart,
not a single trace.

Bryan Woolley

IN JEFF DAVIS COUNTY

I
THE DAVIS MOUNTAINS

Some fences, some roads, some houses the Apaches
would rather die than live in, if they had not already
died.   The grass is shorter, but Espejo would recognize
the stones.   And Nicholas, and Quanah, and Victorio.

II
THE HAWK

I killed you on this mountain twenty years ago.

142

My bullet pierced the soft feathers of your breast,
your sunlit wings, extended to embrace the sky,
crumpled. You fell like a meteorite. I ran
to you, exulting in boy-manliness, then backed away
from the angry stare of your yellow dying eye.
I pumped slug after slug into you there among the rocks,
afraid. I still hear their muffled thud, the rifle's
echo from the cliff. You soar above me, watching.

III
RUDY

You rang up my beer. We talked awhile of when
you were the fastest halfback in West Texas,
a hero long ago, when we knew each other. Lives
have happened to us both since then, the time
in California, the prison and all, but we did not speak
of that. You left your wife and live with someone
else's, they say, in sin. You never minded
sin, and your smile is still the same.

IV
THE DEAD COW

You lay in shade of a liveoak tree at the foot
of Casket Mountain, ragged hide pitched like a Bedouin's
tent, dry and empty. Coyotes spread your bones around
you long ago, to bleach, to be no more a part of you.
The child inquired about your eyes, and how you feel.
Buzzards ate your eyes, and you do not hurt.
You are falling into the ground to be grass,
and there will be another cow.

V
MT. LOCKE

On Mt. Locke you gaze at stars and shoot laser beams
at the moon. British scientist in cowboy clothes,
you explain it. The telescope entertains us with how
small we are. Harvard's machines in Cook Canyon say
cattle will die of what is happening on the sun.
We are grass and rain, Victorio knew,
and Espejo, and Nicholas, and Quanah.

Late Hunter

When we graduated from Players' Square High School on that mild summer evening in 1958, I felt that everything was perfectly in its place and I made myself a wish that nothing would ever change. It was later that very night, of course, that our classmate, Bobby Mack Billings, was killed in an automobile crash (with a whiskey bottle in his hand). But because that was just the end which many folks had long been predicting for him, I agreed with Reverend Cooper that it was a part of the Eternal Plan.

On the next Monday morning, two of the other boys left town to join the United States Navy, little Sue Anne Higgins learned to make chocolate sodas at Waugh's Drug Store, and I went to work in the First State Bank as Mr. Baker, the bank president, had promised. And so it was a pleasant summer filled with swimming parties and softball games on the square and grilled cheese sandwiches at Waugh's, and several weddings.

That fall, many members of our class, like raven-haired Sue Anne Higgins, enrolled at the Cotton County Junior College in Dry Creek. And there it happened, as perhaps it was intended, that some of them met their true loves. Little Sue Anne met a boy from the north of the county whose name was Binks Hunter. And when, two days after their graduation from the college, they were married in our little church, I don't believe either one of them could have felt more completed in his dreams.

They certainly did look happy as they stood there between the banks of calla lilies and chrysanthemums and phlox facing Reverend Cooper: pretty Sue in her long white dress and blond Binks dressed in black. Brother Cooper did not preach a sermon but he did offer them some wisdom "in the vernacular," as he put it. "My children," he told them, "if you play it square with the Lord, why then, the Lord'll play square with you." I repeat his words here because they were words I tried to live by myself. Sue blushed when he said that and she just looked down at her bride's bouquet which was a petite arrangement with Lily of the Valley and Baby's Breath in it. Later, when she got ready to toss it, some of the folks near me said, "Catch it, Prentiss!" But I only smiled above their heads and threw my rice.

Three days later, the happy couple returned from their honeymoon in Fort Worth and we had us a first rate mechanic in our town. Binks had chosen practical mechanics for his studies at college and folks gave him a great deal of practical experience in a hurry. From the day it became known that he actually understood things like overhead valves, he never lacked at all for the business we had mostly given to old Wallace Peek before that.

It happened that he came to my cage at the bank with his first deposit and that was the first time we actually met. He was a muscular man with grease on his cheek and a striped mechanic's cap pushed back on his head. "Did you have a good day?" I asked him.

He said, "Yes," and smiled and called me by my name, so I guess someone had told him who I was.

"Why don't you come out to the square on Sunday and play ball with us?" I asked him.

"I'd like that," Binks said.

"At three o'clock," I told him; and I have always liked to think we became friends right then and there.

On Sunday I arrived early and just sat for a while on the splintery old home team bench and looked out over the green square from which our town had taken its name. Actually, it is a block in the center of town on which nothing was ever built. It has been kept that way for nearly a century. There was a stout wire backstop near the northwest corner and a single hackberry tree stood in the southwest corner.

Our only ground rule applied to "Old Hack," as the tree is called, and was started as a joke. The rule is that any ball which hits "Old Hack" is a home run; the joke is any ball hit that far can't help but be a home run. And only two men had ever hit it that I knew of until old Binks made himself the third on that first day he came out to play. At least, that is how most folks remember it. It seems to me he hit it the day we played the Dry Creek Cotton Strippers for the championship, which would have been two or three months later.

But everybody remembers the pitch he hit. It was a changeup from an old farm boy who had once broken his catcher's nose with a rising fast ball — right through his mask! And that was how fast you expected his pitches to come at you. Most of us would have swung twice at that slow one and couldn't have hit even the fastest ball out to "Old Hack," and so we really mobbed Binks with congratulations. He called it an accident but the truth was he had an eye like a Kodak. We had lots of good times and won the county championship two more times in the next few years before everybody quit playing ball and the square grew up in weeds.

That first summer, though, is the one I like to remember. Often I would get cheese or tuna fish sandwiches and potato chips and cherry cokes in paper cups from Waugh's and meet Binks and Sue Anne at his shop for lunch. I liked his shop for it was always neat and usually it had the good banana smell of fresh lacquer. I often said — and said it to his face, too — that Players' Square would fall to pieces if we didn't have old Binks around to keep things together. Why, he could fix almost anything made from metal. It seemed to me that he prized a broken thing which he could fix above a brand new one; and other folks said so, too.

At the end of that next summer, their first child was born, a white-haired little girl who looked just like an angel to me. Sue and Binks were twenty-one when she was born and they had already decided to name her Angela if they had a little girl. But they were not yet twenty-five when she fell like jelly in the early afternoon sun and died before Binks could get home from the shop.

Angela had not been what folks would call "right" for a year or so, but Dr. Sanders had not been specific about it. There was a reason, when she died, that he had to explain it to them very carefully. Her affliction was hereditary, he said, and extremely rare. And always fatal. Once in a million conceptions, he said, no more. Sue Anne cried. Oh, no, no, the doctor assured her; there was no need for concern. The odds against so rare a thing occurring twice to the same parents . . . It was unthinkable. Everyone was happy then, when, three months after we saw the tiny pink coffin safely to its berth, their second child was born. Pretty Boy, I called him, and everyone else called him Tibby; his name was Mark.

When the boy was born Binks gave us cigars from a stale old box which could only have come from Waugh's, and Miss Massingill shooed us out of the hospital waiting room to smoke them in the noon sun; and I knew that everything was in its place again. The next day, Binks did a valve job on Mr. Baker's pickup and brought me the check to open a savings account in Pretty Boy's name. He had in mind some sort of formula for adding to it regularly and I suggested a fixed amount each month. "No," he said and decided on brake jobs. So for the next four years he brought me the proceeds from every brake job he did and I recorded each one faithfully in that little black leatherette passbook. The account grew almost as fast as the boy and I thought it most wise of Binks and Sue Anne to be preparing for his future.

Binks Hunter was a man so full of surprises that I am still astonished when I remember some of them. No one knew it, for example, when he took up painting.

The way it came out was that he and I and Sue Anne took Pretty Boy to the county fair at Dry Creek. We wandered through the booths around the limestone court house and ate home-baked sugar cookies and perspired even after dark in the summer breeze. Then I said we ought to try the weight game and no one minded. That is where a man guesses at a person's weight and if he misses it over three pounds either way, he must forfeit a prize. Sue Anne laughed and refused to do it and the man wouldn't guess at Pretty Boy; so I gave him my quarter and he sized me up to the very pound.

Then the man said, "How about you, Buddy?" Binks grinned his usual grin and gave the man a half dollar, just to please us, I think. So the man handed him back a quarter in change and said that ought to have lightened him up some. "You'll still go one seventy, though," the man said; and Binks stepped onto the scale.

Well, I'll kiss your Aunt Martha if it didn't read one hundred and eighty eight pounds or if that poor man ever said a word at all! His poor face was just sort of distrustful. Binks chose Pretty Boy a calico frog full of beans and we all walked off smiling. I remember I said that maybe Binks had some of his tools in his pockets and Sue Anne said, "Fatty." But it wasn't either one and he just grinned instead of saying anything.

After that, Pretty Boy and I were playing with the bean bag over Sue Anne's shoulder when Binks led us down the alley off the east side of the court house square. It was all lighted and they had stretched banners above it between the Duke and Ayres and the barber shop; the banners said Alley Art Festival. The first painting we came to belonged to Miss Mary Lorraine Peckham who had brought glory to the county seat for years with blue ribbons for her landscape paintings. That year her entry was a scene of bluebonnets by the bend in a little dry creek bend. It was titled "Lover's Bend" and a red ribbon was hanging across it.

"Would you look at that!" I said, surprised that Miss Mary had not taken first place; but the three of them had moved on to the end of the alley and had not heard me. They were standing with a group of folks in front of a large painting which sported the blue ribbon. It was titled "Players' Square" and I had never seen anything like it. You could tell right away that the vantage point was the home team bench; Milton Attaway was at the plate squared away to bunt and Soup Perkins was at third just straining to begin his dash. Any person who knew them could have recognized every member of the Dry Creek team in the field; even the outfielders were clearly identifiable and yet they were in the background.

"That's no painting," I said, "that's a photograph." The picture interrupted a moment, a spark of time we had all lived through. The ball was in midair halfway to old Milt; in just a second his bunt down the first base line would score Soup Perkins and win the county championship. I was just about to express my disappointment that it didn't show me or Binks either when Sue Anne pointed, for my benefit, to the card on it and I was saved from one more time of opening my mouth only to change my feet.

"Mark Walters Hunter — Players' Square — First Prize," the card said. But nobody had known Binks was a painter, not even me. And certainly not Miss Peckham who appeared about that time to be introduced to Binks. She was maybe sixty years old, the kind of lady who fans herself with a dainty handkerchief and stirs up the powder at her throat where she has put too much of it. "The hackberry tree is just marvelous," she said to Binks. And he thanked her.

On the way home I had to say several times that I just hadn't known he painted; I said, too, that it was a terrific picture. Finally, Binks said, "Everyone needs a hobby."

"Hobby, your Aunt Martha!" I told him. "Why you could make it your real vocation."

"No," he said, "I couldn't. I'm no better than a camera; but I would like to have the time to develop myself."

Whatever else he might have said I don't know because Pretty Boy squealed when his daddy spoke and then he drooled a stream out on Sue Anne's shoulder and hit me square in the face with the bean bag.

I thought he said frog when he did it. "Didn't you?" I asked him, but his parents only laughed. So I leaned back in the rear seat of their station wagon watching the headlights fall on the landmarks which brought us closer to home and I saw that painting over again in my mind and could almost smell the chewing tobacco and leather and Neatsfoot oil all along the home team bench.

Binks won first prize at the Alley Art Festival again that next year for a painting called "Dove Season." Mr. Baker paid a hundred dollars for it and hung it in his office at the bank. For that reason, I got to see it every day and seeing it was just like being in the Hunters' kitchen, as anyone who was ever there could tell you.

There is a shotgun standing in one corner and folks who know guns can tell what make it is although only its barrel is visible above the table. The "Eye", as I came to call Binks' vantage points, is in a chair pushed back from the little kitchen table. About the table are two regular chairs besides the one you know you are sitting in as you look at the picture, and a high chair. I always maintained that you could make out a bit of egg yolk on the corner of the high chair tray; but no one else seemed to notice it. The table is bare except for a blue figured china plate on which three shotgun shells lie together and it is those shells most folks notice. And they are perfect. No, they are better than that. They are the exact shade of Winchester red and there isn't a brush stroke showing on them; a camera could not have caught them clearer. The brass base of one of them is toward the "Eye" and the figures No - 12 stamped on either side of the primer are so delicately done as to appear engraved.

But it was the plate itself I loved; it has a little chip at the near edge and was my favorite because I had eaten so many fine meals from that very plate. Although Mr. Baker wouldn't sell it to me, he used to hint of leaving it to me in his will. "Or," he liked to say, if there were folks around to grin at me, "it would make a nice wedding present."

On the day after that fair and Binks' second award, we celebrated

Pretty Boy's birthday. Sue Anne made me wear a silly cap and hold the little fellow on my knee, which was trying for me because he seemed so fragile. Actually, he was fat, but I could never get Angela's illness out of my mind and felt that I should be extra careful with the boy; so I chattered away at him like a sentimental old maid. "Goo-goo," I said to him but he only stared at my silly cap. Everyone said he was quite the talker for his age, but I had never heard a word out of him. "How old are you today?" I asked him, but he pretended not to hear me, just pouting his little mouth and closing his eyes tightly.

When he opened his eyes to peep at me I held two jelly beans just out of his reach and opened my eyes very wide to him. "Are you two years old?" I asked him.

"Less," he said, squealing, and I gave him the candy.

"Goo goo," I told him, not knowing what else to say.

He stared at me a moment. "Goo goo, Lu-self!" he said with disgust and won my heart forever. That was two days before his first falling spell. And then, after twenty-four consecutive monthly assurances to Sue Anne that 'Tibby is fine, just fine,' Dr. Sanders said that perhaps it was . . . thinkable.

But Binks never seemed to let himself think about it; certainly he did not ever talk about it. Still, I believe he must have felt it all of the time. He repaired and made new everything he could get his hands on. He took on more and more brake jobs, making his deposits with the passbook and with neither of us saying a word about it, for finally I knew the purpose of the account. Binks had expected it from the first.

When I say that he repaired things, since he couldn't fix what he most would have wanted to, I mean that it even showed up in his painting which grew beyond what he called the camera effect. It was my privilege to be present when Binks made his first sketch of the "Old Home Place," as the painting was to be called. That painting was the overall favorite of his work in Players' Square and, needless to say, it won the blue ribbon at the festival that year. Hands down.

What had happened was the county had bought the mineral rights to the place where Sue Anne had been raised before her folks moved into town. Her little old daddy, Runt Higgins, saw in the newspaper that the county intended to tear down the old house to get at the gravel and sand beneath it and so he begged Binks to paint a picture of the old home place before it was gone.

They were due to bulldoze it on a Monday and so there was no chance for Binks to sketch it except on that Sunday beforehand. I went along mostly to amuse Pretty Boy who did not often have such an outing and would need watching-after. We arrived at the old place while the grass was still wet because Binks wanted to see the sun on it at several angles, as he put it. While he was unloading his gear I was lifting

Pretty Boy over the fence with me and trying to get him to talk. "Goo goo, lu-self," I told him, but he only rolled his pale eyes and opened his mouth at one corner to drool a stream into the grass.

Stepping over the fence beside us, Binks did not say anything; he just wiped the boy's mouth and turned away. He stood a long while looking at the old house and the windmill and the trees. "I don't see why they are so damned anxious to tear down what is about to fall anyway," he said at last when he had turned to us and tousled his son's hair.

And it was true. Why anyone would want a picture of that old place was more than I could understand. You had to get up close to tell that the house had been painted yellow, for most of the paint was long ago gone. The porch was not safe to walk on, the roof had most of it fallen in, and the whole place was just a ruin of what Runt must have remembered in his old mind.

But Binks worked all morning from different vantage points and without saying a word unless I pried it out of him and at noon we ate the sandwiches Sue Anne had packed for us. By that time, Pretty Boy was exhausted and Binks asked me to take the child home in the station wagon while he finished his sketch. When I returned he was through and waiting for me beside the gate; he never even looked back at the place when we drove away.

Folks who had known the old yellow house in its heyday said the finished picture was so real they expected to see one of the Higginses walk out the front door just any time. Binks had restored the old place as he painted, making everything fresh and new and strong. Wherever a post had rotted out or a window had been broken or boards had sagged, Binks had replaced them, redone them. Runt himself said the picture was so true to life that it took him back twenty, thirty years. And I told Binks, I said, "Now see, you are more than a camera, for what you have done here is to make everything the way it was; you have preserved here a thing so that it can never change."

Everybody in the county wanted to own that painting. Of course, it was never for sale since it belonged to Runt even before it was done; but I liked to think it belonged to all of us. I said at the time that "Old Home Place" was a painting with a message, an example of how things could be kept as they were intended, if only we would all do our best. And other folks said about the same.

But then, before another year could get by, Pretty Boy Tibby Mark died in his sleep and Binks did not go to the fair again. We gathered at the cemetery on a misty morning crowded about the spot next to that other little grave. Poor old Reverend Cooper, tottering around the edge of the fresh grave, comforted us with the holy scriptures. I remember his reading some of my favorite words from the Book: "All things are possible to him who believes." And I remember little Sue not making a sound and poor Binks just turning away.

And he still looked bad to me the following morning when he showed up at my cage in the bank and handed me the little leatherette passbook. It was one of those awkward moments when I could not think what to say; for his part, he just searched the wall behind me as if trying to find something to focus on. "Well," I said finally.

"Cash," he said, "for the people." He meant the Peabody Funeral Home and did not wish to say it.

"Sure represents a bunch of good brake jobs," I said, busily figuring the interest.

"They didn't stop anything," he said. He then slid a check under the grating; it was signed by old Wallace Peek and made out in the amount of five hundred sixty eight dollars. "For the tools," Binks explained. He asked for the money in traveller's checks.

Even with all that, I did not let myself understand that he was leaving, not until I had followed him out to the curb where pretty Sue waited in the old station wagon loaded chock full.

"Are you going on a little trip?" I asked. And Sue Anne said something I couldn't hear while Binks was shaking my hand, his pale eyes focused somewhere behind me. "What are you going to do?" was all I could think of to say.

"Paint," he said.

"Wait," I said. And then I heard myself ask, "What will I do?" Just like a child. But I couldn't help it. Nothing seemed familiar, nothing certain. I bent over to look into the car and held tightly to the doorpost and heard the quick sound as Binks started the engine. "No!" I said.

"Can't be helped," he said, looking straight at me for a second; "things change."

"Damn you!" I cried. But he wasn't looking at me any more, had not seemed to hear me. "You'll be back," I told him, thinking of the plots on either side of their babies in our cemetery. And then I ran, ran right around the car to her. "Sue Anne," I was saying.

But she only pulled my red face down to whisper in my ear and kissed me on the cheek. I could not hear her, only see her lips moving as if it were a silent nightmare I was having. She put a big square piece of cardboard in my hands, waved, saying something else, and they drove away. And me, I just stood there in the middle of the street staring after them until they turned the corner past the old ball field and were gone.

That was not the moment I left Players' Square, nor even the moment when I knew I must. It was the terrible moment when I saw that everything had already left me, had crumbled and couldn't be fixed, had left me looking desperately for something to grab hold of in the midst of that shallow, dead sea where I stood.

And all I could find was the gift they had left me. It turned out to be

Binks' original sketch of the old home place, the way he must really have conceived it.

But, hanging as it does now in a plain pine frame above my fireplace, it still bears no more resemblance to that old place than a shadow on the wind. It is mostly swirls and streaks like decaying Spanish moss; and goodness-knows-where his "Eye" was, for nothing is quite in focus. Nothing but the top of the old windmill gives it away at all. And there are times, glancing at it over my cup or above a child's head, when I wouldn't know even that from a gray sun or a dried zinnia only for those two, three vanes missing in the old wheel.

Jane Kopp

Waking in West Texas in the Fields

I-40 at midnight, the bucking wind —
we left it to sleep in a field
                              and woke
in fresh air

sun was warm along the taut barbed wires
alfalfa, sweet smelling, somewhere

(I had dreamed the horses of the Parthenon —
their necks, torsos plunging through all that wheat)

meadow larks were everywhere

Hectic Saturday, and It is Raining

                    Leaving
child with a cold in the car, and standing
soaked on the paper boy's porch in darkening air
(no one is there), I am
staggered by the wide, white flash —
race back (skull fracture of thunder) —
but the child is calm, enfolded by the fever. We
drive on. "Wet" county thirty
miles and back, I resort to radio. "Farm residence
of Roy E. Highfield demolished, half a broiler house
torn away," town we have
left. It is moving where we are going now,
storm cell fifty thousand feet high. Almighty
God, looking
at the lifeline in my hand,
turning up the child's, watching
all the windows (euphoric, oddly),
watching the rear view, singing
(suddenly at the child's request):
        "Oh my loving brother,
          When the world's on fire,
          Don't you want God's bosom
          To be your pillow?"

                    Somehow
the storm goes on by, over Crow mountain.
("New home up there completely destroyed, roof
lifted off, new furnishings out in the rain"), and
later, gin and dinner wine snug in the trunk,
we are scudding back westward,
the child's nose flowing still, face wet
clouds black as death. To cheer him (rain still
furious, lashing), again I sing, now "Sweet
bunch of daisies/Grown in the dell,/Kiss me
once, darling —/Daisies won't tell," teetotaling great-
grandmother's favorite, "Give me your
answer,/Oh sweetheart, do:/Darling,
I love you,/Won't you be true?" — sunset,
my face all wet, too, slopped by tears,
and we are speeding, flying toward her dream
of the West of Apocalypse, washed, and opening skies

Howard McCord

YSLETA, TEXAS, 1947

My theology began
with a whistle made of a bird's wing.

Unthinking, I had killed
a buzzard,

> he had settled to the ground
> like a mountain
> in a great exhaustion

and above the stench
had stripped the bones of flesh.

I dried them in the sun,
cut four holes
in the big wing bone

> One for lips
> Three for fingers

The bird was made of death,
with wooden eyes,
and the flute hissed more
like a snake than it sang
and the blowing made me dizzy.

But I was young
and full of nonsense
and thought the dizziness
was to dance to.

I did not know that it was a blasphemy
of death, or that the steps
spelled out I was condemned
and would know fiercer lips
on my own bones before I died.

from THE SPANISH DARK

II

And the Spaniard?
One walked eight years in my country
seeing without Indian eyes the crucifying
thorn, the rocks that work penance
into the feet, the water promised tomorrow
and the food two days more.
The ignorance of the Spaniard.
The armor, the heaving horses,
the monks sweating in habits,
the naive vision of conquest.
The existence of truth, the possession
of the ego. The nakedness of the lost one,
Theon walked the desert at night, the wild things close by.

Additionally there is the Spanish Dagger.

Cactus
twelve inches hawse-rough fiber pointed
with the hint of yellow venom inside.
Right through a boot.
Get one in the calf and it aches.
You've moved the point around inside
somehow and there is a bruise meshing
with the puncture. The poison made
my knee joint ache. I was chill
and hurting and I wanted to stop
and hug myself into my past.
The Spaniards, too.

I was born a Mexican in space
but not in time, as the Bostonian
is born an Englishman in space
but not in time. The land is Mexico,
the border is a delusion of the whites.
The sand belongs to both sides of the river;
it blows back and forth, back and forth.
Everybody born in the drainage of the Rio Grande
is an Indian or a Mexican.

After the Spanish conquered it they

turned into Mexicans. The land wins.
The Indian wins.
Because the Mexicans turn into Indians
if they live in the land.
The land only loves Indians
who plant it easy and pat the ground
to call the water down the row
and it comes licking along the corn stalks
like a puppy.

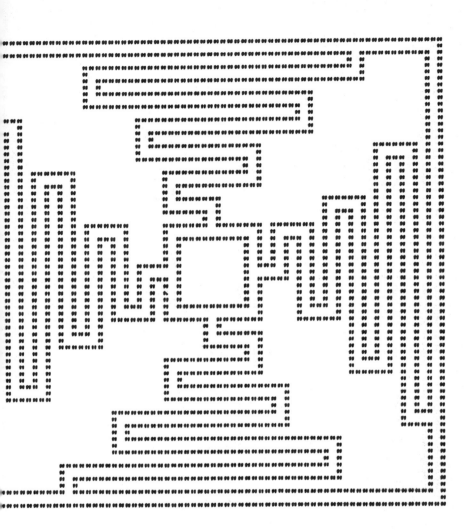

New Mexico is the epicenter of the old Southwest, for it is the focus of nearly all those things one thinks of as truly Southwestern. It lies on the roadmap more than halfway between Dallas-Fort Worth and Phoenix, those two cities Erna Fergusson called the easternmost and westernmost on the southern base line of the vast triangular area of **her** Southwest.

Splitting the state north to south into two almost precisely equal halves flows the Rio Grande, whose valley is the homeland — the blood's country — of the ancient Pueblo cultures of the sun people, the men and women who possessed this river and its pillared land long before the Spanish came on horseback and in oxcarts to claim it in the name of God and King. At first these alien Spanish came for treasure. Somewhere between the oceans, and in a northerly direction, beyond the valleys of Oxitipar, far from the mines of Zacatecas, went the story, there was another land of gold and silver. In the year 1530, Nuño de Guzman, President of New Spain, held captive an Indian who said that he had seen for himself this land of riches. As a small boy, he had gone with his father, a trader of brightly colored feathers, and had seen in that distant country through his little boy eyes "seven very large towns which had streets of silver workers."

If the Spanish never found the treasures of which the Indian spoke, they did find, wrote Pedro de Castañeda, a soldier with Coronado, the first Spaniard to lead an expedition to the upper Rio Grande, "a place in which to search for them and the beginning of a good country to settle in." And the Spanish and Mexican history of New Mexico for approximately three hundred years thereafter would be informed mainly by the twin urges of settling the land and of conquering the sun people and their neighbors, Apache and Navajo. Even though there was much intermarrying so that the modern Chicano natives of the Southwest are a mixture of Indian and European ancestry, the old struggles between the Spanish and the Indians left a badly scarred tribal memory. A young Jicarilla woman speaks in a burst of ferocity of the descendants of the Spanish in New Mexico today: "They hate you (the Anglos, blue-eyed latecomers to the Southwest) so they can forget more easily what they did to us!"

The ancient Southwestern struggle of peoples — the old epicentric conflict — occurred not only between Spanish and Indian. It had gone on before the Spanish first came God knows how long between the native tribes themselves. And in this earlier struggle, Apache and Navajo had been bitter enemies of the Pueblo people. Regularly these hunting and skirmishing tribes raided Pueblo cornfields, stealing slaves, tools, food, whatever of value they could carry off; no doubt they often ran down the women and children as they flew screaming for protection toward their villages. Even today, the Navajo think of the town dwelling Pueblos with a mixture of respect and contempt, while the Pueblos think of the Navajo as ignorant, barbaric, and untrustworthy. Often these attitudes are revealed in the talking, singing and dancing of the Pueblo people; memories of the old atrocities remain. Several years ago I went to a Christmas dance at Zia Pueblo. Leaning against one of those yellow mud buildings which edges the plaza, I watched while two Indian clowns repeatedly interrupted the feathered dancers. These clowns were made up to appear very stupid and very ugly. One of them, a disgusting little hunchback, kept waving and poking his cane at the dancers while his companion yelled insults at them. Finally several dancers broke away to push and shove the clowns off and out of sight among the houses. They were accompanied by hoots and shouts from the crowd about those "awful fellows who live out west." The whole comic action threw the Zia spectators into fits of laughter. One of them explained to me, after he had regained his composure, that those "fellows who live out west" were the Navajo (whose home is in western New Mexico and northeastern Arizona) and that the clowns had been acting just like the stupid and silly Navajo could be expected to act.

Most of the historic conflicts in New Mexico centered around the Rio Grande Pueblos which stretch today from Isleta on the south to near Taos on the north. Include the Jemez River Pueblos of Zia and Jemez and also the old Pueblo of Picuris, near Peñasco. Appropriately, the same river-inscribed landscape, marked by bosques of cottonwood, tamarisk, and willow, contains New Mexico's two main cities, Albuquerque and Santa Fe.

Although Albuquerque is the economic center of the present-day New Mexico, Santa Fe is the true historic center of the state. Here the combined warriors of the Pueblos burnt the Spanish out in 1680, drove them south to El Paso del Norte, where they stayed until de Vargas led his soldiers north again in triumph to the rotting adobe walls of the old capital. Here the Spanish and later the Mexican governments maintained their offices and managed to rule the land and the people who settled thereabout. And here came General Stephen Kearny by force on an August day in 1846 to proclaim to all New Mexicans: "You are no longer Mexican subjects; you have become American citizens. I am your governor; henceforth look to me for protection." Acting Governor Don Bautista Vigil's reply to Kearny suggests many of the conflicts of identity which still haunt the New Mexican mind: "Do not find it strange if there has been no manifestation of joy and enthusiasm in seeing this city occupied by your military forces. To us the power of the Mexican Republic is dead. No matter what her faults, she was our mother. What child will not shed tears at the tomb of its parents?"

But the Anglo-Americans had already begun to crowd into New Mexico before Kearny arrived. In the 1820's and 1830's they hauled trade goods with mule and ox teams over the Santa Fe Trail from Missouri. Shortly, mountain men down from the Rockies to the north discovered the pleasures of wintering in Taos. Blue-eyed Norteamericanos continued to come throughout the nineteenth and into the twentieth centuries. They came to ranch, to mine, to farm, to run the railroad, or to get away from wrecked land and busted hopes back in the Middlewest. Often they took the land by brutal and illegal means, not yet entirely forgotten by New Mexico's dispossessed and their descendants — those Spanish-named people who scrabble a living out of the small farms in the high country or who make their way in the barrios of places like Albuquerque — in Martineztown and Barelas.

What New Mexico is besides its history, its prickly mixture of people, is a very special climate, landscape and sky. In most places it retains its natural beauty. Even the developers of the spreading suburbs of Albuquerque and the architects of the geometric bunkers and the concrete corridors of the new downtown Duke City-Convention Center-USA have not succeeded in hiding the Sandia Mountains from vantage points all over town. Step to one side or the other nearly anywhere in Albuquerque and you can still look at the Rio Grande Valley stretching away southward toward Los Lunas and Belén or you can see the bulwark of Mt. Taylor seventy miles to the west against the reddened evening sun. It is difficult indeed for little men to dominate so grand and richly colored a landscape as this.

Although space and aridity characterize most of New Mexico, there is a look about almost any part of the state that marks that part as different. Whether you enter the state from north or east or west, it is very soon apparent — in fact it is actually apparent at about the time you cross the state line — that you are now no longer in Texas or Colorado or Arizona, but that you are in New Mexico.

From the west there is the land of the Navajo, **Dinetah, The People's Land.** Red sandstone cliffs, wind-edged arches, deep canyons bitten through arid land. The Hubbell Post at Ganado. Window Rock. Even, Gallup. All these are New Mexican places, although the state of Arizona years ago stole Ganado and Window Rock, capital of the Navajo Nation. Western New Mexico **is** Navajoland, and Navajoland extends eastward along the Santa Fe Railroad all the way into the buzzing spraddle of Albuquerque in the center of the state. Navajoland is bunches of ragged sheep, it is thin horses standing by yellow pillars, juniper fires blowing in the night wind, the smell of sage and the look of rabbit bush. It is pickup trucks with four in front and six behind — always behind are the younger women with their children, especially the little boys with chocolate eyes — rattling over miles of gritty red roads in windblown April and May and June.

From the east you recognize the state when you drive out of the Panhandle on old number 66. Somewhere west of Amarillo, a little before you actually get to the state line, you know that you are arriving in New Mexico. Here the high, grassy flattop of north Texas with its fat whiteface cattle and its scattering of oil rigs shades over the Caprock into the long reddish sandstone escarpments of east central New Mexico. Along about here you begin to see prickly pears and, anywhere west of the Caprock, the roadrunner, the cocky, unmistakeable state bird.

But my favorite way of entering New Mexico is from the north, by coming south out of Colorado — from Denver, Leadville, and Salida — into Costilla and Questa or Tres Piedras and Española. Here you begin to recognize New Mexico a hundred miles before you actually reach the state line, after you cross the Poncha Pass at over 9,000 feet. At that very point the green in the landscape — the color that dominates Colorado — disappears, the country begins to stretch out ahead and off to the east and the west toward distant gray hills and ridges. There is dust blowing — the wind always blows here — the color of the landscape is a general dismal, the cover a universal sagebrush, the spread of sky enormous. Teddy Blue, the old Texas Trail cowboy turned Montanan, once rode through this country, "the water warm and bad, and dust gritting in everything you ate." Teddy didn't stay long. What little he remembered, he summed up thus: "To show you what that country was like they told a story about a tough guy who got killed there, and as soon as he got to hell, he wired back for his overcoat . . . The Rio Grande was boiling mud, the sand drifted like snow does in Montana . . . All I ever seen in that country, except sagebrush, was Mexicans and goats."

Here in the San Luis Valley today one sees, perhaps, little more than images of what used to be. Yet these images suggest richly the kinds of knowledge and sympathies and tensions essential for understanding much that New Mexico has been and still in part remains. Some time ago, on a golden fall day, I returned home from a trip to Denver. I stopped in Leadville for pie and coffee in a Main Street cafe, crossed the Poncha about two in the afternoon, and rolled on southward into New Mexico across those gray sagebrush flats. I passed Conejos and Antonito and came to a little, meandering stream where I saw an action that

162

seemed to me to cinch up and girth about much of what New Mexico means.

It was a cattle drive, a fall roundup, and the cowmen, Anglo- and Spanish-American riding together, eased their three hundred or so head across a long, chest-deep, muddy waterhole. A Spanish horseman broke from the bunch — he wore the vaquero's folded-brimmed black hat, the slickworn chaps, the large-roweled spurs, rode the silver-trimmed saddle of his breed — and dashed ahead to meet a waiting pickup. As he passed, he flicked a wave and gave a smile. Tougher than his own saddle leather, intensely proud of his horsemanship, after a day of gritty, dusty, bonecranking work, he could still look fresh as the morning itself.

I knew this place. Apache hunters had waded this stream, made camp by this waterhole. Spanish treasure hunters and soldiers of God had soaked off their terrible desert thirsts here. Mexican and Anglo cowmen had trailed their cattle to water for generations past to this very place, following out of Texas the likes of Oliver Loving and Old Man Goodnight.

Now, occasionally, a cowboy lifted his hat or simply a hand to turn a cow about, and now and then a blue-speckled cow dog shot out to nip a heel, but mostly each cowman sat quiet as his horse edged ahead to dip its muzzle and sip and blow the salty water. Behind them — cowmen and their herd and their loyal dogs — spread the whole immense sky of northern New Mexico, the dark round dome of San Antonio Mountain on the near skyline, the massive range of the Sangre de Cristo far to the south and east, the wispy grass blowing restless in the wind. Then the cowmen rode up the bank and worked on toward suppertime in the failing day.

— David Remley

Sandy McKinney

NEW MEXICO: 1540 - 1975

The Conquistadores came, bringing guns,
    helmets, horses, plagues, priests and nuns
       and a stark Medieval tradition.
Nothing remains
    but a few adobe churches,
    some rusty ironwork rotting in the desert
    and their names.
Epifanio, Tranquilino, Celestino,
the missions have melted away. Your names
are the ghosts.
       We want you in vestments and surplice,
       blessing the young lieutenant as he rides in
           bloody from pillage,
       browbeating
       the natives into loving the One True Faith and
         chinga
       the pagan heresies of spiders and eagles
       and the sacredness of the young corn.
           Instead,
you do small farming or auto mechanics
and drink up your welfare check
on the way home from the bank.

Candelaria, Incarnación,
       the sagging cathedral rears itself in state
       on the legend you wear
       as casually as your shoes, Concepción,
         Reina, Inmaculada,
         Ascención.

Rosa, Dolorosa, crowned with Espinosa,
    you hang like crucifixes on the lampposts
       in the plaza
vomiting cheap California wine, a bicycle chain
       the only weapon left to your
         battalion.

       Nancy, Kevin and Cherie
       have come from the University
       to take over "Collections" at the museum.
       Porfirio Reyes Griego
       watches them as he sweeps.

Agapita, Carmelita, Mercedita all
     work
      at Sears Roebuck,
     wearing mini-skirts,
and a Texaco star adorns the breast
of Jésus Gonzales.

Antonia Quintana Pigno

MY UNCLE LOUIE

Suppose, Uncle Louie,
You had a Ph.D.
Acknowledging your excellence
In horsetrack betting; and
Suppose also your
Petrocelli suits
Were from the best shops
In Albuquerque,
Not from Good Will;
That you got a
Good Price on the
"Historical" Speronelli house,
Now broken, unsold;
Suppose, moreover, that
The vegetable stand
You planned
For the corner of Rio Grande
and Indian School Rd.
Drew all the gringo crowd.
Then, Uncle Louie,
Would you be
Less like Don Quixote
With his sad face and
His Windmills
Long gone?

The Miracle of Santuario

While we played marbles and
Dug irrigation ditches
For back yard adobe ranches,
We almost forgot about
Your new shoes and the
Blue satin cape mamá was making
With the shiny gold rick-rack.
When the cherries fell,
It was time
To travel up the mountains
To Chimayó
Where You waited
With outstretched infant arms
For our kneeling approach
And our yearly offering.
From Your small glass dome,
You watched our curious
Watching come nearer
And nearer to see
Indeed upon Your tiny feet
Last September's white shoes
Now scuffed and worn.

Bert Almon

Albuquerque Landing

Flying over this eroded land
I think of the people it wears
down to a wrinkled beauty
those skulls on display
teeth ground flat by flakes
of pumice from the grindstone
that broke corn into meal

more fitting than the way
men break themselves down
my friend at Los Alamos
poet and physicist, makes
bombs, and dreams of escape
to live like an Indian
in the Sangre de Cristo range

and at White Sands Proving Ground
another friend, poet and physicist
tests bombs on the computer
a holocaust on magnetic tape
(more harrowing than explosions
the tidy printout of blast area
and estimated casualties, broken
down into wounded and fatalities)
my friend dreams of heading west
and keeps on punching data

we are near the runway
our shadow a black bird
racing us on the ground
a stand-off as we plunge
to meet our own darkness
the impact is gentle
cushioned by rubber tires

David Johnson

ALBUQUERQUE'S MT. CALVARY CEMETERY

1

Outside Mt. Calvary to the east there's another
cemetery. The graves are mounds of gravel, as if
the hole itself were a vessel pulled over the body.

Most of the markers are broken, crosses of white
pipe are mutilated. No guardian, not a tree, nothing to center this place — the way in and out.

It takes more than coffins to contain death
in the random disarray of this potter's field.
Yellow painted rocks circle two identical graves

Each with plastic roses and a garland of snow.
History has passed this way, parents perhaps
children certainly — someone's.

2

I met an Indian chopping wood in the drainage
ditch, like a coyote moving into the suburbs.
Was he the caretaker, two copper coins for eyes.

With words lost in the humming of the interstate
he pointed to the mountains where an arsenal
is buried, to his logs tied with electrical cord.

He didn't explain why the new downtown looks like
an Egyptian tomb, or how the dead can be outside
the steel fence at Mt. Calvary — or even inside.

SOULFEATHERS FOR ALBERT CAMUS

In Albuquerque 'the relentless
bad taste
        reaches a point of baroque extravagance
where all can be forgiven'
                  The miles
of neon lights along Central Avenue
attract me as no other lights anywhere
I'm a tourist
        nothing more
of this nightly bawdy passage
through the New Mexican plains

Albuquerque is a desert
              During the day
I can be alone with it   I can make love
to it   How can it resist me
helpless as it is   a city of little character
and no repute?   All it asks of me
is that I bring back flowery stories
from Santa Fe
        60 miles away
Santa Fe is a bitch   We would quarrel continually
There would be questions of fidelity

INDIAN CORN

Indian corn suspended from the ceiling
eight ears wired together   One is yellow
one maroon another pink still another black
These colors are imprecise   they harmonize
with, and are, the language that observes them
hanging, at this angle, just above
the horizontal window   This angle
is the eye's
        Another corn is creamy
three others have no words   The numbering
is exact, the sizes of corn descend

from smallest to largest
with two exceptions; again, there is definition
in the numbering
                        These cornshapes have been hanging
around for more than two years, the exact date
of their acquisition lost
though the place, Ácoma Pueblo, remains
They instill no ideas
no fantasies   The mind, holding them, is static
itself suspended; the hand has no impulse
to covet their polished surface   What is of concern
is that, at last, they are visible

THE ANGLO COORDINATOR

As the Anglo coordinator
for the 3rd Annual Southwest Poetry Conference
I have so far failed
to coordinate a single Anglo

I am neurotically troubled
The event is a mere two weeks off
in Durango Colorado
and I freak at the vision
of all those uncoordinated Anglos tripping
over their own feet

I have no doubt the Chicanos and Indians
are in talented hands
but my Anglos, what a confused team
I'll have on my conscience!

None of them knows
the signals I have not yet devised
nor the comprehensive strategy to be used
in delivering our poems
True, the element of surprise
will be on our side
but what we critically lack is the totally expected

Can we depend on the others
to fuck up their lines?   No right-minded coordinator
would risk it   It is time for a
hasty ill-conceived locker-room prayer
something like: 'Dear Almighty of the Anglos
bless our flabby metrics our dull rhymes
and give us credit for lots of guts'

Our Almighty is known to be half-hearted
much lazier and probably more incompetent than theirs
Still, he may help us put together
a potent stanza in the right place
a quick spurt of highly-regarded images . . .

though I think it's really no use
The 3rd Annual Southwest Poetry Conference in Durango
is sure to be a slaughter
You can imagine how guilty I feel

Gerald Hausman

Santo Domingo

My boots stir up
yellow feathers of dust,
sun fire on every stone.

A child playing
sees us coming and cries.
Fat moccasined mother
chases after her,
turquoise squash blossom
bangs at her breast.

The child swooped up
from the white invaders.
I feel eyes of things
sparkle back
from sky-roof antlers,
the child's corn husk doll
eyeless, grinning in the dust.

Johanna Cinader

The Gardener

Lean and tall but bent a little
dressed in clean, ill-fitting clothes
the gardener comes in the morning
on a truck from his home in the county.

It is cold, so he comes in.
He talks of his wife who is sick at home,
his English halting, searching for words.
We drink hot coffee and laugh as we find ways
with his Spanish and my French,
to tell each other of our grandmothers
who knew the same ways of living with arthritis
and growing things.

Joy Harjo

"Are You Still There"

there are sixty-five miles
of telephone wire
between ácoma
              and albuquerque
i dial the number
and listen for the sound
of his low voice
              on the other side
"hello"
        is a gentle motion of a western wind
cradling tiny purple flowers
that grow near the road
                    towards laguna
i smell them
as i near the rio puerco bridge
my voice stumbles

returning over sandstone
               as it passes the cañoncito exit
"i have missed you" he says
the rhythm circles the curve
of mesita cliffs
               to meet me
but my voice is caught
shredded on a barbed wire fence
at the side of the road
and flutters soundless
in the wind

3 AM

in the albuquerque airport
trying to find a flight
to old oraibi, third mesa
TWA
        is the only desk open
bright lights outline new york,
                          chicago
and the attendant doesn't know
that third mesa
is a part of the center
of the world
and who are we
just two indians
at three in the morning
trying to find a way back

and then i remember
that time simon
took a yellow cab
out to ácoma from albuquerque
a twenty-five dollar ride
to the center of himself

3 AM is not too late
to find the way back

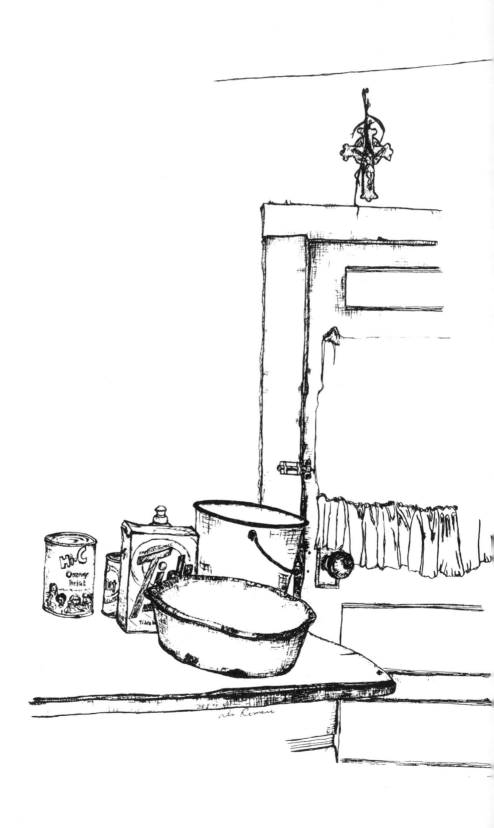

Rudolfo A. Anaya

THE WRITER'S LANDSCAPE:
Epiphany in Landscape

The barrio was a welcome place to drive into that afternoon. The summer afternoon air was thick with dust that rose from the feet of children playing and from the workers who trudged down the dusty streets. The dust swirled in clouds behind pachuco-laden cars, and it covered the sweating boys of the barrio who played baseball in the street. The dust settled over the towering elms and the house tops of Barelas, like a veil pulled by the golden fingers of the afternoon sun . . . Jason listened . . . Around him children called and ran to meet their fathers, neighbors visited across fences and paused in their small talk to turn and wave. Smiles were in the soft air, and so was the fragrance of roasting chile verde and hot tortillas, supper for the hungry workers. The air was heavy with the damp smell of just-watered gardens, dirty with the bad smell of sewage that drifted up from the sewage plant in South Barelas, and acrid with the salty sweat-smell of the grimy workers from the railroad yard.

This selection from **Heart of Aztlan** illustrates my concern for conveying my sense of place and people to the reader. Although the passage strives to capture an actual barrio scene it does not — and neither does my statement about conveying my sense of place — limit me or trap me into being only a recorder of an empirical reality. Quite to the contrary, my interest in writing is to explore the magic in realism and in that sense my immediate landscape and my relationship to my region is only a point of reference, but a very important point because it is the "taking off point." It is the place where imagination and the image-laden memory begin their work, and the three forces — place, imagination, and memory — are inextricably wound together in my work.

In speaking about landscape, I would prefer to use the Spanish word **la tierra,** simply because it conveys a deeper relationship between man and his place, and it is this kinship to the environment which creates the metaphor and the epiphany in landscape. On one pole of the metaphor stands man — on the other is the raw, majestic and awe-inspiring landscape of the southwest; the epiphany is the natural response to that landscape, a coming together of these two forces. And because I feel a close kinship with my environment I feel constantly in touch with that epiphany which opens me up to receive the power in my landscape. I don't believe a person can be born and raised in the southwest and not be affected by the land. The landscape changes the man, and the man becomes his landscape. My earliest memories were molded by the forces in my landscape: sun, wind, rain, the llano, the river. And all of these forces were working to create the people that walked across my plane of vision. And my vision was limited until I was taught to see the stark beauty which surrounded me. I was fortunate to meet a few, old ancianos who taught me to respond to my landscape and to acquire the harmony which is inherent between man and his place.

So in **Bless Me, Última,** Antonio's eyes have to be opened by Última so that he can see for the first time the beauty of the llano and the valley, and he can begin to sense the latent energy in the landscape:

> . . . She took my hand and I felt the power of a whirlwind sweep around me. Her eyes swept the surrounding hills and through them I saw for the first time the wild beauty of our hills and the magic of the green river. My nostrils quivered as I felt the song of the mockingbirds and the drone of the grasshoppers mingle with the pulse of the earth. The four directions of the llano met in me, and the white sun shone on my soul. The granules of sand at my feet and the sun and sky above me seemed to dissolve into one strange, complete being.

Antonio has described his first epiphany with his landscape. He has opened himself to the power in the earth and he has been transformed, as we are all transformed when we feel the surge of energy that flows through our landscape. Whatever tension exists in the man:place metaphor dissolves in the harmony of the epiphany.

While growing up in Santa Rosa, New Mexico, I spent a great deal of time along the river. I came to know the river very well. A great deal of the time I tramped up and down the valley alone, and in those early formative years I was haunted by the soul of the river, that tremendous energy of the place which I later called the "presence of the river." That presence, which was the same power I felt on the open llano, touched my primal memory and allowed me to discover the river gods and the other essential symbols which were to become so important in my writing. It was those times when I surrendered myself to the surge of energy that I felt the potential of the epiphany.

The power of the earth is reflected in its landscape. And each one of us defines our relationship to the energy of place according to our particular world view. Energy flows from the earth, and as one learns how to receive that energy one also learns how to give of one's energy to dissolve the polarity of metaphor and create the unity of epiphany. In **Heart of Aztlan** Clemente Chávez seeks the strength that will help him become the leader of his people and he remembers this energy of the llano:

> Suddenly he stopped and remembered that there were certain spots of earth on the wide llano where he had once stood and felt the elation of flying. Yes, the power of the earth surged through him until he felt himself soaring over the landscape . . . He had gone once to the old sheepherder they called el hombre volador, and he had asked the man if he could explain this strange feeling. The old man had laughed and said that the dark secrets of the earth were only for those who were willing to search to the very core and essence of their being.

And as time is also energy, it fuses the epiphany between man and place. When Clemente has learned how to respond he can reach out and touch the heart of the earth, and his epiphany is described thusly:

> Time stood still, and in that enduring moment he felt the rhythm of the heart of Aztlan beat to the measure of his own heart. Dreams and visions became reality, and reality was but the thin substance of myth and legends. A joyful power coursed from the dark womb-heart of the earth into his soul and he cried out I AM AZTLAN!
> My heart is the heart of the earth!
> I am the earth and I am the blue sky!
> I am the water and I am the wind!
> I walk in legends told today and turn and recreate the past.
> I pause and give the future time to grow.
> I am the image, and I am the living man!
> I am the dream, I am the waking . . .

The pregnant power of the epiphany is described here. At that moment time is infused with power. As man and woman at the peak of their love break the shell of solitude that holds them apart and in tension, man and place achieve a similar climax in the realization of this essential metaphor.

But how is this relationship useful to the writer? How does the power of the epiphany translate itself into the writer's task? My sense of place helps to define my center, and that center becomes the point of view from which I observe life. The discovery of place was very important to me, and very crucial to the writing of **Bless Me, Última** and **Heart of Aztlan.** My writing before that discovery was busy duplicating false models; it had no flavor to it, no characters, no story. So it was very important for me to realize that I didn't need to traverse the world suffering the slings and arrows of outrageous fortune to find the raw materials for my fictions, and what I really needed to do was to stand still and discover my sense of place. From memory I recalled the epiphanies and their power charged my imagination into recreating that universe where the stories could be played out. Now, in that lonely act of writing when I struggle with my craft, I aim to duplicate the power of the epiphany. The relationship I feel with the earth fuses with time and memory and imagination and creates the scenes, characters, images, symbols and themes that are woven into the story. Sitting quietly behind the typewriter I evoke the epiphanies sleeping in memory and the flood begins. The writer thrives on energy, and energy is what the epiphany rekindles. Characters awaken and move, they speak, and they bring with them their own landscapes, old impressions, joy and sadness, fortune and misfortune as they come to fill the writer's lonely room and to discuss the task at hand.

So the landscape of the southwest has been very important to me as a writer. Here time, or a sense of timelessness, permeates the earth-features, and it is that sense of timelessness which lends the vision to the epiphany. I have already likened both the spiritual and sensual aspects of the epiphany to a deeply shared human love. It is our ability to love and to make human connections that is necessary to our well-being, and it is that feeling of strong love that envelops the epiphany I described. And just as the natural end of all art is to make us well and to cure our souls, so is our relationship to the earth and its power. I do not merely mean the awe and sense of good feeling which we experience in the face of grandeur and beauty in nature; I mean that there is an actual healing power which the epiphany of place provides. In **Heart of Aztlan,** Adelita, Clemente's wife, suggests this:

> "You see," she spoke earnestly to her daughters, "once there would have been the land to make him whole again. A man who met defeat could go out on the land, and the earth would make him well again. It might take weeks, or months, or years, but always the man who looked found himself in his earth and he was well again. . . . Well, things have changed, and your father, he is a man lost in a foreign land —"

These characters who have become separated from their land and sense of place become frustrated, alienated human beings. They lose their center, and most devastating, they lose their source of redemption. Does this separation also bode ill for the writer? Is the writer separated from his sense of place further estranged from the redemption in the epiphany? And if so, what is the vision of the world which he presents to guide us through our fragmented, often frightening, modern reality?

Memory has been a constant companion in my writing, and I found that it was the haunting beauty of those early epiphanies which I learned to recall that triggered the latent images in memory. Some of the characters of memory were characters composed of river mud and water. Those that came from the llano were as restless as llano wind. I

178

peered closely into their souls and discovered that they not only reflected their landscape but that they **were** my sense of place! The raw sensual beauty of my encounters with the presence of the river and the llano and the wind and rain and sun had become a part of me! All those times of haunting beauty and poignant sadness were stored in memory, and they could be aroused to energize and support the creative act! I became intensely aware in my writing of the process by which the landscape and its epiphanies had become incorporated into memory and how the same energy and emotion present at the actual epiphany could be used in writing! I felt I had found a natural reservoir that was as deep as I cared to explore.

Obviously this explains only a small part of the creative process that occurs in writing. The sources of energy that drain into the mental and emotional five-finger exercise are bound up in other areas of this complex act. The characters themselves recreate their own energy and often clamor to write their own stories. The private writing place becomes a madhouse, and the writer a mere guide as to the course of the characters' lives.

The landscape can always expand. At this point in time I can choose whether or not to expand my landscape. In many ways I already have, but I find that which is honest to me and therefore to my writing comes from my deepest felt experiences, so I choose to stay at the center of the place which is providing me energy, and whose energy is healing me because the exploration into my world is a process through which I come to know myself and my earth better. For the moment, I am content to continue this exploration, and to convey to my reader the center of my universe. It is our task as writers to convey our landscape to our readers and to work through the harmony of this essential metaphor. When the writer has incorporated his sense of place into his art and when the entire sense of the landscape — characters, emotion, experience, detail and story — permeates his craft, the reader will respond, and that response is the beginning of a new epiphany.

Leo Romero

THE GOAT'S CRY

My grandmother took the young goat
and slit its throat
Delicate cords cut in the glass air
I fled from the sharp knife
from the gush of hot blood
which had stained my grandmother's hands
which the earth drank greedily
In the air the goat's cry
shattered clouds, opened and closed blue doors
I cowered inside the house
where I ran after seeing the sun's face
in the blade of the knife
saw the sun drinking the blood
which was so warm, which burned
I listened to the incessant crying
the goat's agony filling the sky like smoke
I was helpless and trembling
listening to the severed throat
to the blood cry, elastic cords snapping
a cry jagged as broken glass
until the goat's cry finally left the sky
and my grandmother was calling me
to wash my hands, to drink of the blood
the still hot blood which she held in a pan
a pool of life, bright life, the sun
O the sun was full and very large
Drink of the blood, drink
Earth, sun, hot blood, O drink
of the life which is all life, drink

EL REY DE LAS PAPAS

The Potato King they called him
He lived in Lucero canyon
or did he live in canyon Flechado
The old woman's mind is blurred
It was so long ago
She sits so patiently
only a rock could seem more at ease

What about the Potato King I ask
That was when there were many people
in the valley
He would grow lots of potatoes
The old woman looks at me serenely
She bore twelve children
the youngest is forty-two
It was so long ago she repeats
for the sixth or seventh time

DURING THE GROWING SEASON

Nowadays it is growing corn
that attracts my attention
like girls in short dresses used to
The girls in Mora did not interest me
half as much as the corn growing there
It is not that I have become less virile
but that I feel priorities must be made
during the growing season
It is with affection that I gaze upon
the rows of slender green cornstalks
growing vigorous and resplendent
Before this beauty feminine charms pale
It is no wonder that the Indians
have their corn-gods and their corn-dances
Twenty dancing virgins dressed in finery
is the closest we can come to this beauty

David Kherdian

Cerro Gordo

Spiraling smoke from a round Mexican oven
beside an adobe house of straight lines
natural wood
and primitive carvings.

A relationship:
red clay,
the earth
and man's dwelling.

The mud and fire of his life
from which he emerged from God
to which he has given back himself
as himself.

Arthur Sze

1000 camino piñones

who loves white? & winter sunshine?
& cabernet sauvignon grapes?

she fired us as soon as we finished the porch:
made excuses, complained to

the carpenter that she was going broke.
look at the indian kachinas

in this house. look at the 15th century hand-carved
spanish antiques. she hired a mexican

to dig that ditch for the adobe wall,
& paid him in cash.

L.S. Fallis

At Silver Creek

no
snow
falls
here
nor
summer's
rain

butterflies
are
but
shadows
on
illusion's
veil

nothing
real
yet
nothing
false

only
Kasyapa's
rose
growing
in
the
mid-
day
sun

Paula Allen

GRANDMOTHER

Out of her own body she pushed
silver thread, light, air
and carried it carefully on the dark, flying
where nothing moved.

Out of her body she extruded
shining wire, life, and wove the light
on the void.

From beyond time,
beyond oak trees and bright clear water flow,
she was given the work of weaving the strands
of her body, her pain, her vision
into creation, and the gift of having made it,
to disappear.

After her,
the women and the men weave blankets into tales of life,
memories of light and ladders,
infinity-eyes, and rain.
After her I sit on my laddered rain-bearing rug
and mend the tear with string.

WOOL SEASON: 1973

In Cubero
days too hot, arroyo dry
dust marks the road that forever crumbles at the edge
it will rain next month. Now
time to get the wool in — paid up, settled,
like in the good times when wool sold by the tons
even out of Cubero.
Now it's petroleum all the way, and the arroyo gets deeper
the road narrows a little every year.
Old Diego died in the bottom of the arroyo
a couple of years ago. They say he was drunk,

missed his way in the dark. They found him in the morning.
The old huge boulders I climbed have shattered and moved downstream
in summer floods. The heavy hum of fat flies is the same.

What do the people do when they can't sell their wool?
How do they settle for the lard and mutton and flour?
The kids' clothes, the ladies' shawls, the shovels,
tires and gas?
The wool lies heavy in the barn now, season after season,
unsold, unwanted. No one even tans the hides.
They can't survive much more. Being punished for no crimes.
The skin of my thought is bloody wool, stuffed
with gorging ticks like the packed sacks of fleece.
Don't play in the barn where the wool is stacked
they used to warn us kids.
you'll be killed whether you've murdered anyone or not.

Catherine Stetson

Preparations

Men sit by fires in the night
along the steep banks of the Rio Grande,
fishing. Fires burn in the eyes
of the fish they are trying to catch.
We stop for a few moments
in the cold dark —
in Taos, the foot-racers pause
in their preparations.
We are all waiting
for the same shadow
which passes quietly
just before dawn.
We know it by the fire
which burns in its eyes,
and we know that dawn is near.

Joe Lafferty Ought To Be
Ashamed of Himself

Everybody in Clovis liked Joe Lafferty, the livery stable man — everybody, that is, except Bud Kilgore. Being a young fellow, Bud fancied the girls, but he was plumb ashamed of the way Joe Lafferty talked about them. Joe told Bud that he never said anything in his life that he was ashamed of, but still Bud wondered. He thought that Joe told pretty bad stories, the sort of things a man shouldn't talk about. Maybe the trouble came from Bud's youth and inexperience, because Joe Lafferty had a good reputation all through the eastern half of New Mexico, being especially well liked around Clovis. In fact, Joe Lafferty was a regular old-timer.

Bud Kilgore's Dad, who was an old-timer of old-timers, told his son that Joe Lafferty would die for a friend. Every time Bud pushed his Dad hard for more of an answer, the old man just smiled and said nothing. Bud wondered about it a lot: he began to think that his Dad was too old to understand things any more. One day he decided to ask him point-blank what he meant by saying that Joe Lafferty would die for a friend.

"Say, Dad, what do you mean? You say Joe would do this and do that. Just what would he do?" Bud asked him.

"Joe would give you the shirt off his back, son." The old man smiled, as if it should be plain enough to anybody.

Still the question stuck in Bud's mind. For the life of him, he couldn't understand how Joe could have such a good reputation and make the cracks he did. For instance, whenever a young fellow rented a buggy to take his girl for a Sunday ride, Joe Lafferty always wisecracked, "Watch out you don't push the dashboard in." And he didn't care who was standing around.

It was things like that which stirred Bud up. His new girl was the preacher's daughter, and he was going to want a nice-looking buggy to take her out in for a Sunday ride as soon as he worked around to it. Finally, on Tuesday he made a date for the next Sunday. It was his first date with the preacher's girl.

The next day Bud started worrying about the buggy and how Joe was going to talk.

Bud couldn't stand thinking about it for very long, so Wednesday afternoon he started down to the livery stable to pick one out. The buggy that caught his eye was a brand new shiny black Peter Schuttler, trimmed in yellow with a big red rose sewed on the leather dashboard. Joe, who was busy working the stiffness out of the new harness, was as jovial as usual when he saw Bud looking the buggy over.

"I want to rent that one," Bud said finally, pointing to the Peter Schuttler buggy that Joe had just harnessed. "I want to rent it now so I can try it out a little before Sunday. I'll bring it back to you Sunday evening."

"All right," Joe said. "You'll be the first to use it, but I guess it's all right to let you have it now."

Bud was relieved that nothing had happened. He paid Joe as quick as he could and was about to get in and drive away when he heard Joe gurgling down in his throat the way he always did when he was about to make a crack.

"You want to be careful about that flower there, Bud," Joe remarked. When Bud turned around he was pointing at the rose on the leather dashboard and had a funny grin slanting across his face.

Bud got red all over inside. The next thing he knew he had hauled out his gun.

"Damn you, Joe Lafferty," he said, "you keep your damn mouth shut or I'll blow your gizzards to hell and back."

He noticed that Joe flinched a little, but since Joe didn't do or say anything Bud started walking away. Then he decided to turn around and come back. He came back while Joe was putting away the rent money for the buggy.

"What do you mean sayin' that, Joe? I'm takin' the preacher's gal out for a ride Sunday, and I don't like it. Damn it, you're goin' to respect the preacher's gal here in Clovis. I'm tired of hearin' your wisecracks. Honest to God, Joe Lafferty, you ought to be ashamed of yourself."

"Go on, Bud, forget it. Take the buggy now, and try it out. Use it all you want to, and bring it back Sunday night. It's brand new," Joe repeated emphatically, "so take care of it."

That seemed to be the end of it. Maybe Joe was just worried because the buggy was new. So Bud drove it on home to the ranch.

But as Sunday drew near, Bud began to worry again. He simply couldn't get over being suspicious of Joe Lafferty. Try as he would, he couldn't understand how his own Dad, being the old-timer he was, could say that Joe was such a fine man. The more he thought about what Joe had said, the worse it got. Sunday afternoon, when he came in from the corral, he stormed over to his Dad.

"You are as wrong as hell, Dad — about Joe Lafferty, I mean. He's crazy to talk the way he does. What makes you think he would do anything for a friend?"

"Bud," his Dad explained, "you got to remember that Joe is older and more experienced than you are; you got to remember that he has been here in the livery stable business a mighty long time."

Every minute that his Dad was talking, Bud was thinking that he was simply getting too old to understand people any more. Finally, Bud decided to tell him just what Joe had said about the preacher's girl and the buggy. When Bud told him, his Dad sort of cackled and grinned foolishly. Seeing the old man act that way made Bud ashamed of his own Dad.

"Has it got to where nobody in New Mexico respects a woman?" Bud asked him.

And then his Dad said something surprising.

"How do you know that preacher's gal is a woman?"

That sort of stunned Bud. Of course he didn't know whether she was a woman or not inside her bonnet and dress, but what did that have to do with it anyhow? His Dad was certainly too old to understand women any more, he decided, or maybe it was just a way of the old-timers to act foxy about it.

"Dad," he said, "I've never been out with the preacher's gal before. But let me tell you something. No matter what you, Joe Lafferty, or anybody else says, it won't change things. I'm goin' to take her out for a buggy ride this Sunday."

For the first time Bud felt that he really knew more than his Dad, and this sort of made him feel disgusted. He walked in through the house out to the back porch, took off his six-shooter, and washed his hands and face clean of the filth from the corral. But even after he washed his hands and face, he was not entirely through being angry. He was still going over it in his mind later on that Saturday night at supper time. When everybody gathered around the supper table, Bud Kilgore said sort of sudden like to his Dad and to all the hired hands around the table.

"I don't want to hear anything more about Joe Lafferty in this house. Whenever you get to thinkin' of him, just wait and mention his name out at the corral or in one of the bunk houses because I'm damn tired of hearin' him talked about." Everybody looked at each other, but nobody said anything.

Sunday morning Bud Kilgore really dressed himself up. He oiled his gun, polished his boots, shined his big belt buckle, tied his red string tie, shaved his face smooth and clean, tucked in his white silk shirt, and creased his gray Stetson. Bud thought all the fixing up was worth it when he saw the preacher's daughter that afternoon. She was dolled up, too: Black patent leather shoes, blue silk dress, and light blue bonnet. To Bud, she was as pretty as a picture, with her pink complexion and her blue, blue eyes. And he could tell she really liked the new buggy.

She stretched and squirmed on the leather seats to get the feel of the squeaky new cushions. She reached out her legs as if testing the roominess between seat and dashboard. Then she sat up and looked at the flowered design. Next she bent over and tracked the full form of the rose that was sewed there with her soft, white fingers.

"My, what a pretty rose," she declared.

By then Bud had taken the road around the shady side of Wild Horse Mesa. He slowed the horse so he could talk with her better.

"It's mighty pretty, isn't it?" he said, just making conversation.

"The dashboard?" she asked.

Bud was startled at that because when she spoke he was looking, not at the rose at all, but down at the roomy leg space between seat and dashboard which the new Peter Schuttler buggy featured. He wondered if she had noticed, if her remark meant anything.

"There's sure lots of room," she added.

There was something in the way she spoke that made him get hot all over, and his stomach seemed to crawl around inside of him. Did she mean anything special? Bud felt limp and excited when he drew back on the reins and turned around to look at her. But since she was gazing straight ahead at the dashboard, he couldn't tell what she thought, and he couldn't see her eyes for her bonnet.

"Yes, the dashboard," he managed to reply. What he was remembering was his Dad asking him if she was really a woman. She talked about the dashboard a mighty lot, it seemed to him. When he was sure enough wondering if she was hinting at something, he had to slacken up a little bit on the reins because the horse had stopped to eat grass alongside the road.

"That red rose is real pretty," the preacher's girl continued. "The red against that black leather is real pretty."

Still harping on that dashboard, Bud thought to himself. He decided that maybe he should hint around a little to lead up to what she was really thinking.

"I bet you'd be surprised at what the livery stable man always says to the fellows about the dashboard," he said.

She laughed at that and leaned towards him with a knowing look in her eyes.

"I bet you I wouldn't. You mean Joe Lafferty. I've known him a long time; he's a fine fellow, Joe is. You're wrong if you think he'd surprise me. I know him too well for that."

Outside Bud went suddenly cold, but inside he was sweltering. A thin mist of perspiration had broken out all over him. He asked himself what Joe knew about her. Had she really pushed in the dashboard? Was that what Joe meant? He wondered. Of course Joe would see the buggies when they were returned to the livery stable after every ride. Maybe that was what Joe was hinting at all the time. Joe would certainly know if she ever really had.

"You know how Joe is," he stammered. "He's always talkin' about the girls. He's always warnin' fellows to take care of his buggies. Keep them clean and 'don't scratch the dashboard,' Joe always says."

"Don't worry about Joe Lafferty. He's got no room to talk," she said, squirming around again and sidling up to him even closer.

"Do you mean . . . ?" But then he reasoned she surely wouldn't go for a fellow as old as Joe.

"I mean I wouldn't trouble myself about dirtying up his buggy. He gets paid for it." She gripped the dashboard as if she meant business and looked square dab at him.

Later that afternoon the preacher's girl reminded him that she had to get back to town. "It's getting late," she said, "and I have to sing in the choir."

It was then that Bud turned the buggy around, slapped the horse on the rump with the reins, and hurried back towards Clovis. They were so late getting back that he had to let her out before going to the livery stable. When they reached the church, she slipped in at the side door so she could take her place in the choir.

Driving on from the church to the livery stable, Bud began to wonder what would be the right thing to say to Joe. By the time he reached the stable he had his mind made up.

"Here you are, Joe," he said, handing him the reins. "I'll be needin' one of your buggies again next Sunday."

"Not this new Peter Schuttler; you'll not get it again," Joe said, bending over with a cloth to polish the leather dashboard.

Keith Wilson

THE DAY OF THE RABBIT

> Jackrabbit: *a shy, swift creature*
> *with round, shiny eyes, fur*
> *that ruffles in the wind*

One Sunday, they rounded us kids up,
promising a picnic and loaded us into pickups;
chattering we rode through the dust, screaming
with joy at the bumps, any high fly through the air.

190

At the ranch all was nearly ready:
a huge beef turned and smoked on the spit,
pickles in barrels, beans in great clay pots,
red chilis crumpled into jagged flakes
and dropped into the bubbling brown sauce.
Dutch Oven biscuits, hot & steaming
being sampled by the cook

The pickhandles were piled just beyond.
Each of us was given one, the details explained
by the potbellied rancher: we were to form
a huge circle, about two feet apart.
The men would join us, then we would close.

Later, moving slowly through the grass,
we scared up several rattlesnakes, various
small rats, a bird or two. The dust closed
on a tight pen in the center and there they
were: over a hundred rabbits, cottontails
& big Jacks milling, trying to break free.

Then the rancher took a pickhandle from one
of the boys and, laughing softly, walked to
the pen and hit one of the rabbits, breaking
his back. The rabbit screamed high & shrill,
went on screaming, he hit another & another,
soon all the boys were in there, hitting, blood
all over them, the big eyes of the rabbits
shining out of the dust, their screams cutting
the air, boys shouting & the older men sat
back, watching, smoked their brownpaper Durhams
& smiled, thinking of the rich feed to come.

— Cambray, New Mexico, 1936

ZEB

— short for Zebediah, late come
mountainman, part-time prospector
now grown stiff in the joints.
Unshaven but not bearded, bushy
eyebrows hanging over blue

At 83 my empty rifle moves smoothly
up to his shoulder, the hammer falls:
"A little stiff in the trigger, son,"
he says and looks away

       his half-wolf dog
moves, with him, flank brushing the
old man's leg, big flat head down
he watches

   Once I made the mistake
of trying to touch him; he growled
deep in his chest. "Don't do that,
boy," Zeb said softly. "He'll take your
hand off." And hobbled back to his
son's house, his lame old dog beside him.

HILL MAN

— Albuquerque, New Mexico

First he and his wife lived here
with their Spanish daughter
& stunted Indian-Spanish
son-in-law.

Then she died and he, tall,
whip-hard, stood alone in the neat yard
his new clothes too big for him
choosing not to see suburbs surrounding him.

—Staring toward the high, pale mountains
of his manhood, where his wife and he
tended sheep in the blue air . . . .

Once he took my blonde baby
held her in his arms and said
"Que linda tu eres, Chica." Gently.
He drew the sign of the Cross
on her soft forehead, for witches
he said, were everywhere, still watch
from the mountains and would curse
a beautiful child praised
and without protection.

Jim Ruppert

WILLIAM BONNEY 1859-1881

Why do they all write about you?
Every poet in the
west
hands you a gun between the bars
faithfully leaps the balcony with you
blows away two dim-witted deputies
and rides off to new inspiration.
In that leap, Lincoln county lives.
At the courthouse, I stopped the van
and wondered where you landed
to make such an impact.
West
the mountains rise defiant
old El Capitan shrivels
like a pimple on your ugly buck-toothed face.
Between you and Albuquerque lies
Trinity Atomic Bomb site, malpais
and lost treasure buried on the missile range

by some mad friar.
The landscape is impossible.

Real bars confine a dummy
in the Billy-the-Kid Museum jail.
Ed Sweet, an old snake-oil salesman
and his wife Billy
hold your profitable past open
10 to 7 daily.
It gets top billing over a
Prehistoric Indian God Ed found
in a dark cave at Acoma.
Fort Sumner cemented your grave a few years ago
buried you with two friends
ever concerned with your company
even to the grave.

your favorite hideout
Fort Sumner.

I slide my face into the hole
where your face should be,
the only picture of you
cardboard, life-size, stiff as Belle Star
or Wyatt Erp beside you.
Someone takes my picture there.

You keep Fort Sumner mythic,
mindless of its genocide past
not like before with the Maxwell's money
but in a fort, a picture
and the poets on the Long Walk to your grave,
The children with plastic guns
The Navajos dead in Bosque Redondo.

you came from the
east
so did I
though I drove 6 hours from the
west
to this meeting
blind to ambush.
You shot us all in the back
and beat it to Juarez.

besmilr brigham

The Sky Is A Circumference

> *a man, walking the canals*
> *come up from mexico: the*
> *Chamberino house*

when we let him out of the car
he stood briefly —
                    the law, *el ley;* picking him up
how he walked with confidence

full in an own law, his variation
'I have come to where I was going—' and
you, the mayordomo! he has
his own Mayordomo

who knows no borders
who does not stop with mountains
whose hand
is placed over seas and rivers (his
land)
        feet on the earth. we sit in the car

stopped by the unbending bonds of
our insignificance . .

in all his body
we feel the sharp im-prudence of birds, as birds
have. we feel we cannot touch him. his eyes
are not on us;
his eyes move in some lost air space, apart from

the hot flat fields and work buildings

Stanley Noyes

SKULLS

Locomotive 384 of the D. & R. G. (built in 1911)
stands with five cars attached
in a green valley north of the Cumbres Pass

while a half-dozen Hollywood grips attach
with planks and chains a platform for lights, camera,
cameraman outside the engine's window;

the stack coalsmokes from the firebox, *chuff-chuffing*
periodically into clouds torn blue by wind
while steam sizzles loudly from a tube behind it;

Barbara, stand-in in 1890's hat, leans out the cab
watching grips hammer, twist wrenches. Her
husband, Ben, who robbed the train this morning,

loafs on the bank above, at his hip a Colt
.45 Frontier Model neatly holstered,
gazing down at old 384 and the movie idlers. Then

slowly up the valley a rider on a dark pony,
figure in cowboy hat, faded denims,
heads at a walk for the train and the movie crew.

Ben has spoken of an old sheepherder who
didn't seem to speak English *or* Spanish, and who
that morning kept riding into scenes, magnetized.

Now he nears the locomotive, riding easily
on a steady dark brown pony who eyes the hissing
engine but comes ahead. All idlers watch the herder.

"Hey, come here," one cries. "Hey, *primo*," calls another.
"He's deaf," someone says. "Baaaaaa," gargles another,
a lamb. But the old man rides along the train, looking

carefully, as if to set it hard in his mind, and waves,
one courtly swing of the arm, and smiles, a
grizzled, nearly round, toothless hole.

Then he's gone, a figure firm in the saddle
of the little dark horse, and all is the same, yet
changed. Who is this old man? What does he remember?

Ben has picked up two bleached cow skulls in
good condition, though of polled cattle. They bring
15 bucks apiece in Santa Fe tourist stores.

"THE LYRE-HORNED CATTLE"

— James Schevill

"Lyre-horned" — I heard that metaphor *thrum* one
morning when four of us saddled up
(me on Buck) and rode into the pasture
back of red corrals, and early sun
was white and grass brown and wet when
Johnny Hubbard and George Turner and
Ike Eidson and I trotted across the
field toward the brahma bulls grazing.

There was a pest of spiders that year,
their filaments shimmering everywhere
in the grass, and when we had circled
the brahmas, were loping back
whooping, whistling, slapping our thighs,
I remember that herd of great bulls
heavily loping toward the corrals, with threads
of light floating between some horns:

Abruptly the morning rang, struck from
an instrument I'd never heard, a lyre,
but wish I could see or hear once more.

197

E.A. Mares

Entry from Las Vegas Journal

Carl Wickham drinks at the Plaza Tuxedo Bar
and talks about his flying days
and about growing up in Roswell
where the gringos didn't like him
because he talked funny English
and the chicanos didn't like him
because he looked like a gringo.
"Estaba cabrón en high school.
That was tough country down there.
It was fight all the time and all the way.
Even the Air Force wasn't that bad.
Hell, I used to fly super Connies
damned near all over the world.
Eso estaba cabrón sometimes, too.
Once I had to fly from Frankfurt to Brasilia
with a heavy piece of machinery for a power plant.
The thing had a part that wouldn't fit in
so they tore a hunk out of an old Connie
ready for her last flight, leaking oil
from all four engines and the landing gears.
When they put that machine in her,
with a part sticking up through a hole in the roof,
she kind of hunkered down like a fat turkey.
I let the engines build up power
'til the whole thing was trembling,
then I let her go, balls to the wall,
and I never thought I'd get off the ground.
She just kept rolling and the buildings
at the end of the runway kept getting bigger.
I finally got her in the air
but never higher than two thousand feet.
I'd dive to get air speed,
then climb for elevation, lose air speed,
dive and climb again, dive and climb,
I went humping clear across the Atlantic.
Three hundred miles out I called Rio,
and they cleared a path for me
all the way to Brasilia.
Sixteen hours across the Atlantic
and fighting that old Connie all the way.
When we landed, they unloaded her,

tore her apart and sold her for scrap."
"I bet you got good money for that job," says the bartender.
"Five thousand dollars and I blew it all in two nights.
It was a rough flight and a rough good time.
Estaba cabrón, but it was worse in high school."

Kathleen Dale

Lunar Eclipse; Chama, New Mexico; May, 1975

The heavy coated collie
hung around our cabin
that whole week.
Hourly pathetic cries
were licked up by our own
locked up
blood dripping Lab.

I trust dogs.
Trust
that their cocked ears
catch what I miss.
He padded heavily,
discouraged, after us
down to the river
to watch
the night's eclipse.
   He lay silent,
   his own waning
   silver outline.
   No howling silhouette.
   No longer comic.

Light tugged back
from the full moon
like skin from a fruit,
    or, reversed,

like life pushing its way
into this brown
nugget of dust.

A shadow's birth.
Dark searchlight,
swinging on its axis,
hitting something solid
on which
            to print itself
by which
            it seeks,
            at last, a third
            dimension.

            Were the moon not there
            we would be less full.

The river
in the coming darkness
doesn't stop,
nor the spring frogs' songs.
Why did I think so?
Even my booted feet
beat out a rhythm.
The river
carrying its load of winter snow
and fish wrapped tight in silver
hurries into this darkness
rushes toward this opportunity.
    It casts no shadow;
    we cast into it
    its anti-shadow: shards
    of China's morning white sunwater
    bounced off a pale
    dead stone.

Darkens.
Two-dimensioned
shadow of a dog
slinks from the river.
Three-dimensioned
shadow of a dog
breathes softly at my feet.
Thin lens of redearthed shadow

pushes hard against
the moon.
Who casts?
Our minds
are cocked
like waiting
muscled
arms.

Stars come out
like game,
form a backwards questionmark
around the fire red ball

       orange circlet

       dark hole
       in the center
       to poke a finger through.

Shadows must be thicker
in the middle.

We still don't know
still can't explain it all
to our own children
even with mother, father, child
holding grapefruit, melon, orange
          playing
earth, and sun, and moon.

Why the bloodrimmed crown?
And where's the shadow of the earth
now wandering
        its
        flung self untouched,
        again
        imaginary?

And today
that mottled, realistic dog's
still straining
toward our
dark black bitch.

Harvey Mudd

Poem about the Water

My neighbor came today
to complain, as he does each year,
about the government,
which is ignorant and remote,
about the porcupine
that eats his corn,

and about the water,
which is not enough.
   They take more than is theirs
upstream, he says.
   Come then, we'll go, I say,
and talk to them again,
especially to Romero,
who has no paper for his water.
   And someday, my neighbor says,
we will take the rifle,
and not the paper.

And so we went,
in his old truck, which remembers,
he always says,
when the water was high in the ditches,
and remembers Roosevelt,
and hauled bricks for the W.P.A.
The grass, he says,
from here to Antonito,
stood to the running boards
in the old days.

          We went
as we have gone before,
tired and resolute, and grim
as farmers. The dust of the road
coated our faces,
as with pollen
for the ceremonies of middle summer.
And his brown dog
prowled behind us on the wooden truck bed,
alert with anticipation.

* *

The sheriff came today,
with questions.
I showed him the ditch,
which is not wet,
and the corn leaves
which are dry as treaties.
They, upstream, say this,
and you say different,
he says.

And I say,
we went about the water,
as we do each year
in middle summer.
We took the paper.
We did nothing.

Can I see the dog?
he says. *No,* I say,
and point to where we'd buried
him in the sage.

When we did
I could not look,
for the familiar head
had been shattered
by a rifle bullet.
We wrapped the stiff body
in a grain sack and laid it
gently, three feet down.
We were in Romero's yard,
standing in the sun by the truck.
Romero said
that he did not take too much,
and that his corn was nearly dead.
Then the shot came,
from the ditch bank,
a good shot, a hundred yards.
It was not Romero
because we were with him.

We will have a meeting tonight
in the school house, my neighbor says.
We will decide what to do.

203

We will read the paper again,
as we have many times before.
The paper says the water belongs
to our valley; and it always did
until so many farms came in
above us. We will decide, as always,
to do nothing.
The government does nothing.
They pave roads we will never use.

The Holy Man

Old Juan Ocampo
is drunk again.
He sits in the middle
of his bleak yard
while dust, chickens,
dogs, and children
revolve around him.
He removes,
one by one,
the spokes
of a bicycle
wheel.
He says he does it
to confuse the Lord.

Drought

A dry time
for a long time.
Ninety days without rain.
The dust rising
and filling a thousand miles
of sky.
The cowboy says,
"We can hold on,
rock bottom,
ten days more,
then we sell."

The papers say
it's the worst time
in sixty years,
since the records began:
cracked earth
and cows dying;
ranches folding
and the people
moving to the jobs
in Lubbock
and El Paso.

Then rain.
A great cloud
rolling out of the Guadalupes
and across the Pecos.
Rain clattering on the roof.
We push up the window
and watch the stain spread
on the ground.
I ask if he thinks God
is in the thunder.
He says *yes.*

Denise Chávez

Baby Krishna's All Night Special

Homer Dill smelled like old baba on softened grey handkerchiefs.

The first bus had left and the rest of us survivors were a paleworn lot. I was what I considered to be the only normal-looking one among the ragged Greyhounded veteran crew of syncopated travelers.

The crippled man in the seat in front of me erratically thrust his rearranged pelvis out to those of us who didn't have the sense to look away. (Always in the midst of varnished-over absurdity, I am the one who stares, frankly and without guilt!) I stared at the man's zipper. He was later to vanish into the night seats of the 6:20; he was later to shrivel up that daylight ambiguity of his and meld it into the jar and whir of Lubbock and Big Spring. The only illumination that would remain for me would be the vision of him right now: flailing arm, thrusting penis, shadowed sense of man, fully grown, tormented and pure.

What remained was that brat of a child, his topknot a medal to some perverse god of calm and reason. The child of God? This fat whining crushed-over bully flown from the flesh of some holy Krishna's union, some towel heads cunt, this **thing**, eating and spewing brown candy-colored droplets, crying and moaning in the women's restroom with swaddled orange sheets clutched to Nero-belly, the age old crotch of the elect, staring spiritually goggle-eyed as the Mother, with softened voice chanted drops of water, the cleansing of hair with grainy pink soap, there, in the lavatory, at 2:00 a.m.

What remained was Albuquerque, this was another time, what remained was Albuquerque, and the tarnished surreal flow of coffee in vein, anguish in heart and rent in soul. Flattened ass of me in quartered seat, the Master flashes his face. "Have you read this book?" asked a turtled man of a copy of Einstein's Greatest Hits. "No," I've lost my voice, "May I see it?"

Who are you, where are you going, and why do you clutch **this** to your breast, while we, vagabond crowd of thoughtless profiles, seep by, exuding daylost time and anticipated wish? You, veteran of Vietnam mind, whitesocked and blue serged, holding to your rounded fattened ears a cassette: classical music in the heart of Albuquerque morning.

Do you see the man with sunken eyes and no eyelids? Deformity is a requisite for the all night special. Do you see the young country couple with child, the holy family in transit, fleeing from Herod America?

The two singing teenage sisters seduce with virginal flattery the long haired young man in the faded nehru shirt; he's from West Virginia, my name is Nora Lou, and you? The trio sings long into the miles of Billie June and Emma Mae (Née Cunt). Romances flicker and die with motorized time. The tread of acid-thoughts eats away the asphalt silence.

I am afraid of the man across from me. I imagine his shadow to be an evil time-enfolded thing; he is dark hawk of dream; he is phantom lover of no face, he is D.

It began in the lobby, bringing in all those suitcases, the remnants of three and a half years of graduate school, a marriage of sorts and whatever else had manifested itself to me as art and wonder.

I felt as if I would fade away and die. Outside the depot, the known ache and the hanging on. I was leaving Dallas. I was leaving D. I felt as if the earth had been lifted up from me. I was flying, a mutant bird, dying, choking in some deadly airsack of my own creation.

When did he come up, this partner in Hell?

Homer Dill: eighty-five years old, from Georgia. A retired deputy sheriff. He told me of the time he had to go and arrest someone, for who knows what offense. Loitering among the living? Carousing with the dead? Homer saw the man in the distance, cutting wood. Why didn't Homer run, then, with excuses, staring that vision in the face, knowing his freedom? The man lived on the farm, in, as I saw it, flashing by Texas-browned night Georgia-green day, in peace with the wife and crickets.

The wife said to Homer, "There he is out there, go and find him." She did not say, "Who are you, what do you want?"

Once handcuffed, the man said, "May I change my shirt?" to which Homer, kind bastard, replied: "Yes, but hurry." That's when she came up to them, alarmed by the silence, by the broken thread of metal splitting wood noise. That's when she came up. "He's out there, go and find him."

She had a gun. "Put that gun down, woman," the man intoned, but this was after he'd changed his shirt and was ready to leave.

What if she fired? Homer didn't know what he'd do. The only bullet that had ever flown his way had stopped somewhere near his hatband, flew right through there like a bat out of, if you know what I mean, flew through there and missed.

"The only thing I miss, the only thing I miss about them days is the chain gangs. They got work done then. All they do nowadays with criminals is let them check out library books."

"Look at this." Homer shows me his wallet, a synthetic leathered receptacle for a wad of twenties. "Just sold some land in Georgia. Where you going to, young lady?" "Home," I remember. "Where are we going, always home." Novalis. I read that quote in Vermont one winter when I was going mad. The only thing that entertained me at the time was filing the calluses on my feet. It was such mundane and tedious work. It **engrossed** me, that was the word. The results were uncomfortable, unsuccessful. I kept filing. Novalis.

I try to look interested. I am hoping Homer will slip me a tax-free wad there on the bus as we speed by Buck's Gun and Dog. Gun and Dog? The bus driver is talking quietly to someone about Corney Hawkins and Little Dickie. I make a mental note to remember those names. I know them. When Homer gives me the wad I can go home and become a writer and spend my days rearranging my drawers.

"Where are **you** going," I ask, as I notice his pitted thick hands close over my future. I am becoming aware of his acrid breath and foul, darting tongue.

"I'm going to visit my daughter in Tucson, Arizona, probably stay there until Spring." I know where Tucson is.

I think about what time of the year it is. I look outside, blur of light lit hamburger moon. D. once said that if I felt myself fading away I should look at the sun, the moon. Stop the bus! There is no moon. D. has left me unprepared for the real darkness.

The overhead light flashes Homer to me. He gets out a blank check. Will I find the mythical patron at last, in the form of this diseased dreamer? Homer writes his name and address on the check, only it is illegible. I do not tell him. I stuff the whitened reminder of night in my purse and sigh. I will give you and Emma Lou a call when I get to Tucson, Arizona, yes siree!

I'd hoped for money.

Homer: eighty-five years old. Bulbous nosed and veiny, smelling like a yeasty old rag, telling stories.

We got off to have breakfast. I ordered a grilled cheese and a hot chocolate. What possessed me? It was a foul meal, and long. Homer was my date. "I'll buy your meal, young lady," Homer says and grabs the ticket from the countertop, but when I get to the cash register the dour-eyed waitress refuses to believe "the gentleman" is paying for the check. Née Cunt keeps repeating, "But that's **her** check." "Listen," I growl, "he's paying for it." "Oh," she connects and suspiciously. She is laughing at me. I feel nauseated. How many more miles can I travel with this man?

The smell of eggs on breath. It is 4:30 something by this present time inside my all too present head. The smell of eggs.

Riding, the bus lights constant mistress of my sleeplessness, I place my hand near my nose to keep from gagging, gagging from the egg breath. I smell my flesh to keep from gagging from stories about crime in Georgia. It becomes later and later. I see Homer's teeth in halflight. I can find no dreams to fill the miles. His food is spotted on his greyed white shirt and the collar is twisted with bus sweat, like a sick dog's ear it waves to me. I don't think I can go on listening and I yawn artificially. "I think I'll go to bed." Homer moves in secretly, longingly. "Now you'll be a good girl, won't you?" I say yes, yes, to myself and yes again. This time I will certainly try. Homer moves back, clucking old man, hen-ridden old man of this all-night special. I try to sleep. Cluck. Cluck. Who will bring me luck?

Eyes closed to wet glass reality. I cling to D. I cling to D. There is no moon.

Cluck. Cluck. Who will bring me luck?

Lynn Strongin

ALMOST WINTER

Grass is the color of smoke.
But only sun burns
above this town with streets of mineral names.

Coal, Silver, Lead.
An illicit leaf fire burns somewhere,
sheets are stiffened by ice on the lines.

Cinder days. No praise for the dark chill coming.
But a bird likes to gain the top of a fir still:
bob up & down, like a finch in water.

Roughen the texture of the map.
Toughen the knowledge we can't go back home.
Outside, the pool's surface will double the flame in its dark mirror.

Who is my protector?
If I'm in no state of grace,
bring me into one.

Coming Back
(for Susan Dewitt)

1.

June storm clouds blowing in from Taos Mountain.
Ten miles away across dry sage and sand
rain palace builds:
gray ragged pillars rinsing down
to slake the valley. Sun shines slant on us
still picnicking, but wind
a rumor bruits along the eastern slope
of pinon ridge, cold, loosely circling.
Soon.   Soon.

Pack up kids, friends, and stumble for the cars
and hit the road before it gets washed out.
Big drops mean business. Bounce
along the ruts sheepherders' wagons made.
Sagebrush scrapes metal doors and undersides.
Jackrabbits spook
in splendid hoodhigh leaps.
                        This hot stale air
inside the car tastes safe. My little son
squirms on my lap to get a better look
at where the rabbits go. A day should end
like this: Amazing Grace
we sing, and take the bounces hard and clean.
The next car eats our dust. We're heading home.

2.

Main road. Hard dirt.
A pickup slows, stops, signals us to stop.
Old couple, hollow, slackened throats and jaws,
but eyes as bright as nickels, staring in.
We'll do, but only just. I know the look.
How much
an acre did we give, where from,
how long, how many, name and job and age
who do we know and what?
Be sure the kids stay clear of rattlers,

neighbor's boy killed two
a few days back a little ways away,
and glad to yes be seeing you drop in.
I speak to them as to a microphone;
a public broadcast.   Let's get out of here.

A mile clear of their tallying and talk
and we spot something humping in the dust
they left behind.
                                    A broken snake
heaving himself in arches, tying knots
trying to unwind his beige and golden braid;
the belly plates gleam pearl
except where blood seeps red along the seams.
Undone.   Undone,
his agony a shield to shut us out.
Here, where all other things cohere,
color to colors, cloud to sky to rock,
hell's idiot rhythms hold him.
He jerks at angles, jerks and tries to rear
straight up in air or bore directly down
in dirt, his chosen path
no longer horizontal   secret smooth
past choice   past any motion making sense.
Not venomous, not this one. Only big;
now monstrous. Thrust and jerk. We cannot bear,
and cursing we back up and run him down,
crushing his head to make him quiet, flat,
more for our sake than his.
                                        Sick, looking back,
I see him lie like rope along the road.

A few more drops and then the wind lets down.
Dull sun, limp air.
The storm breaks somewhere else, and we go home.

Susan Dewitt

Tsankawi

(for Patricia D'Andrea)

Careless people?   They broke a lot of pots,
and left the sherds, and left obsidian chips, a broken arrow-point,
Tsankawi litter that we don't pick up
. . . for future generations . . .
both ordinary ware, grayed black,
and special, both-sides-painted, hand-held curves,
the Sunday best, whenever Sunday was.
Sherds that lie under what we call
wild-mountain-desert gold-cup,
flowers no book will cover,
the day after rain.

We have no book to read the numbers by,
we guess:
cool caves have cradle holes, and holes
for gods or snakes to enter in.
The path around the mesa says   ·
left-foot, right-foot,
and sometimes two feet deep
on tufa light as dreaming
walking on a drum.
We go the way it goes,
left-foot, right-foot
and two feet deep where snakes and faces smile from rock,
welcome, beware.
Cool caves to keep a house in.   Dungeons.   Graves.
Kivas.   Cradles.   Beds.
Empty.   No one to say, because.

We make our answers up, without the book,
we think
of Tslakwk the Abominable, seven feet tall,
who pushed his people out of caves he bumped his head in,
and over to San Ildefonso.
We decide
he kept the rebels in these dungeon caves,
and marched his people off the mesa top,
left-foot, right-foot,
to heavier valley earth,

leaving for guards around Tsankawi peace
the potsherds, faces, caves, the quiet gods.

*

The death-caves of Los Alamos
honeycomb all these mountains: keep off.
Faces, gods, snakes and potsherds are forbidden here.
No guide books say, beneath this pinon-juniper (and look
how they have grown together)
likes a pit of steel.

Anick O'Meara

AT NIGHT   NEAR THE EDGE

of small towns in the Southwest
I have seen the desert
gather its darkness into a knot
and begin to rise in skin
of a mastodon returned angry
at this tawdry leech
drilling for its blood

A bloated yellow moon roves
crablike across the shrunken sky
cancerblind claws grope earthward
By day there is the cold high glide
of a white hawk's waiting
for the stones to die

Deep in far-off cities
a desert tendril weaves itself
through my body   dust moves in
to cleanse these concrete
eye-sockets in which we shelter

LEAVING NEW MEXICO

Too long here
to follow the body's
leaving   this octopus sun

ensnares   forever   black
watermelon-teeth
gnaw at our eyes

as we move in Wisconsin
Tweezers of desert darkness
pluck our flesh

out of Ireland   back
into coffin-colored sand
Among skulls of luminarias

death silent and clean
as a cry under the sea

William McGlothing

CARVING: AT EL MORRO

Here is the place where wind works best.
The rock itself, but more the thankfulness
and wasted time
carved one-quarter inch in stone.
Centuries of chipped pause.
Wind breaks shallow scrawl into air,
this scratching in of lies
giving wind a grip.
Grim rock made easy.

Names are gone, these markings
merely fingerholds
for the breaking down of stone.

Grit in my teeth, kicked up by wind
is what the names become.
I spit them back, want to trace the words,
but *the process must not be hurried.*
I come here alone in winter,
snow and coolness strange
in this place so known for thirst.
Always it was first the water,
then the name, remembered.

Cool fill of rain and melt,
cool blue eye in the blinding face of rock.
Unlike these dimming carvers
I have given no names away.
I hold mine on my tongue,
taste the dust.
Nothing saves me here — not death,
dust or thirsty company.

This time of year the pool is frozen.
Nothing to write stone about.
But something mars the plane of ice.
A shape of color.
I cross the warning cable, venture out,
ice feels deep enough to hold,
more than rock dust scratched on water . . .

> In the center, a bird, wings fanned
> like rain, frozen, color of all water
> in a dream of fire.
> Somehow warm, outline shaped in melt,
> carving wings of heat.

My sudden thirst as heavy as the sun,
I want to cup my hands and drink.
But high blank walls draw me in and down,
and wind, the only sound,
demands I leave my name.

Mei-mei Berssenbrugge

Rabbit, Hair, Leaf

1.

Some child left the cage unlatched
and George's rabbit hopped out with timid interest
while they were all inside eating cake,
drank from the acequia where they found prints
and got its throat torn by a dog tame enough not to eat it.
Their own dogs were lapping crumbs from plates.
The rabbit with the velvet nose was only one he loved
because it was gentle like him, but others, too,
more responsive though less like clouds were slaughtered
or died of their hearts: birds, a turtle who hibernated
too long. He still stares at chickadees scrabbling
on the snow-patched earth and wonders if he could love one.
His most sensuous dreams are of a golden horse.

2.

Hair scattered on bare dirt
where an old woman has combed it
instead of going straight and smooth keeps falling
and the flesh that holds it keeps letting go,
what isn't pecked away by coal-colored birds
or dragged a small distance by the coyote eating hair and all.
The tiny tail-bone I found on a hill,
bleached and tapered as a rat's nose,
or that big fist of cow thigh by the cottonwoods
has nothing to do with the cloud we stepped through
accidentally, or the quick breath at the back of our necks.
It is the animal in you smells death
though the real smell has gone to sage,
that makes you start to run, but the ghost in you
makes you stay on the tenuous patch
of meadow fog on dirt. Eerie there are no bones,
only white hair thick as milkweed
and big as a man with arms spread,
so clean and old most of what's eaten it
likely dead, too.

3.

I picked up some yellow leaves you bled on
and put them in a book.
I always thought the body died slowly,
letting go as much as it understood at a time.
Angry as you were in a minor way, it went to dirt
growing into something with any water at all.
But a dead horse in the stream, eyes gone,
fouls what flows through it.

Ralph Walbridge

Winter

The horse in his long hair
comes over to the barb wire
where I stand

The mesa to my west
is fleeced white

The green pinons bolts
of strength
setting the mountain to hold

"Come here, I love you,"
I call to the horse

He approaches to where
the irrigation ditch runs
stands one foot on the ice

bends to drink the cold water
running beneath

Robert Lloyd

nightfall

in the Jemez Mountains
above the Valle Grande

these pines
stand for it
    calligraphy
stand to be stood among
to return to it
standing
a script of forms
upon the land
moving against skyscape
as i move across the earth
          the pines
scribing both the rooted
and the animal view
        against cloud
          the volcano rim
          and across
the palimpsests of air and light
            and the eye
and evening clear
        the meadows
close
as the sky uncolors
        days-eyes in clearing
             underfoot
        and stars in clearings
             overhead
obscured by clouds
        only the brushstrokes
of these pines stand
over this closed circle
now without horizon
  the evening cleared
    to the closing black
and my eyes dilate
to tracelight
before the reflex
        narrowing at the human
circle of a single lanternlight
beamed square

from the cabin windows
    circled
at my walk home
   these encircling pines
      now must be strode to
      to be found and touched
         until morning
                          then
into lanternlight and sleep
only these pines brush
blackness
only the eyes can read
                kalligraphia
            in beauty it is written
            in beauty it is written
            in beauty it is written
            in beauty it is written
blackness
only the eyes wrote
                 where

VI 1966

Karen McKinnon

The Loop

I want two windows made
in the adobe wall
around the patio.
One on the south
to frame the Manzano mountains
    there at the east to keep
the Sandias rising.

We already have a window

on the three volcanos over
the kitchen sink
which is why it happens
that I begin to think
of windows in walls
how we want to be opened
yet closed   held close
enough to be open

how the kitchen now looms
    and ripens with sunset
holds itself full
in the nectarines
set in the bowl
on the table

how a frame
when it opens from a poem
being made with the windows
not yet built
in the adobe wall
around the patio
will measure
the fill
of what can not
be contained.

Crossing

for Dan

Have we always been close to
something luminous as this lake
    the one called Holy Ghost
we drove to after work today
near the red clay of the Jemez

There is still movement underneath

this earth and further up   high
on the plateau of ashes
from an old volcano   the holy spirit
wakes in the wind

This is Indian land you said — only
40 miles from Albuquerque   while
I watched the mountains recede
in the rear-view mirror and felt
it would be an ill omen not to turn
around   look back at them

Here it is dusk now   a mauve and
silver one   trout leap in flash
reflections of the stars overhead
    we notice again how fast
night darkens in October

You begin to build a fire while I
search for more wood by the light's
last coherence   I think of that other
fire we made in the forest one night
above Santa Fe   and hold them both
in mind as something sought and found
    and so confirmed

We have been together so long we can't
see each other apart from the places
I have realized with you   you have known
with me   now this hollow in the desert
rimmed rose with sandstone   the rib-cage
of rock on that hill   these thin cat-tails
whispering on the edge of the water
    their stalks nodding with the air's grace
tonight   this lake   fed by springs
underground will define us in some other
time not yet arrived   we'll remember
that we once camped for a weekend at
Holy Ghost Lake and paid the $3.75
for a permit from the Indian
who appeared in a red GM pick-up   though
we were fishing only in imagination
    casting our lives now   then

Dulce Station, 1955

In mid afternoon, five old Indians walked over from the bench between the Bureau of Indian Affairs office and the general store, to sit in the shade in front of the depot. I watched them cross the tracks, then I went back to reading the week-old **Albuquerque Journal** I had spread across the desk in front of the window next to the tracks.

The minister from the mission up the road came into the office.

"Train been in yet?" He was a pale, gaunt man, in his early thirties.

"Not yet."

"I'm expecting a shipment." He walked to where I was sitting and lifted himself up onto a clear area of the desk beside the paper. He motioned toward the Indians outside.

"The old ones sit around all day in the shade and the young ones sit up half the night in the bar at Lumberton."

I glanced out at the old men sitting peacefully on the platform.

"I can't understand it," he said. "All I get up at church are the old women and children."

"Maybe they have their own religion."

He laughed in a way that meant I was naive about Indians. "Oh, they've got a religion, all right. At least, they call it a religion. I'd call it something else, though. Ever hear of peyote?"

"I've heard of it."

"Well, they have all night sessions with it. God knows what goes on. They won't let a white man in."

"Maybe it isn't as bad as you think."

"It's a narcotic. Just like any other. They have hallucinations and call them visions."

I looked out the window. "Those old men?"

"Oh, no. Those old fellows have that much sense, at least. It's the young guys."

"Maybe they need it," I said. "They don't have much else."

His eyes began to show excitement. "That's why I'm getting in this shipment. Sent to Kansas City for it. It's a kit with molds and some sacks of plaster of Paris." He got up from the desk and walked around to the window on the other side of where I was sitting. He leaned across the desk and peered up the track.

"I'm setting up an operation so they can make things for the tourists," he said.

I looked out at the mesquite and chaparral that lined the tracks and dotted the desolate country stretching for miles beyond the general store. "Not many tourists around here," I said.

"Well, maybe not tourists. I thought we might take them to the state fair. Get people interested in the mission work." He walked back around and sat down. "Time's running out for these people," he said. "They don't know there's a world outside the reservation."

The first clouds of black smoke appeared down the track. I folded the paper and watched as the train approached the station. When it got past the section house, the engineer sounded four blasts of the whistle and I pulled the semaphore board to green. After he answered the signal, I went outside and opened the baggage room door with a switch key and pushed the baggage cart out onto the platform. The minister followed me out and stood by the old Indians.

The train pulled on by us and came to a stop so that the first box car behind the engine stood adjacent to the baggage room door. The brakeman from the head end came back and opened the car door.

And then, as if by signal, a dozen dogs appeared, barking wildly, leaping in the air, their skin the color of shale, stretched taut over their ribs. The brakeman swung his club at them while I pushed the cart up to the box car door. Then he went inside and carried out chunks of meat wrapped in heavy paper slung over his shoulder. He tossed them on the cart.

"Better pull that inside before the dogs get it."

I wheeled the cart inside the baggage room and pulled the sliding door shut while the brakeman threatened the dogs with his club. Then he closed the box car door. The dogs ran to the baggage room door and continued barking.

The minister walked up beside the brakeman. "Anything in there for me?"

"Nope," the brakeman said. He walked back up and climbed aboard the engine.

The train pulled away from the station. As the caboose passed by, the conductor stepped out on the rear platform and tossed off a new copy of the **Albuquerque Journal.**

The minister followed me into the office. "How long before another train?"

"A week."

He looked defeated. "I thought sure the shipment would be in today. I've got some people up at the mission waiting to set it up."

"Maybe another week won't hurt," I said.

"Well, it won't help."

After he was gone, I sat back down before the window and opened the new copy of the Albuquerque paper. An hour later, the owner of the general store came across the tracks with two young Indians. The two boys carted the meat back to the store over their shoulders, the dogs suddenly reappearing to jump in the air and snap at the meat. The man came into the office to sign the freight bill.

"Did the preacher's shipment come in?" he said.

"Not today."

He pulled a chair out from the wall to the center of the room and sat down.

"He thinks he's gonna save the Indians," he said. "Goes around tellin' everybody in sight. What he don't know is the Indians don't want savin'. And maybe they don't need savin' either."

The old men outside had moved with the shade from one side of the window to the other.

"Maybe not," I said.

"He's like that fella up at Lumberton that's been tryin' to get 'em to build shanties with his lumber. He don't know how easy they can build wickeyups without his damn lumber." He paused. "These Apaches been livin' the same since I got here in thirty-nine. Only difference is the oil money. Now they buy pickup trucks, but they don't carry anything. They just burn up the road between here and Lumberton. You've seen 'em, ain't you?"

"They go by the house every evening."

He laughed. "They sure burn rubber," he said. "Good thing the traffic's only one way."

"Still, it's no way to live," I said. "Especially when you consider the way it used to be."

"But they don't know. Their grandparents lost the country. They been on the reservation all their lives. Only a few of the old timers remember how it was before, and they don't remember too well."

"Just the same. Something should be done."

"Like what?"

"I don't know. It just seems someone ought to be able to figure out something."

He leaned forward. "Look here, where'd you come from?"

"Denver."

"An' how'd you get here?"

"Train to Chama. Then I caught the mail truck over here."

"An' that wasn't no highway from Chama, was it?"

"No."

"Did you see any traffic?"

I shook my head.

He leaned back in his chair. "Well, somewhere between Denver and here, you left the twentieth century behind. I know, I came here from Tulsa years ago. And I still get out once in awhile and drive down to Santa Fe or Albuquerque. I know what it's like out there in the world." He paused. "But I always come back. I don't wanta leave, no more than those old Indians outside the window."

He stood up. "I quit worryin' about it a long time ago," he said.

He went out through the waiting room. I watched him as he walked past the window, waved toward the old men, then made his way across the tracks to the store. Pretty soon the old Indians got up and walked across the tracks and around the government building. I couldn't see where they were headed.

I finished the newspaper and locked the office. Then I walked over to the store. Flies were buzzing around inside and everything looked as if it had been there too long, but I bought a pound of bologna and a loaf of bread anyway and walked up the tracks to the old section house. The screen door banged behind me as I went up on the back porch and into the kitchen. I put the meat and bread in the refrigerator and took a drink from the bottle of cold water I kept on the top shelf. Then I heard a whining at the back door.

One of the dogs from the depot was standing by the steps outside, looking up through the screen door. He stared at me with hungry eyes. I got out the package of bologna and took a piece out on the porch. I opened the door and tossed it out. The dog snapped it out of the air, wolfed it down in one gulp and stood waiting for more. I went back to the refrigerator and brought back two more pieces. But those disappeared just as fast. Finally, I brought out the whole package and fed them to him one by one. When they were gone, he was still waiting.

I went back into the kitchen and made myself a fried egg sandwich and opened a can of fruit cocktail and sat down to eat. Afterwards, I went out and sat on the front porch. The dog came around the house and lay down beside me, looking as thin and hungry as he had before I'd fed him. I reached down and petted him. His hair was short like bristles, and there wasn't enough even to get matted with burrs.

After a while the pickup trucks started up the road in front of the house toward Lumberton, raising huge clouds of dust that hung in the air long after the trucks had disappeared over the hill. The dog chased after each one. Four of them went by and then the dust settled. The dog came back and lay down beside the steps. Pretty soon he was asleep.

"Why doesn't anybody around here feed you?" I said. "Or any of those other mutts, for that matter."

He perked up his ears and looked at me. Then he went back to sleep. I got up from the steps and went back inside the house and went to bed.

About midnight I woke up. The pickup trucks were coming back over the hill from Lumberton, their motors gunned and tires spitting gravel as they angled from one side of the road to the other. As each one neared the section house, the dog raced down the front steps and out across the hard ground to the road, barking loudly. When the last one had passed, he came back to the steps and crawled up on the porch. Then I heard him sigh heavily in a way dogs do just before they doze off. And I knew he'd be there when I woke up in the morning.

Harold Littlebird

coming home in March

partying by a river near Ellwood City, Pennsylvania
getting loud and high
keeping company with people I met
empty cans of past party-ers
and broken glass
a song from numbed mouth coming out
weakily bouncing back through the quiet
we all stood by the tracks and laughed at my song
"hey little Indian, sing that again"
"yeah bird, again"
song building
louder, clearer
"that's far out, man"   "you're all right, Littlebird"
"yeah, far out, bird"
— away in winter
when men of the pueblo, young and old
sing the season, and the village echoes
the heart-throb of the drum beating strong —
a wind in the trees
moon climbing high
stars shining brighter and brighter through cloudless sky
singing my heart deep into the night
holding on, remembering
lump in my throat growing harder

William Oandasan

Coupishtye

> *(with appreciation to the
> Pueblo of Laguna)*

The drummers drum.   The dancers dance.
The singers sing.   All in Praise
Of the Coupishtye.

The People form a Circle,
Round the Sacred Place.   There,
Near the Center, to the North,
Enchanting drummers and singers sit.
Upon the Sacred Place, the Gods dance.
The People, the Gods, the Sacred Place,
All together with the Coupishtye.

The song and the dance flowered, with the first dawn.
Today, they bloom, with the first dawn.
Tomorrow, they will bud, with the first dawn.
This is the meaning of the ever green tree.
All together with the Coupishtye.

The song and the dance were one, in the beginning.
And this was beautiful.   The deed and the word
Were one, in the beginning.   And this was beautiful.
The end will be as in the beginning.   And this is beautiful.
All together with the Coupishtye.

The drummers drum.   The dancers dance.
The singers sing.   All in Praise
Of the Coupishtye.

George Perreault

DREAD

a sudden rush
geese low in the sky
air brittle as october grass

my body hollow with dread
our shaman
not yet returned
from the western hills

on our way to albuquerque,
a swirlihg, flexible image:
tumbleweeds breaking their backs in the wind,
and our car going in a straight line as usual
breaks/breaks the spell of the image.

Keeping Warm in Santa Fe

Walk on the sunny side of the street;
Don't be ashamed to wear a jacket.

Remember:
The sky isn't cold blue but just clear.

Open your veins to the sun;
When you start feeling better, send pictures
To your friends in the East
So they can see how healthy you are.

When you get tired of walking,
Stop and sit on a bench in the park or
Lean against an adobe wall,
Close your eyes and let sun caress.

When you are hungry, find a
Cafe where you can eat
Beans and green chilies — they
Have more flavor than the red ones.
Eat until·you start sweating and your head clears.

If you live in a basement and it's cold
At night, light the gas heater;
Tell everybody to gather around the heater so they can get
Warm.

Before going to bed,
Take a good look at
The lights from moon and stars;

Don't forget them,
They'll warm your dreams.

In the morning, if you're still cold,
Jump out of bed, and make hot chocolate
With cinnamon and whipped cream on top because that's a
Mexican idea
And if you're still not warm yet,
Slide back into bed and make love easily.

Joseph Somoza

seasonal change

Las Cruces

the yellow grass
reflects a paleness in the world
that came over us last night
as we drank coffee

seeping through chinks
into our home
while we shuffled in our slippers
looking for an ashtray.

the children slept. we stared
at corners in the walls, grabbed hold
of what we thought we were.
we felt the urge to hear voices on the radio.

and this morning, yellow grass
piles of leaves under the locusts
all along the streets turned white

our legs
directing us to places

J. Mackie

PASSAGES

VIII.

> No ideas but in things — W.C. Williams

No ideas but in things   is a dialogue
At 6 this morning   the sun was 4 red
wedges in the cobalt   cloud strata
east where the Manzano and Sandia mountains
slope into a valley   Venus was the morning star
and the wind was off the west mesa where the sky
was still night   At 9 the wind bent the high
grass in half   by the woodpile I worked
A nuthatch on the rock wall   a seed
in its bill   the size of its eye
angled its head   its black peak
pointed north to cumulus clouds
that were a storm on the hill   It blinked
as I left with a load of cut cedar.

Carol S. Merrill

Georgia O'Keeffe once lost an easel in the red hills
Never found it again.

The earth folded round her tools
and the blue, green streaks through steep arroyos
hint the secret.
Deep veins of gold somewhere
let go little flecks and crumbs,
Tempt leaden men to shake water,
claw dirt and grovel for purity.
O'Keeffe's painting found half-buried

in sand and water one spring.
Maybe she just bought pigments for show.
Found a place where canvas mounted already and fertile, hot
jutted volcanically from old soil.
She had shovels and brushes,
     Artist-archaeologist showing us
     The inner walls of our own sky
     ourselves, our skulls
     our hands and inner folds of earth
     moving and grinding growing receiving
     sun giving green leaves and song
     and Bach and paintings
     heaved forth from narrow hips
     full formed and conceived of the
     heat of sun, cool of moon
     and damp breath of ancient oceans.

Herb

You were a seventy-year-old mandarin,
Your blue work shirt collar turned up.
You doused all your brown face wrinkles
Because the best water is next to smooth stones.
You raised your head dripping with melted snow.
Every evening you came in for dinner dripping sweat
after irrigating, popped a beer and breathed loudly
Untying shoes with the concentration of a Zen monk.
With your precious fly rod you showed me
How to pull up on the line at the latest precise moment
So the feathers landed very lightly in calm water
Next to the rush over rocks.

Augustine Primavera

Augustine Primavera, despite his last name, which is Spanish for Spring, was born in the middle of the cruelest winter the Sangre de Cristo Mountains had ever experienced.

His mother would sit by the adobe fireplace and rub her enlarged belly feeling Primavera's tiny feet kick the walls of her womb. Strange kicks. Unlike her previous child, this child seemed desperate to leave the dark and warm solitude of her cave. Had little Primavera known, in that dark and nourishing labyrinth, that outside its walls lay a world of ice and frozen dreams, he would have never desired to break the comfort of his chains.

Unlike her other pregnancies, Flora Primavera spent this pregnancy in endless day dreams. Nonsensical dreams filled with palm trees, ripening dates, decaying mangos, and glowing memories of warmer climates that were the roots of her childhood. She had not easily adapted to the higher altitudes of her husband's home, but after twenty years of marriage and seeing the Sangre de Cristos turn magenta with her husband and his animals in the foreground she rarely thought of any other place as home.

Here, up high, in these dizzying heights, she had helped build home out of dark fertile adobe bricks. Here she had tended the lambs during the lambing season; here in the village Campo Santo she had buried their first child.

Now she sat by the comfort and warth of the corner fireplace and let herself become intoxicated by the rich aroma of the pinon-scented fire. The tips of her fingers slowly caressing her rounded and heavy breasts, she smiled inside with a glow of deep contentment. Despite the severe winter with an early accumulation of more than two feet of snow and the landscape outside her window frozen in a pale blue dream, she felt secure for herself and child knowing he would not be born until March's snows had become part of the red brown earth that was this high mountain village.

Diego Primavera, Flora's husband, perspired amid December's early blizzard. The pinon wood had to be prepared and stacked outside the kitchen door. The animal's quarters had to be secured, the way to the well and soterano had to be cleared; the soterano contained all their stored food. He thought himself prepared if he took the precautions to seal it well and protect it from scavenging animals. He was a religious man and after each task was completed he mumbled a prayer in his secret way and gave thanks.

With every bead of perspiration turning a translucent blue as it dropped from his forehead onto his heavy eyelashes and then briefly clouding his vision, his thoughts stole away from his tasks and found comfort and confusion in the vague notion of Flora's expansive belly and her joy in this late gift. He considered her years; she was older now. She was still as beautiful and sensual as when they had first met, but he realized that time up here was both kind and cruel. With gentle frozen crystals slowly descending from a darkened sky and changing his outward heat into an invigorating chill, his thoughts became tranquil and pacific amidst his labors. He realized the baby was due in the Spring.

Because God has destined and blessed Northern New Mexico with paradoxes, the people here reflect their lives and gather their strength for living from Nature. Within this aura of the mystical and unpredictable the people have cooperated and joined the stream of universal survival by unconscious consent, so it was not unusual that the illusionary peaceful tranquility of the previous day was broken by a knock on the door that evening.

In the kitchen, Flora Primavera made room for their neighbor of two miles away. He refused, stating it was urgent that he speak to her husband. The anxiety on his face shattered the warmth and peace of the pinon-scented air; he brought with him the pale blue cold that drenched the exterior landscape and made the moment as fragile as a crystalline icicle.

It would be cruel to the memory of those high mountain people to describe in detail the torment which the brave men must have endured searching through those frozen canyons. It is sufficient to say that Diego Primavera and a party of men from the village led a fruitless search, hoping to find his neighbor's young son. Some bottomless canyon, the heavy suffocating snow, the wretched cold, the darkened spirits and hopelessness not only claimed the young boy and his goats but the entire party.

The village women, especially those older women whose husbands were lost in those days, can still be heard wailing in the wind during those lenten months that are set aside by our people to remember the dead. The village had, for all practical purposes, been violated of its strong mature men.

The village is strong again because the younger men have now grown to maturity. Augustine Primavera, his mother dead in giving him life after the news of her husband's disappearance, knows his legacy. He remembers neither of his parents, though his father is almost a folk hero and his mother is remembered as a mystery from a warmer climate. The village, like Augustine Primavera, goes on. But like Augustine Primavera it never takes for granted the gift of life, or forgets how precarious its place is among these snowy peaks where the people would rather die than leave.

Leroy V. Quintana

Hijo Del Pueblo

he was born
in that small town
of my youth
and lived there all his life

had been a prisoner of war in Korea,
when he returned
the nuns would send us
to his house
so that we might sell him
holy statues or stamps
with pictures of saints

they were of the opinion
that god had spared his life
and he should show his gratitude;
he very quietly turned away
our sympathy

the nuns didn't like him
and thought he was an infidel;
he never even bought
a raffle ticket

. . . .

Outside the continental bus station
in albuquerque
stoned black dude
cool in his cool clothes and clogs
and hat

talking to two drunk navajos
cowboys in ten gallon hats
tells them he's been through gallo, new mexico
once

Blue, The Sacred Lake

for Keith Wilson

"Here are the mountains,"
he said when I asked him where Blue Lake was
placing one hand on the table
his knuckles and fingers forming jagged peaks

then placing the other hand near the mountains
the Taos Indian told me
"And this is Blue Lake,"
holding it in his cupped hand

Then the mountains became a hand again
as he reached for his beer
and the copper butterfly
on his blue-studded bracelet
flew over sacred waters

Turquoise skies above,
and below

James Taylor

NEW BOOTS

Augustine, old Pueblo man,
Has cut the heels
Off my boots.
He has stitched deer skin
Around the soles.

I put them on,
Wobble, feel like dancing,
Walking just that much closer
To the earth.

TAOS: ON THE DEATH SIDE OF TOWN

I have seen them arrive
from cities; no, not many
with good intentions,
merely an addendum
of some previous trauma,

Seen them shop at the bars,
carousing through gin and genitals
with either sex, preaching,
always too loudly, the importance
of the moment.

Some, hawking the art de jour,
creep back to their quaint caves,
convinced of their own importance,
counting the day's sales.

A chatter of books never written
fills the lounge; canvasses are jessoed,
the colors stay in the mind.

"I wouldn't even want any children."

"He shot himself in his studio, right after his opening."

Eventually, the bafflement, the tears,
the midnight siren toward the hospital,
the excuses for pills and despair.

And they come again along the streets,
the dusty streets that are only bothersome
pathways to the next party or affair,
the dinner parties, the food pushed aside:

they are hungry,
and there is plenty,
but, now, at this fine moment,
are disgusted by the act of eating.

Stan Renfro

from White Pueblo:

Broken thunder echoes through clouds'
purple chambers, from the rim
of canyon to the rim, —before
our porch, ponds, swept by dimpled rain.
The back porch flows rivulets from tin.
Lightning cracks near, thunder opens
door!   Deluge to back away from,
flowers bouncing under hail,
and then the cool air after rain
of breezes swaying forests turned dim,
mud a place for deer tracks before morning
lights more
          canyons.

Clouds would roil white in sky,
turning gray-blue underneath, shuddering
slopes of scrub oak with slants
of rain or hail, to stop,
and break apart in light and leave
willows gemmed with rainbows,
               shimmering breezes.

Rocks dried first; shadows last.
The river frothed, sounded more solemn
for tones of hours, then cleared
by evening light — frogs hopping
near boulders,
            and the red ridges
turn purple,
      then spire into darkness.

Ken McCullough

THINGS TO DO AROUND TAOS

Get up after a nightmare in which some dead men have your house
    surrounded
Wash thoroughly, chant, meditate, do yoga
Eat a lot of yogurt and bananas
Write twelve letters and look over the rough draft of the short
    story you're working on
Put a little cognac in your coffee and pretend you're an aristocrat
Walk into town and go stand around the plaza in your black hat
    pretending you are Billy Jack
Hope that Dennis Hopper sees you and puts you in his next paranoid
    movie
Pay a dollar at the La Fonda Hotel to see D.H. Lawrence's dirty
    paintings, or think about it, anyway
Pay fifty cents to go through the Kit Carson House
Be amazed when you find room after room having nothing to do
    with Kit Carson
Read about what Kit Carson did to the Navajos' peach orchards;
Plan to desecrate his grave
Plan to make a pilgrimage to Blue Lake if you can get permission
Plan to make pilgrimages to Mesa Verde, Canyon de Chelly, Chaco
    Canyon and Oraibi
Plan to do Sufi dancing some Sunday out at the Lama Foundation
Go into the shop next to the Kit Carson House
Have the woman who runs it follow you around to make sure you
    don't rip anything off
Go to the bookstore across the street run by a woman with cruel
    eyes
Buy one book, rip off two
Go to the Harwood Library and look at the death carts upstairs
Walk to the Post Office in the late afternoon to get your mail
Drop in at Dori's Bakery
Curse Dori's jovial face as you sit there eating pastry after
    pastry
Start home, get splattered with mud by some redneck in a pickup
    just as you're admiring your picture on a poster of a contest
    you've just won
Get home and do some more chanting, some more yoga
Read *The Penitentes of the Southwest*
Sit in the yard with your shirt off feeding crackers to the sparrows
Watch a magpie beat up on a solitary sparrow

238

Go to the laundromat and do clothes
Forget to turn the knob from "cold" to "hot"
Be the last one out as the lovely senoritas sweep up
Have fantasies about them as they lean over in their tight jeans
Go home and dress up entirely in black
Go to La Cocina and drink brandy, hoping a rich young widow
    will see you, be impressed, and say let me take you home with
    me and be your Sugar Mom
Make eyes at the cocktail waitress
Check out her profile against the fluorescent lights
Imagine skinny-dipping with her on a moonlit night out at the
    hot springs in The Gorge
Give a skier hard looks when he catches you perusing his bunny
Be awkward when some lady asks you if you've found Zoot Finley yet
Be embarrassed when a member of the group playing nods a friendly
    hello
Wish it was summer
Hear from everybody that D.H. Lawrence was the biggest fascist
    that ever lived
Go across the street and hear Antonio entertain the turista
Stand next to a couple from Denver and develop instant rapport
Dance a flamenco with Benjamin, drunk simpatico from the pueblo
Tell the couple your life story
Bid goodbye to Benjamin in his blanket as he is being tossed out
Go to Los Compadres and be the only Anglo there,
Finish your beer and leave in a hurry
Go to a dance at Casa Loma,
Feel like a child molester
Go back to La Cocina and ask the cocktail waitress if she'd like
    to go for a drink at Antonio's
She says yes, you go, she finishes half the drink and leaves in
    a hurry
Talk to the guy you're left standing next to about Ireland
Go to the Men's Room and notice you still have a big glop of
    mud in your left ear
Make a date with the barmaid with no intention of keeping it
Sneak out and get splattered by some mestizo high school kids
Get in your mud-splattered battered car, drive home, find the
    phone number of a friend in New Orleans, drive out to a freezing
    phone booth
Punch the phone when it eats your only dime
Drive home again in a swoon and go off the road into a snowbank
Leave the car and walk home to leftover black-eyed peas, a cold
    bed, and the dead men surrounding your house

Barbara Mor

the bicycle & the sewing machine are
wonderful inventions said Gandhi

& when the bicycle fails
30 mph winds / 7 miles to go
up a slow 2-lane road
wind across the pastures
bending small trees
30° / breath of the snow mts
raw in yr throat

trucks zooming past
lean their speed / against you
abate, wind
abate / just 1 hour
but it doesnt

wild sage / beginning to rattle like knives
& lead wheels / road of thick water
thighs / prisoners on a rack
7 miles / against the winds will
walking uphill / pumping downhill
& walking is easier

sky whistling / thru yr carved ears
& every direction turns
into the earths huge lungs
song of a maniac
grass tatoos in yr skin
mt-razors on yr knucklebones
& yr nose / running cold snot

abate, wind
abate / just 1 damn hour
& it wont

because the wind / wants to know you
it wants to know you

& when the sewing machine / fails
& electricity fails
& the easy cloth fails
& nakedness & the beginning / are close

chip a stone edge
cut a spear
hunt thru the mts
kill a deer
strip its skin / cure the hide
clean the rib
carve a bone needle
twist gut into thread
puncture holes
pull the needle / thru the soft hide
make a shirt
make pants / make shoes
for you to wear
to hunt the next deer

because the rock / the forest / the animal
want to know you

because youve come / into their real dream
& they want to know you

Joseph L. Concha

Deer mother
you sat at the head
of the valley
like a beautiful song
your image came to me
without wind
the corn pollen
lay at your feet
the fur on your back
was like a dream
looking at me
in the dawn of winter
the warmth of your womb
sent clouds of steam
towards my heart
that left me
feeling like a lover . . .

Leslie Silko

Lullaby

The sun had gone down, but the snow in the wind gave off its own light. It came in thick tufts like new wool — washed before the weaver spins it. Ayah reached out for it like her own babies had, and she smiled when she remembered how she had laughed at them. She was an old woman now, and her life had become memories. She sat down with her back against the wide cottonwood tree, feeling the rough bark on her back bones; she faced east and listened to the wind and snow sing a high-pitched Yeibechei song. Out of the wind she felt warmer, and she could watch the wide fluffy snow fill in her tracks, steadily, until the direction she had come from was gone. By the light of the snow she could see the dark outline of the big arroyo a few feet away. She was sitting on the edge of Cebolleta Creek, where in the springtime the thin cows would graze on grass already chewed flat to the ground. In the wide deep creek bed where only a trickle of water flowed in the summer, the skinny cows would wander, looking for new grass along winding paths splashed with manure.

Ayah pulled the old Army blanket over her head like a shawl. Jimmie's blanket — the one he had sent to her. That was a long time ago and the green wool was faded, and it was unraveling on the edges. She did not want to think about Jimmie. So she thought about the weaving and the way her mother had done it. On the tall wooden loom set into the sand under a tamarack tree for shade. She could see it clearly. She had been only a little girl when her grandma gave her the wooden combs to pull the twigs and burrs from the raw, freshly washed wool. And while she combed the wool, her grandma sat beside her, spinning a silvery strand of yarn around the smooth cedar spindle. Her mother worked at the loom with yarns dyed bright yellow and red and gold. She watched them dye the yarn in boiling black pots full of beeweed petals, juniper berries, and sage. The blankets her mother made were soft and woven so tight that rain rolled off them like birds feathers. Ayah remembered sleeping warm on cold windy nights, wrapped in her mother's blankets on the hogan's sandy floor.

The snow drifted now, with the northwest wind hurling it in gusts. It drifted up around her black overshoes — old ones with little metal buckles. She smiled at the snow which was trying to cover her little by little. She could remember when they had no black rubber overshoes; only the high buckskin leggings that they wrapped over their elk-hide moccasins. If the snow was dry or frozen, a person could walk all day and not get wet; and in the evenings the beams of the ceiling would hang with lengths of pale buckskin leggings, drying out slowly.

She felt peaceful remembering. She didn't feel cold any more. Jimmie's blanket seemed warmer than it had ever been. And she could remember the morning he was born. She could remember whispering to her mother who was sleeping on the other side of the hogan, to tell her it was time now. She did not want to wake the others. The second time she called to her, her mother stood up and pulled on her shoes; she knew. They walked to the old stone hogan together, Ayah walking a step behind her mother. She waited alone, learning the rhythms of the pains while her mother went to call the old woman to help them. The morning was already warm even before dawn and Ayah smelled the bee flowers blooming and the young willow growing at the springs. She could remember that so clearly, but his birth merged into the births of the other children and to her it became all the same birth. They named him for the summer morning and in English they called him Jimmie.

It wasn't like Jimmie died. He just never came back, and one day a dark blue sedan with white writing on its doors pulled up in front of the boxcar shack where the rancher let the Indians live. A man in a khaki uniform trimmed in gold gave them a yellow piece of paper and told them that Jimmie was dead. He said the Army would try to get the body back and then it would be shipped to them; but it wasn't likely because the helicopter had burned after it crashed. All of this was told to Chato because he could understand English. She stood inside the doorway holding the baby while Chato listened. Chato spoke English like a white man and he spoke Spanish too. He was taller than the white man and he stood straighter too. Chato didn't explain why; he just told the military man they could keep the body if they found it. The white man looked bewildered; he nodded his head and he left. Then Chato looked at her and shook his head. "Goddamn," he said in English, and then he told her "Jimmie isn't coming home anymore," and when he spoke, he used the words to speak of the dead. She didn't cry then, but she hurt inside with anger. And she mourned him as the years passed, when a horse fell with Chato and broke his leg, and the white rancher told them he wouldn't pay Chato until he could work again. She mourned Jimmie because he would have worked for his father then; he would have saddled the big bay horse and ridden the fence lines each day, with wire cutters and heavy gloves, fixing the breaks in the barbed wire and putting the stray cattle back inside again.

She mourned him after the white doctors came to take Danny and Ella away. She was at the shack alone that day when they came. It was back in the days before they hired Navajo women to go with them as interpreters. She recognized one of the doctors. She had seen him at the children's clinic at Cañoncito about a month ago. They were wearing khaki uniforms and they waved papers at her and a black ball point pen, trying to make her understand their English words. She was frightened by the way they looked at the children, like the lizard watches the fly. Danny was swinging on the tire swing in the elm tree behind the rancher's house, and Ella was toddling around the front door, dragging the broomstick horse Chato made for her. Ayah could see they wanted her to sign the papers, and Chato had taught her to sign her name. It was something she was proud of. She only wanted them to go, and to take their eyes away from her children.

She took the pen from the man without looking at his face and she signed the papers in three different places he pointed to. She stared at the ground by their feet and waited for them to leave. But they stood there and began to point and gesture at the children. Danny stopped swinging. Ayah could see his fear. She moved suddenly and grabbed Ella into her arms; the child squirmed, trying to get back to her toys. Ayah ran with the baby toward Danny; she screamed for him to run and then she grabbed him around his chest and carried him too. She ran south into the foothills of juniper trees and black lava rock. Behind her she heard the doctors running, but they had been taken by surprise, and as the hills became steeper and the cholla cactus were thicker, they stopped. When she reached the top of the hill, she stopped too to listen in case they were circling around her. But in a few minutes she heard a car engine start and they drove away. The children had been too surprised to cry while she ran with them. Danny was shaking and Ella's little fingers were gripping Ayah's blouse.

She stayed up in the hills for the rest of the day, sitting on a black lava boulder in the sunshine where she could see for miles all around her. The sky was light blue and cloudless, and it was warm for late April. The sun warmth relaxed her and took the fear and anger away. She lay back on the rock and watched the sky. It seemed to her that she could walk into the sky, stepping through clouds endlessly. Danny played with little pebbles and stones, pretending they were birds' eggs and then little rabbits. Ella sat at her feet and dropped fistfuls of dirt into the breeze, watching the dust and particles of sand intently. Ayah watched a hawk soar high above them, dark wings gliding; hunting or only watching, she did not know. The hawk was patient and he circled all afternoon before he disappeared around the high volcanic peak the Mexicans call Guadalupe.

Late in the afternoon, Ayah looked down at the gray boxcar shack with the paint all peeled from the wood; the stove pipe on the roof rusted and crooked. The fire she had built that morning in the oil drum stove had burned out. Ella was asleep in her lap now and Danny sat close to her, complaining that he was hungry; he asked when they would go to the house. "We will stay up here until your father comes," she told him, "because those white men were chasing us." The boy remembered then and he nodded at her silently.

244

If Jimmie had been there he could have read those papers and explained to her what they said. Ayah would have known, then, never to sign them. The doctors came back the next day and they brought a BIA policeman with them. They told Chato they had her signature and that was all they needed. Except for the kids. She listened to Chato sullenly; she hated him when he told her it was the old woman who died in the winter, spitting blood; it was her old grandma who had given the children this disease. "They don't spit blood," she said coldly, "The whites lie." She held Ella and Danny close to her, ready to run to the hills again. "I want a medicine man first," she said to Chato, not looking at him. He shook his head. "It's too late now. The policeman is with them. You signed the paper." His voice was gentle.

It was worse than if they had died: to lose the children and to know that somewhere, in a place called Colorado, in a place full of sick and dying strangers, her children were without her. There had been babies that died soon after they were born, and one that died before he could walk. She had carried them herself, up to the boulders and great pieces of the cliff that long ago crashed down from Long Mesa; she laid them in the crevices of sandstone and buried them in fine brown sand with round quartz pebbles that washed down from the hills in the rain. She had endured it because they had been with her. But she could not bear this pain. She did not sleep for a long time after they took her children. She stayed on the hill where they had fled the first time, and she slept rolled up in the blanket Jimmie had sent her. She carried the pain in her belly and it was fed by everything she saw: the blue sky of their last day together and the dust and pebbles they played with; the swing in the elm tree and broomstick horse choked life from her. The pain filled her stomach and there was no room for food or for her lungs to fill with air. The air and the food would have been theirs.

She hated Chato, not because he let the policeman and doctors put the screaming children in the government car, but because he had taught her to sign her name. Because it was like the old ones always told her about learning their language or any of their ways: it endangered you. She slept alone on the hill until the middle of November when the first snows came. Then she made a bed for herself where the children had slept. She did not lay down beside Chato again until many years later, when he was sick and shivering and only her body could keep him warm. The illness came after the white rancher told Chato he was too old to work for him any more, and Chato and his old woman should be out of the shack by the next afternoon because the rancher had hired new people to work there. That had satisfied her. To see how the white man repaid Chato's years of loyalty and work. All of Chato's fine-sounding English talk didn't change things.

II

It snowed steadily and the luminous light from the snow gradually diminished into the darkness. Somewhere in Cebolleta a dog barked and other village dogs joined with it. Ayah looked in the direction she had come, from the bar where Chato was buying the wine. Sometimes he told her to go on ahead and wait; and then he never came. And when she finally went back looking for him, she would find him passed out at the bottom of the wooden steps to Azzie's Bar. All the wine would be gone and most of the money too, from the pale blue check that came to them once a month in a government envelope. It was then that she would look at his face and his hands, scarred by ropes and the barbed wire of all those years, and she would think 'this man is a stranger'; for 40 years she had smiled at him and cooked his food, but he remained a stranger. She stood up again, with the snow almost to her knees, and she walked back to find Chato.

It was hard to walk in the deep snow and she felt the air burn in her lungs. She stopped a short distance from the bar to rest and readjust the blanket. But this time he wasn't waiting for her on the bottom step with his old Stetson hat pulled down and his shoulders hunched up in his long wool overcoat.

She was careful not to slip on the wooden steps. When she pushed the door open, warm air and cigarette smoke hit her face. She looked around slowly and deliberately, in every corner, in every dark place that the old man might find to sleep. The bar-owner didn't like Indians in there, especially Navajos, but he let Chato come in because he could talk Spanish like he was one of them. The men at the bar stared at her, and the bartender saw that she left the door open wide. Snow flakes were flying inside like moths and melting into a puddle on the oiled wood floor. He motioned at her to close the door, but she did not see him. She held herself straight and walked across the room slowly, searching the room with every step. The snow in her hair melted and she could feel it on her forehead. At the far corner of the room, she saw red flames at the mica window of the old stove door; she looked behind the stove just to make sure. The bar got quiet except for the Spanish polka music playing on the jukebox. She stood by the stove and shook the snow from her blanket and held it near the stove to dry. The wet wool smell reminded her of new-born goats in early March, brought inside to warm near the fire. She felt calm.

In past years they would have told her to get out. But her hair was white now and her face was wrinkled. They looked at her like she was a spider crawling slowly across the room. They were afraid; she could feel the fear. She looked at their faces steadily. They reminded her of the first time the white people brought her children back to her that winter. Danny had been shy and hid behind the thin white woman who brought them. And the baby had not known her until Ayah took her into her arms, and then Ella had nuzzled close to her as she had when she was nursing. The blonde woman was nervous and kept looking at a dainty gold watch on her wrist. She sat on the bench near the small window and watched the dark snow clouds gather around the mountains; she was worrying about the unpaved road. She was frightened by what she saw inside too: the strips of venison drying on a rope across the ceiling and the children jabbering excitedly in a language she did not know. So they stayed for only a few hours. Ayah watched the government car disappear down the road and she knew they were already being weaned from these lava hills and from this sky. The last time they came was in early June, and Ella stared at her the way the men in the bar were now staring. Ayah did not try to pick her up; she smiled at her instead and spoke cheerfully to Danny. When he tried to answer her, he could not seem to remember and he spoke English words with the Navajo. But he gave her a scrap of paper that he had found somewhere and carried in his pocket; it was folded in half, and he shyly looked up at her and said it was a bird. She asked Chato if they were home for good this time. He spoke to the white woman and she shook her head. "How much longer," he asked, and she said she didn't know; but Chato saw how she stared at the box car shack. Ayah turned away then. She did not say good-bye.

III

She felt satisfied that the men in the bar feared her. Maybe it was her face and the way she held her mouth with teeth clenched tight, like there was nothing anyone could do to her now. She walked north down the road, searching for the old man. She did this because she had the blanket, and there would be no place for him except with her and the blanket in the old adobe barn near the arroyo. They always slept there when they came to Cebolleta. If the money and the wine were gone, she would be relieved because then they could go home again; back to the old hogan with a dirt roof and rock walls where she herself had been born. And the next day the old man could go back to the few sheep they still had, to follow along behind them, guiding them into dry sandy arroyos where sparse grass grew. She knew he did not like walking behind old ewes when for so many years he rode big Quarter horses and worked with cattle. But she wasn't sorry for him; he should have known all along what would happen.

There had not been enough rain for their garden in five years; and that was when Chato finally hitched a ride into the town and brought back brown boxes of rice and sugar and big tin cans of welfare peaches. After that, at the first of the month they went to Cebolleta to ask the postmaster for the check; and then Chato would go to the bar and cash it. They did this as they planted the garden every May, not because anything would survive the summer dust, but because it was time to do this. And the journey passed the days that smelled silent and dry like the caves above the canyon with yellow painted buffaloes on their walls.

IV

He was walking along the pavement when she found him. He did not stop or turn around when he heard her behind him. She walked beside him and she noticed how slowly he moved now. He smelled strong of woodsmoke and urine. Lately he had been forgetting. Sometimes he called her by his sister's name and she had been gone for a long time. Once she had found him wandering on the road to the white man's ranch, and she asked him why he was going that way; he laughed at her and said "you know they can't run that ranch without me," and he walked on determined, limping on the leg that had been crushed many years before. Now he looked at her curiously, as if for the first time, but he kept shuffling along, moving slowly along the side of the highway. His gray hair had grown long and spread out on the shoulders of the long overcoat. He wore the old felt hat pulled down over his ears. His boots were worn out at the toes and he had stuffed pieces of an old red shirt in the holes. The rags made his feet look like little animals up to their ears in snow. She laughed at his feet; the snow muffled the sound of her laugh. He stopped and looked at her again. The wind had quit blowing and the snow was falling straight down; the southeast sky was beginning to clear and Ayah could see a star.

"Let's rest awhile," she said to him. They walked away from the road and up the slope to the giant boulders that had tumbled down from the red sandrock mesa throughout the centuries of rainstorms and earth tremors. In a place where the boulders shut out the wind, they sat down with their backs against the rock. She offered half of the blanket to him and they sat wrapped together.

The storm passed swiftly. The clouds moved east. They were massive and full, crowding together across the sky. She watched them with the feeling of horses — steely blue-gray horses startled across the sky. The powerful haunches pushed into the distances and the tail hairs streamed white mist behind them. The sky cleared. Ayah saw that there was nothing between her and the stars. The light was crystalline. There was no shimmer, no distortion through earth haze. She breathed the clarity of the night sky; she smelled the purity of the half moon and the stars. He was lying on his side with his knees pulled up near his belly for warmth. His eyes were closed now, and in the light from the stars and the moon, he looked young again.

She could see it descend out of the night sky; an icy stillness from the edge of the thin moon. She recognized the freezing. It came gradually, sinking snow flake by snow flake until the crust was heavy and deep. It had the strength of the stars in Orion, and its journey was endless. Ayah knew that with the wine he would sleep. He would not feel it. She tucked the blanket around him, remembering how it was when Ella had been with her; and she felt the rush so big inside her heart for the babies. And she sang the only song she knew to sing for babies. She could not remember if she had ever sung it to her children, but she knew that her grandmother had sung it and her mother had sung it:

> The earth is your mother,
>   she holds you.
> The sky is your father,
>   he protects you.
> sleep,
> sleep,
> Rainbow is your sister,
>   she loves you.
> The winds are your brothers,
>   they sing to you.
> sleep,
> sleep,
> We are together always
> We are together always
> There never was a time
> when this
> was not so.

R.P. Dickey

INDIANS

The truth is they're like anybody else,
despite our racial romanticism or theirs.
Oh this one'll insist on his Indian-ness
so we'll lay a quarter or half on him
on the Taos plaza, and that vocal committee
up in Dakota so we'll give them back some land
their forefathers grabbed from another tribe or from animals.

We call it ours, they call it theirs,
and we both should know what we're full of.
Know what I mean? That's the traditional
bitch, and unsentimental as hell's going to be
if we don't massacre our collectivistic self-deception
and find out about, say,
                        Augustine Bad Shoes
out at the Taos Pueblo or Ben Black Elk
who just died up in Keystone, South Dakota,
after "bullshitting tourists," as he told me,
for nearly thirty years at Rushmore
under the big funny faces of four presidents.

Big historical defeats come in cycles
or something similar, despite the Iroquois
League of Five Nations of around 1570 or
the United Nations of 1945; those other defeats,
simple, daily, a series of them we all know about.
That's what we have in common. Come on, come *on.*

From my cut-rate Scotch and cluttered study
I type up and xerox a Vita, a data-sheet,
bunch of glory statistics leaving out failures,
mail it around trying to get readings, to show off;
ol' Ben drove up there to Rushmore every day
from his Schlitz in cans and one-room tarpaper shack—
buck and a half for Kodaking him in his feathers,
three with your kid posing at his side.

SANTO DOMINGO CORN DANCE

Each beat of the drum's a round drop of rain,
the stamping of the dancers' feet is rain,
their heartbeats and breathing resound as rain,
the fringes on the men's moccasins are rain,
their feathers are iridescent sheets of rain,
the toes of the barefooted females are rain,
the women's hair runs thick with black streams of rain,
the billions of motes of dust underfoot are rain,
the chunks of turquoise a lighter shade of rain
than each needle in hundreds of evergreen sprigs,
the links and clasps and rings of silver are rain,
even the billions of beams from the sun become rain,
and then the actual rain, onto the earth,
for the corn, O always the actual rain,
there it comes, then it comes, and it comes.

James L. White

Navajo Moon

(Navajos believe they have always lived on the moon.)

We landed from darkness into the dust of light and out
of the great shadows stood The First Mountain Around Which
Was Moving. Above us *mah-ee*, the coyote, scattered stars.
Old *shumasan* floated past the ship's porthole tending her
sheep in space. In one crater white figures danced *Yei-be-
chai* with pine boughs and fox tails. The moon smelled of
wine and fried bread and mutton stew. Old Navajos in turquoise and silver floated about the small fires. Near
another mountain was a sign saying "Eddie's Club" where

the Wingate Valley Boys played "Last Train To Gallup." All through space floated great horses of blue, yellow, black and white. Some had lightning for breath and fire for hooves. We left, knowing this was a holy place.

When we returned to earth we reported nothing living on the moon, which seemed the only intelligent thing to do.

The Death of Simon the Laguna

The snow was ruthless
along the road to Grants
the day Simon died.

After the priest
they painted his face yellow and blue.
A cap of cotton
that he return to the desert and sky and Sandia
Mountains.

His mother shrunken in grief,
fumbling the missionary's beads,
in the small corner of her life.

Simon escaped them all:
the old chants and funeral dinner,
slipped past the mission church,
and the last drink at Cecil's Bar.

He took his own heaven:
one last mean-assed quarter horse,
Howard Major's stock,
a chute fighter,
gyrated into time,
twisting in space,
Simon hard at him,
eternally . . .

Losing Their Circle

"High in the mountains where your
crest more perfectly matches the moon."

                    Laguna Deer Chant

Two dead deer ties to a station wagon
stare milky-eyed into Fred's Cafe
at their killers having coffee.

Poet's animal trapped forever in some basement freezer
without pollen drawn from their mouths,
giving them back to the pueblo people,
guiding us to spirit places:
Tsetijiin, (man's mountain)
Lukacukai, (woman's mountain).

They join other deer looking for their circles,
(not killed the right way)
and hunt the world all over,
trying to find their shadows.

Foster Robertson

SPRING WATER, TEA LEAVES   AND TIME

In a hot cup of water
a few good tea leaves
makes the taste of the water sweet to drink.

Too many tea leaves, however,
turn the tea to bitter.

Of course,
if the water has come from

too far away,
if the water has come too many
dusty hundreds of miles
from a too much harried River
to a dry rim metropolis,
if the water has travelled so far,
how can Sorrow not be evident?

Not even the tipleaves
from the happiest, highsunned teabush
can make such water sweet,
can take from the water that ache.

Al Neely

A SINGING

All through last midnight we heard a wild singing
from the top of the south ridge behind this post,
and we have snow from before this morning
to fall and whiten much of this day.

Sky, last night,
was clear as deepest crystal,
closed only between wings of passing and advancing cloud,
and some say here that there has been
one too many yeibhitchei dances sung . . .
the dances are bringers of snow.

The wild singer tells not time nor season
by yeibhitchei,
and he only answers the last evening round call of the dogs
who have asked coming night a watchword question.

Many of the questioners slept before answer was given.
A few waited,
and they were silent after wilderness replied in song,
giving down a faroff hymning in a lost voice
in the mourning music of a night walker.

254

Ramona Weeks

MESA VERDE

I drove through Mancos to the tall mesa
where deer and wild cows walk on licorice sticks
in the dark. The windshield ran with water.
I reached Far View at ten, and the hotel clerk
said, "Darling, you're a mess." He gave me wrong
directions because I got there late. The bar
showed bare ostrich necks, tall gullets of bottles
rising out of the pithouse. "Sleep well, dear,"
the man told me. I slept, hemmed in by forebears.
I dreamed of Richard Wetherill, racing a storm

out of Mancos to round up stray cattle,
riding upcanyon, the world turning silver
in snow. He reined up parallel to a cliff
and saw the stone city, cupped in the cool
mammoth webbing of spruce, an ancient tower

of mud carved on the face of that winter.
Until the storm broke, he was the keeper
of silent cities, cliff homes with burnt
ridgepoles dark as arrowheads, warrens
which smelled of absence for the last time.

He rode back, deciding how to tell Charlie.
Tell him that the moon looked like pig iron
compared to the ruins, that the gadabout
people just picked up and left one bygone
day. Migrated. Rolled off like cold walnuts.

Looking for summer. Looking for water.
And I looked up under my greasy hat,
spied the ghost city in snow. Some of its dust
was caved in, but the pure stones shone; the wideness
slept. A cocoon of a world, Charlie. All ours.

You can bicycle now past Sun Temple.
The park service shuts some areas off;
but, warmed by the mesa, I lost myself
on forbidden sites. "Ten ruins visible
from road." And much more to see from the closed

side of the unsorted canyon: the flare
and rudeness of sage, broken grindstones
the color of bread in the weeds; on beyond,
diggers taking a smoke in a kiva.
At the raw selvage of sandstone, the sand

began to melt. Each switchback of thunder
made it slide, pushed a fine rain of dirt
onto the midden, a black cloud ripping
its sleeve. Light snagged for a blackeyed moment
on what could have been skulls of Charlie's strayed
cows.

John Brandi

GALLUP, SUMMER 1976

Wake up at Seig's
    Ya-Tah-Hey Liquors, across
from the Puritan Bakery
        two Navajos mend the street
a white lady checks
            trashcans for change

I buy sweet wine, sit
on a bench advertising First Indian
    Baptist Church, watching
missionaries play baseball
            on a flooded diamond
        I dream of times
            "when . ."
            & the way people bring upon
                themselves
                what they receive.

256

GALLUP, WINTER 1975

Dark-hatted people
    walking away from pawn shops
smelling of coal
            in the snow
        on a Sunday afternoon
                —twenty below.

AT MESA VERDE

Ute-Liner, Travel-Craft
Weekender, Pace Arrow: man from
Walla Walla, wife from
        Savannah, kids born in
            Arlington, face backwards
        3000 miles
                playing war
        in a Coupe de Ville
                —to get here.

Rangers
give directions to
    the snack-bar, not in metric
            but: "Ten Winnebagos down"

Matadors, Gran Torinos
Starcraft & Sportsman   all empty
                    Americans pulling up to
Man   the Sun Temple
in Louisiana
drawl, asks   "This where they sacrificed
                    their victims?"

Up a 30' ladder
thousand feet above Mancos Valley
    Gioia wears no underwear

vacationing executive turns to his
camera-eyed wife:
"Got it on
infinitive?"

Balcony House
tour proceeds, scout-leader
behind me secretly whispers
"Gotta time this vacation just right.
Wouldn't know what to do with
any extra days starin' me in
the face"

(his foot in pre-Columbian toehold)

& the dark-eyed chick
from Boulder
dressed in Forestry Dept. green
gives me the rap on Anasazi
menstrual pads
under a red
handprint   in Longhouse Ruins.

That same night
after the tourists left, we
climbed into an old kiva
smoked hemp, found corncobs & hanks
of grey yucca

Watched a white rainbow
over Montezuma Valley, stoned
I carried myself away
"Ten Winnebagos down"
& 13 centuries back—

To how it was "then"
when America was still
without
Name—

258

Arizona's history is one of influx. Her motto, "God enriches," hints at her curse: God gave the state such riches that they are coveted by too many. In the 1880s the Southern Pacific brought settlers in droves. In 1912 Arizona became the 48th state in the Union. By the 1920s tourists were flocking to the state because of its climate. True, the Depression reversed the trend temporarily. But the economy revived with World War II and the subsequent rise in manufacturing throughout the Southwest. In the decade between 1960 and 1970 the population grew by over 33 per cent. Today Arizona has the distinction of being the nation's fastest growing state. What draws visitors and new residents in such a flood?

Arizona fascinates because it is a land of contrast, even irony. Its plant life ranges from the subtropical organ pipe cactus of southwest deserts to the snowbank primrose blossoming in the snow at 12,000 feet in the San Francisco Peaks. The barrel cactus grows in the hottest desert climates. Men have died within feet of this plant, ignorant of the fact that water lay hidden in its pulp. In the southeastern corner of the state less than 4 inches of rain falls annually, yet a hundred inches of snow may fall over the higher elevations of northern Arizona.

The newcomer expecting a land of sand dunes is surprised at the diversity. The Grand Canyon, the great gorge which the Colorado River carved out over the centuries, cuts through a plateau of solitary peaks in northwestern Arizona. Even in December, with the wind blowing and the red-rose Canyon wrapped in a biting cold, packs of tourist-laden mules wind down to the Colorado on the famed Bright Angel Trail. The quaint El Tovar Hotel, built in the early 1900s and modeled after a German riding castle, lures tourists with its huge stone fireplace and its command of the South Rim.

A series of cliffs stretches east to the Painted Desert, the Petrified Forest, and the vast reservations of the Navajo and Hopi. South of the Colorado River rise the San Francisco Peaks, sacred to the Indians. The extinct volcanoes jut above the tableland and shadow Flagstaff, home of Northern Arizona University, the burgeoning institution which began as a sleepy teacher's college.

The central mountains lie south of this plateau region and extend in a southeasterly direction diagonally across the state. The area covers some 32,000 square miles rich in copper, lead, silver, gold, and timber. A drive along the Oak Creek Canyon road snaking south from Flagstaff to join the freeway from Phoenix is still worth the fight with other motorists. Northern Arizona University students still wear out the seats of their pants zooming down Slide Rock, the slickest place in the bouldered creek.

A region of desert basins broken by piney mountains dominates the southern part of the state. Here are Arizona's two major cities, Phoenix, the state capital, and Tucson. Phoenix is the center for an electronics industry. The city came into its own in 1889 when the legislature designated it as the territorial seat of government. Some cultural offerings rescue Phoenix, though it is plagued by unwieldy size and unplanned growth. Its first multi-racial housing got started after World War II, with row on row of houses, each the same, each on its uniform plot of ground. Later developments have shown no improvement. The sky darkens with pollution. A drive from Phoenix to Mesa, a much smaller city east of Phoenix, used to be graced with views of mountains, rolling hills, desert growth. No more. The two cities link arms — businesses, industry, subdivisions without end. Arizona State University sits in the middle.

Tucson lies south of Phoenix, snuggled in mountain ranges and ICBM missile sites. It is close to Nogales, gateway to Mexico and to drugs, and is the home of the gigantic University of Arizona. Tucson currently finds itself embroiled in charges of racial discrimination in its schools and citizen uproar over water rates. The city just ousted all of its pro-environmental council members. The desert areas surrounding the "Old Pueblo" have been less ravaged by developers than Phoenix has been — but Phoenix had a head start. Almost three-fourths of the state is federally controlled as Indian reservations, national parks, forests, wildlife refuges, and wilderness areas. Thank goodness — for otherwise the hungriest of all developers, Arizona's, would have munched still further than they have.

New residents flock to the state because they see Arizona as a mixture of cultures. The Indian crafts, American citizenship, the supposedly violent and colorful territorial history, proximity to Mexico — all these bring newcomers. Arizona has more Indian lands than any other state. The largest tribes are the Navajo, Hopi, Walapai, Papago, Apache, Havasupai, and Pima. Among the more prominent Indian ceremonies is the Yaqui Easter celebration, taking place both in Phoenix and Tucson. Late into the night the Yaqui dancer, a deer head atop his own head, performs a sacred rite as musicians chant and play on violins and homemade drums. He mirrors the movements of the animal as he dances until the dawn. It is a strangely mesmerizing sight.

262

Summers, camera-laden tourists crowd the annual All Indian Pow Wow at Flagstaff and the Hopi Snake Dances in northern Arizona. Today, Anglos comprise the majority of the population, with Chicano, American Indian, Black, and Oriental following. Its most ancient citizen, the Indian, mixes the least with the others. His lands change the least. The separateness is in part due to his certainty that his ways are superior. Yet the Anglo accepts best those who would change and become as the dominant racial group. Relations between Anglo and Chicano are for the most part relaxed, an intermingling of equals, at least when money is not a factor. But the poor still have the worst lot, and the poor minority has it hardest of all. New arrivals from Mexico and the Blacks whose dialect is thickest have almost insurmountable problems. Many Chicanos are completely Anglicized, having lost their Spanish, the ties with Mexican relatives, and for the most part the foods and customs of their forefathers. No one really is to blame. Some Chicanos fight this and make a conscious effort to retain their music, language, customs, foods, and their communities within communities. And this is better.

The largest religious group is the Roman Catholic, largely because of the high percentage of Chicanos and Indians. Among the Protestant sects, the Mormons are quite influential. Mormon agricultural settlements date back to the 1860s, when the first white men made irrigated farming a principal means of livelihood. The Chicano population maintains prejudice toward this group, a suspicion dating back to the loss of land to Mormons with superior understanding of land laws. The Mormons have been close-knit and good managers of investments, with profits usually falling within their own group.

The temperature, humidity, and sunlight attract out-of-staters. Eighty per cent of the state is arid or semi-arid. This makes the southern part of Arizona a mecca for tourists and winter "Snow Birds." Summer temperatures of over 100° are common at the lowest elevation — these are excellent for some medical conditions. The clear, often cloudless, skies of Arizona create the light that artists and astronomers prize. Consequently, Tucson is a haven for artists, and nearby Kitt Peak Observatory a gathering place for scientists.

People hungry for a sense of history come to study and remain. Historians say that Arizona has been inhabited for at least 20,000 years. White explorers invaded the state in the 16th Century. Of the Indian groups they found, the Apaches were most war-like, the Pimas most peace-loving. Many times the soldiers' bullets made no distinction. In 1540 Coronado failed to find the legendary cities of gold, but his men stumbled upon two modern-day treasures: the Grand Canyon and Indian villages, famed today for their intricate and unique crafts.

In 1700, Padre Eusebio Francisco Kino, foremost of the Jesuit missionaries, founded San Xavier del Bac just south of Tucson. The mission is still used by the Indians and is known locally as the "White Dove of the Desert" because its domes shine for miles. It is its own world of arches, clay statues of saints and fascinating sculpture. Tucson itself was a small Indian village before a Spanish garrison moved there in 1776.

American traders began to frequent Arizona early in the 19th Century, followed by small numbers of settlers. In 1850 a frenzied but short-lived mining boom occurred over gold and silver strikes along the Gila River. Yet territorial recognition didn't come until 1863. From 1860 to 1886 fighting between whites and Apache Indians ravaged the settlements. When the Apache chief, Geronimo, was captured and "removed" to Florida, the warfare ended.

Today, manufacturing is the state's major source of income, followed by mineral extraction. Mining is at present a plus and a question mark. It means money, but the industry also bargains for lax pollution standards. Consequently, Arizona's once clear air suffers, resulting in a rise of lung afflictions. Are corporation profits more important than health? Many Arizonans seem to think so. The Four Corners, the one place in the nation where four states touch, is an area of once cathedral beauty. Now gigantic black plumes spiral above Black Mesa, place of worship of the Navajo and Hopi. And so Arizona strip mines sacred lands to light Las Vegas and Phoenix.

The most crucial problem caused by the influx of newcomers is water. Arizona is primarily desert. The average rainfall is only thirteen inches; some areas record as little as four. Yet something in the vicinity of 90 per cent of the state's limited water goes to agriculture, often for non-food crops meant for more humid climates. Year after year, Arizona pumps out its treasure of underground water, while the level of the subterranean reservoirs sinks. Perhaps the state needs to face up to its desert habitat. Perhaps it has to stop the wasteful attempts to create an agricultural base that nature never intended. The Central Arizona Project would bring expensive and poor quality water from the Colorado River to the southern part of the state. Some see it as the panacea to end all water shortages; environmentalists see it as a benefit to the construction industry.

Perhaps it is the peaceful, non-manufacturing, agricultural towns in the eastern part of the state that retain some of the sense of space and casualness that once pervaded Arizona. Livestock raising has changed greatly from the 1870s and 1880s, when cattle from Texas and sheep from California and Utah were first driven into the region. The era came to a close because of the cattle wars and the depletion of the lands. Today beef is usually raised in irrigated pastures with grain rations. Yet the romantic cowboy image has a hold on the state. Phoenix and Tucson stage yearly rodeos for its tourists.

Joseph Conrad wrote, "Each blade of grass has its spot on earth whence it draws its life, its strength; and so is man rooted to the land from which he draws his faith together with his life." Some natives feel this indebtedness to the land called Arizona. Some newcomers have transferred this feeling for the land from the states of their birth. But far too many come to Arizona only to plunder its resources, to break the silence of its deserts with thunderous motorbikes and dune buggies, to carve thousands of lots from desert and forest, to wipe their feet on the land.

— Marina Rivera

Franz Douskey

CROSSING ARIZONA

Past the Mustang Drive-In
the *Texas Chain Saw Massacres*
co-hit *Torso*
past Taco Bell imitation adobe brick
past Circle K and Jack in the Box
going south from Flagstaff
into Phoenix and Tempe in false fashion
then into Chandler
no doe-eyed swollen breasted co-eds
seen on every Tempe corner
but Buddy's Market the Mini Mall
Economy Self-Pump Gas.

Southside Liquor Blue Horse Saloon
waiting for the working dead
as is the Pecos Lounge

then suddenly into open space
pecan fields newly tilled.

in knee-high grass ancient bay
lifts his tail to shit.

Now long stretches of green
then oil and natural gas tanks
farm machinery in the fields.
on the other side of the road
sheep and, behind them, mountains.

three bikers sparkle
roar toward Chandler
to live out evil 1950's motorcycle fantasy.

More fields and an occasional peeled billboard.
scrub land of greasewood mesquite
and some rabbit bush growing along
rusting roadside railroad tracks,
a few silos and flat miles
of green cotton seedlings.

Small cemetery at Sacaton;
hundreds of tiny white crosses.
on each desert grave a flag waves.

some sagebrush and one mocking bird
on utility line that goes
past Sacaton land-fill with broken
glass gleaming in late afternoon sun.

Into Sacaton with tv antenna
on top of natural gas storage tank
in front of the Arizona Trader.

Indian kids make circles with their feet
in parking lot dust a half block from Pima Indian Agency.

Now outside Sacaton heading east.
nothing manmade but telephone poles and wire.
on the way to Coolidge two crows lift from
the gray-brown scrub and far away dust rises
from a dirt road. We pass a danger flood warning sign.

Saguaros, the sentinels of the desert,
are far and few between,
short unhealthy brown;
the telephone poles look healthier.

sand has washed across the macadam.
now, except for Blackwater Trading Post
and irrigation pipes, there's nothing
on either side of the road but brown plowed flatlands.

Three miles to the north there's a Big "C"
painted on a mountain.

Coming into Coolidge
rotted out ranch houses junk heap land-fill
waterless liver-shaped swimming pool,
then gravel quarry
and empty side roads that go flat out into mountains.

Knee-high pecan trees look like deformed
crucifixions. Caliente Casa del Sol
and out past the water towers
lumber yards churches and brick courthouse
is the Arizona State Prison in Florence.

Low adobe stores and houses on narrow streets,
a modern ghost town and the vibes from the killings
at the prison adds heaviness to the steps of jobless Indians.

South on 87
Grande Vista Motel, Safeway,
Roadrunner Drive-In,
abandoned Dairy Dell,
Sage & Sand Bar, Sunset Cafe,
into Stage Stop Cafe
where two teen-age girls
stop serving coffee and scream, "It's him",
every time a low slung Bonneville cruises by.

We head south
past former winter home of Ringling Bros. Circus
and in awhile pass bronze plaque
commemorating Tom Mix's fatal car wreck.

Sun setting to the right
seen between the camel humps of mountains.
in the dusk faces and strange configurations
can be made out in the contours of the Catalinas.

87 ends. 84 begins.
Ancient watertank leans briefly in front of orange sunset.
we pass palm trees and sycamores,
The Trading Post Motel in Picacho,
then switch onto Interstate 10
taking the night into Tucson with us.

THE SNAKE

in daylight the snake
with his impeccable simplicity
is forced to keep covered

when the infant desert mice cry out
his scales stampede toward fulfillment
he flicks his tail
says *sshhh*

his colors crackle over sand
hypnotic hairpinned body straightens
layer after layer merges with the earth

eyes trained perfectly
his body stretches
then a snap a transfusion
the air sucks with death

blue night slumps over the dunes
the snake is asleep
a caravan of mice pass through him
going home in cold baffling darkness

TUCSON NIGHTS

close your eyes
you can smell orange blossoms
the scent of holy incense
coming out of a head shop on 4th Avenue

take my hand
and we walk on the sidewalks
of heaven there is magic
in the mountains and there are
lions in the streets
thirsting for water

there but for the Chamber
of Commerce walk children of god
sinuses burning from cocaine
holy holy lovers in Indian clothes
slender in the gut naked in hot moonlight

did I tell you I miss you
orphaned streets
homeless children

Orion's belt
I miss you
Gates Pass
I miss you
Gayatri
I miss you San Xavier
miss the morning chanting
the evening prayers
full moon feasts
everything holy
and innocent

Tucson open your heart
your third eye

I am falling through

Ronald Koertge

Tucson

7:05

Two wranglers in Ford pick-up
getting well on
Circle K
beer.

Man in Pinto pulls up, goes
toward market with
list.

He's bermudas, sandals,
socks, toilet paper
on cheek.

Cowboys take off, ram light
pole: foreheads into
dash and glass.

They laugh, feel blood,
laugh, drive off

into sunrise.

Paula Yup

Summer Song

Paper singeing crispily
crackily
     dry
on a
    sidewalk
one fine
     day
       in Phoenix.

Ramona Weeks

Jerome

From this hotel I look out
at the mansion once occupied
by Winston Churchill's mother
and over the narrow cribs that were the houses of whores.

The cribs seem to float
in the dark. Catwalks, broken, sag over them,
blown by the air's sexual tides.
Douched blue by the distance
the girls walked at night
between epaulets of English torches
sputtering in the torrid wrinkles
of the mountain.

They longed for rich men to whisk them away
by early morning.
Lust trailed like Spanish moss from the catwalk.
Occasional laudanum eased the pain
of watching evening go and morning knock
like a pitboss at the door.

Jennie Jerome and I watch as the curlicues
of brass beds envelop them.
Indians shoot blazing arrows at the
hanging bridges, and the rigging thrashes
with St. Elmo's fire.
The phenomenon is visible from miles
away; only the miners are absent from the scene.

A step from diamond, carborundum
gnaws like a worm at the light where Jennie's castle
raises its mullioned windows. Spiders throw ropes
across the crevasse to the homes of the creatures of joy:
all ghosts now but me, and I sip at unhoused
shadows and fires, a stirrer of shadow and fire.

Ramón Martínez

LEAVING FOR MEXICO

The road has passed before me many times,
like an old movie.
It's faster than time, so that here and now
may be returned to.

Driving south the last time,
I saw the Estrellas dark purple.
Behind them the western sky
filled with dark fast clouds.

Later that night, summer lightning
over the Rincóns illuminated the drizzle
not touched by
the headlights.

Rita Garitano

Exterior Landscapes

in Arizona
mountains surround my home
resting beside the back steps
like a pride of cats

I never imagined waking without them

One antiseptic morning
in Kansas
I looked through a window

land unwound
a bolt of green fabric
torn by the sky

no rock arm before me
to break my fall

272

Indian Burial

Nobody knew about her spot and she sure as hell wasn't going to tell them.

She hitched up a shoulder to scratch the small of her back and took out a cigarette. She held the steeringwheel with one hand, tamped the cigarette to let the bits of tobacco flake loose out on the dashboard.

That prissy Lena with her flowery pack, some silly woman filter to show off dainty and let some man light it for her. What the hell kind of smoke is that? She touched the red circles of the lighter to her Camel.

Men're so damned stupid. Weak and stupid, the lot of them.

She ought to know. Married four times with five kids, twins with that namby pamby Willis, and who'd think he'd even have one kid let alone two at once. Four husbands and not one of them worth the powder to blow him to hell. Twenty-three lovers besides, or was it twenty-four, she always had to stop and count if she wanted to be exact, and "lovers" certainly wasn't the word anyway, not a one of them worth a damn.

In all those years if she'd just found one, even one, that'd given her anything. Anything at all besides some accident that'd come bursting out nine months later leaving her with another squalling brat just when she was getting the others so they could take care of themselves.

But she had to hand it to Matt. He'd had sense enough to take off on his own without waiting to have her throw him out, locking the door and chucking his shoes out a window the way she'd done with all the others when she was sick of them drinking up her restaurant money.

She ground out the half-smoked cigarette, feeling the damp tip where her lips had been. No matter how hard she tried, she never could keep from wetting the paper, and then the clammy end in her mouth always ruined the smoke.

Maybe she ought to get one of those holders with a plastic mouthpiece after all. Matt suggested her getting one once but she'd just sneered at him, having better things than that kind of damn nonsense to spend her money on. She'd kind of hoped he'd get one anyway, let her know it was a gift, let her know he was boss, but he didn't. And a couple of years later he was gone, taking Sammy with him.

She'd never understood that. Sammy wasn't even his own kid but belonged to that lazy Manuel who was her husband the shortest of all and who she was never sure why she married in the first place except that she was angling for his brother Raul and he'd got in the way. And Sammy was certainly no damned bargain with all that dark skin and her blue eyes, but wishy-washy like, staring off into space, floating like loose marbles in his head if she ever shouted loud enough to get his attention. Always fiddling with a pencil or a crayon or some damn thing, one time even drawing up a whole pad she needed for taking down orders. That was the one time she'd seen Matt mad, violent mad, pushing her off from Sammy, jerking away the belt she was beating him with, yelling at her not to touch the kid. He even tossed a couple of dollars on the floor to pay for "the fucking paper." She remembered it exactly, his angry voice using a word she always made clear no one was to use in her presence.

"Oh what the hell." No use spoiling the day.

It wasn't often anymore she got away from the restaurant what with not being able to afford much help and trying to stay open as much as possible. It was funny how with the country getting prosperous again that the food and motel business had gone off so. Of course Flagstaff wasn't what it once was with big chain motels moving in and all. She didn't ask questions when somebody checked in for a couple of hours at the full night's rate, but you still had to change the sheets after, wearing them out with washing.

Well, no use thinking about that either.

Here she'd got the afternoon away and that was what she ought to be thinking about. Getting to the spot no one knew about, digging out in the sun, letting the heat warm her clear through, maybe making that big find she could sell to the museum in Tucson. Matt was good for that at least, getting her onto the digging for Indian treasure. No use thinking about the other crap.

A dense flight of orange butterflies rose ahead, hundreds of them filling the sky, the highway ahead of her, catching in the air currents as the car overtook them, smashing out of control on the windshield, leaving yellow blotches of insect entrails over the glass.

"Goddamn nuisances." It was hard enough to see with the damned glare on the hood and the blacktop without all that mess.

She peered through the yellow-white scum. The car kept hitting into them even as they tried floating, flying out of the way, hundreds more of them.

And the dirt road was along there somewhere. She had to slow down.

There it was.

She turned sharply off the highway onto the road that was hardly more than a wagon path, and great banks of dust rose immediately on each side of the car.

She was forced to slow down even more, guiding the car in ragged tracks hard and stiff as concrete.

Past the first crop of foothills in a little valley sort of place was where it was, where she'd found all the arrowheads that last time.

She kept her eyes half on the rose of the hills, half on the ruts, looking hard through the dirtied windshield, and she was suddenly jolted to see a man beside the road.

She got closer and saw it was an old Indian, hair lank and dirty — looking below a round-brimmed gray hat, shoulders stooped in a greasy jacket too big for him.

As she drove slowly past she saw him dig in the little brown dime store sack he carried, extract a red candy ball and put it carefully in his puckered mouth.

"Old fool." She glanced back at him from the rearview mirror. Standing out there in the middle of nowhere sucking ten cent hard candy. "Probably not a tooth in his head."

But then as she got to the row of foothills she forgot about him. It was right along there, and she had a feeling about her luck that afternoon.

She drove through and got to a spot she thought she recognized, the sagebrush looking right to her. She stopped, stared at it until she was almost sure, and turned off the motor.

No use pulling off the ruts and risk getting stuck in that soft looking dirt when nobody'd be coming by anyway.

She jammed a sweat-stained hat down on her head and got out the shovel and trowel.

Matt'd been good for something anyway. More than the rest of them.

She walked out from the car to where she was sure she'd found the points that last time. A rain had eroded down the side of what looked like a mound and she stooped to look at the gouge in the dry earth.

Sure enough. There were two pot sherds sticking straight out of the water cut. Red clay pieces about the size of quarters but there they were all right. It was the place.

She put down the trowel and started digging in the side of the little hillock. Slow, careful, methodical, watching sharp-eyed each shovelful as it was pulled out of the earth and dumped to the side. Whenever she saw a sherd or a chip of flint or a shred of bone, she stopped, picked it out, and put it aside. At least half a dozen different bowls or pieces of them were in the mound.

Sweat collected under the hat brim, on her upper lip, ran down her backbone and down the crease between her breasts. She always felt like taking off the heavy drill shirt and digging in her bra, but she never did. Matt'd've liked that. All they ever thought about was sex.

To hell with them.

The pile of dirt grew as her shovel dug, lifted, emptied.

Then it happened.

The way Matt described it might when he'd got her interested in hunting for Indian burials in the first place.

The shovel struck rock where there should've been only dry loam. She tossed the shovel down and started with the trowel, scraping off the

275

dirt to expose flat stones laid carefully over something the Indians wanted to protect.

She worked steadily, carefully, laying bare the stones that fitted together like a flagstone walk.

She'd cleared a space about four feet long when the stones ran out.

It was too damned small. She couldn't remember if they were supposed to have flexed burials or not.

Maybe it wasn't a burial after all.

She dug some more, but that was all of it. Only four feet. The end stones went down, encasing, enclosing whatever it was in a stone box.

That's the way it always happened. Just when she had something good going, it all went to hell.

She got down on her knees and started lifting the rocks off the top, afraid she might drag away some and the rest'd fall in and crush the treasure if there was one. But as she worked, she could see the hole had already filled with dirt and she could lift the stones off without worrying.

She started with the trowel again, the sweat running down from her hat to her eyebrows, and she wiped it off with her sleeve. Her tongue felt swollen, dry as the earth as she heaped it out.

She didn't stop to examine any more, just watched as the dirt was lifted out by the trowel.

"Damn."

It was a burial after all.

Not of somebody flexed, but of a kid.

From the size of the skull and the teeth she could see coming out of the dirt, it'd probably been about two years old.

She leaned back on her heels.

Little bone hands lay at the sides of the rib cage filled with dirt. Beside the head was a buff colored bowl and some rough beads curved like they'd been strung on a thread long since rotted away.

She dug carefully again until at last she had it all exposed, the little skeleton, the bowl, the flat stones of the grave floor.

Her hands rested on her knees and she looked down at them. Dirt stuck to them in random patches and the enlarged blue veins at the backs protruded in great ugly ridges. Her hands were old, old like the rest of her, dry and crackled.

She could feel the back of her boots against her thighs.

Out there all alone it wasn't enough, wasn't anything. That old fool Indian in the middle of nowhere sucking hard red candy.

A movement caught her eye and she looked up from the grave.

The mass migration of orange butterflies had reached where she was. They filled the air above her in a thick orange cloud, fluttering like burnt orange ashes, sifting, glittering stained glass wings hazing against the sun.

"God damn you," she said softly. "God damn you to hell."

Richard Shelton

BURNING

1

each day comes here
to its own execution
to its own burning

at sunset the ashes
are sifted and scattered
until they are cool

then darkness walks barefoot
through the desert

2

today the rain kept
coming back as if it had
nowhere else to go

and each time
the desert welcomed it

the gates of the desert
never rust but they open
only to the voice of rain

3

even the Indians were
strangers in this place

our oasis is a mirage
and all day the desert
looks through us

at night it looks through us
and sees its own stars
its own moon burning

Rex Lambert

BELIEVING IN MIRACLES

Tonight in a dream I am searching again
for that lost and frightened child, a girl
of twelve, her given name Susan, just as
I had once done in another dream, long ago.

The first time I saw her, she was smiling
at me through a school photograph her father
had given us. Already her footprints were
disappearing in the sand of a summer desert.

We tracked her five days through that blinding,
desolate landscape, the vision of her face slightly
tanned and lovely, her blond hair sun-colored,
haunting us like a bright and terrible fire.

Each day that passed without finding her, we
fought the sun more desperately for her life
with our hope and beaten bodies, until it consumed
us utterly in a sorrowful knowledge of failure.

Too young to be a bride, the sun took her
then for his own. Now, in my new dream,
the darkness and cold are laying claim to
Susan, and again I am fighting death for her.

The earth is barren as ever, and the wind
is filling her footsteps with snow. The face
in the photograph haunts me still as we
track her over white and frozen tundra.

But the ending does not change, and I am left to
wonder about the next dream and the next failure,
and how I will be able to tell myself and Susan's
father that we must stop believing in miracles.

THE LAST HOHOKAM

Too old to be a ditchdigger
but young enough to dance,
he comes each day at noon
to the white cement schoolyard
with his dime store drum
and gourd rattles,
his loosely woven baskets
and brightly colored hoops,
claiming to be the last Hohokam,
a skillful builder of canals,
and all the children believe him.

Really just a Pima pushing 90,
all the teachers say he's senile . . .
a harmless Indian elder
drunk with age
and bad, home-brewed whiskey.
They stand owl-eyed in classroom
doors, jealously watching
their children as they cluster
eagerly about his feet
like green spring grass,
calling him *Grandfather.*

Grandfather, they shout, teach us
another dance in honor
of the new season. Already
the earth in our fathers' fields,
tilled and seeded last month,
begins to quiver and tremble
like a mare ready to foal.
The warm sun has melted winter
from our legs and made us restless.
Hurry, Grandfather, we are stiff
with hibernation and waiting.

The last Hohokam settles cross-legged
on the hard, uncomfortable ground,
cradling his drum in a nest
of blue denim and brittle bone.
The children scramble for baskets

and hoops, and the one who
is left without snares
the rattles like a prize
in his palms. As he shakes
his fists in the air, the rest
of the children fall into line.

In the white cement schoolyard,
poised at the brink of assertion,
an anxious tendril of children
coils around the ancient dancer
like a thin, nervous snake,
listening to hissed instruction
flicked lizard-like from tongue
through a gap in his teeth.
Then the circle breaks to
movement, slow and deliberate,
and the hissing turns to song.

Baskets filled with flowers and fruit
hover precariously atop the tossing,
tumbling heads, and the hoops gripped
by tiny fingers reel and sway
like frantic birds in the shimmering,
resonant air. *Grandfather*, hunched above
his quivering drum, exhales tradition
from the nostrils of winter, measured
and monotone, like sweet mesquite smoke,
while time resumes its natural rhythm
to the patter of prancing feet.

Yet at full, hysterical stride,
when young, exquisite bodies leap
deliriously sunward like plants
to the frenzied beat of a drum,
rattles, and an old man's chant,
schoolbells clamor their deafening
summons, teachers intrude with threats
of reprisal, and in one bewildering
moment of bedlam the children drop
back and scatter like chaff
to the beckoning safety of classrooms.

And now, alone in the still,
deserted schoolyard, where excited

voices stubbornly linger
like cobwebs under the eaves
of modern, whitewashed buildings,
Grandfather, last of a tribe
of industrious ditchdiggers, rises
and gathers the abandoned relics
of his heritage, having given
his children the Coming-Out Dance
and their first legacy of spring.

Doug Flaherty

SHE GATHERS IN ALL TIME

after a Hopi legend

at her loom
struck with open spaces
feels the unborn kick
the hand in air weaves
a pattern of her mind

Out of her egg shapes
thread by thread
she gives warmth of
her blanket to rest
But with her hands

she gathers in all time
chants across valleys
Her voice bounced back
like a new son on a drum

THE CHILD

after a Hopi legend

washed in cedar water
rubbed with corn meal
and cedar ash rubbed
over his new body
lying in darkness
feels the meal and ash
of his two lives

hears the woman drink
from his bath water
caught up in sound
between the meal
of her fertility
the cedar ash
of his consumed skin

the milky water
from his burst sac
washing him upon earth

Peter Wild

The Cactus

Once there was only one cactus
   a sterile ear
in a land where there were
    no men, nor fish cruising into the sunset,
  nor cats on the mountains.
then it split like the side
   of a building giving birth.
in the rain the parts took root
   they gritted their teeth in the sun
expanding, catching their breath
   going a little deeper, breaking off,
like windmills learning new tricks
   walking toward the inhabited lands.

282

Marina Rivera

Chon

Running through the house, out the gate
you chased me, tortilla in hand, you a
long-legged wolf, me the moppet but fleet.
How would you have done it Uncle?
How open my mouth of sharp, strong teeth
how stuff it down, since my nails were long
and my soles could have struck you in a fine spot.

We'd feast on ice cream but you'd wait longer,
knew how to sit, pretending to grey, to wizen
with the sun's setting that you might frighten
me with stories till the long, low dragging began.
The Indians going home, street dusty, pot-holed,
darkening, figures morose, hunchbacked
in the wagons. You saying how they'd come
for me soon, stuff me in their gunny sacks,
the roar of the wagons growing. I could not
see the mules' ribs but sensed them,
the wagons dragging, not rolling.

Later you would marry, have children,
come to axe our two pet ducks that you
might feast, careful to persuade in my absence,
cautious to gobble yours at home, the ducks
I loved to feed, hear, watch bathe
glistening at us in segments no one ate,
parts too unlike friends to bury.

Returning the tent, you hid the gash.
I can see you shivering,
determined to chop wood in the tent at night,
your strokes fiercer till you brought in
darkness through the wet smile in the canvas.

It was always your flaw:
That you would warm yourself through force.
And always the darkness falling on your head.
Immensely tired, going grey, the nose longer,
face thinner — I know I ought to forgive you.
The hatred of the small, brown child
is the hardest kind to change, Chon.

Seek

We were all colors living there,
Bermuda struggling to green up,
pastel boxes, none of them big.
Barefoot and brown my brother
would let me leap up on his hand
then flip me over and upright,
medal agleam above his belly,
a game in the yellow porch light.
My dad would stand me in his hand
to raise me stiff above the roof,
a ritual since my knees could lock.

But at night before the fences,
hunched in the cool dark,
you'd hide and hope that
no one would find you too soon.
Shadows would raise the hairs
on your thin arms as you crouched
in wait for the anger, for the loss
one small house portended,
for the time when no large hand could
hold you upright, no toss right you,
the years when no one could find you
in this brass lamp's bright light
                    looking back
for a small brown body ready
flatchested, bugeyed in the dark.

Franz Douskey

Tucson

1

Rimbaud must've spent his summers here. A sprawling amoeba-like city carved like a disease from the abdomen of the Sonora Desert. A university town. A geriatric ghetto. A town of citified cowhands who left the long hours of farm work to their shriveling, leather-faced ancestors, and now make their living in construction, chomping on burned down stogies, hawking great gobs of tobacco juice, (arcing brown lungers for distances of twelve, sometimes fifteen feet, before they splat on the steaming cement walks. "'scuse me, M'am.") ogling braless coeds, deliciously tan from Rocky Point who strut arm in arm with grubby, patch-covered freaks.

The university is growing, but it takes the man who never had the inclination to finish high school to do the digging and grunting into calcified earth to get the freakin thing built. In the desert, if you don't farm, if you don't raise cattle, you find a construction job, or maybe find work in the open pit copper mines, when it's available. But no matter what you do, you still find yourself grumbling from bed at sunrise to spend another day digging like a prairie dog into the dad blame ground.

Yeah, this is the city in the desert where tubercular Indians shuffle to and from clinics in their government-issue blue robes and pee-stained, gray pajamas; the brown spittle of tobacco stained into sagging, sullen corners of their mouths. Is this what the white man feared when he came west with his Winchester 94? A withered hunched shadow coughing into a yellow rag? **Man is unable to go anywhere without his diseases, but I am old and do not see a noble life. I . . . when I am alone at night, with the spirits of my ancestors . . . after the coughing and . . . when sleep comes, I cherish most the passing of memory.**

When it rains in the desert, lovers awaken each other; whispering, "listen." When it rains here it's as though someone had used a butcher's knife to cleave open the swollen undersides of thunderheads. Nothing delicate, just a sudden torrent flooding the sewerless streets and underpasses, wrenching utility poles from their moorings, snapping wires with a loud crack, followed by a whirring sound as the broken ends hum through the air like lariats. Arroyos swell to overflowing, spilling across gravel roads and paved streets until passage becomes impossible. Every year a dozen lives are lost, trapped in cars, drowned, electrocuted by the dangling wires, flushed into the next county by the whirling current. The gods have been satisfied and bless the parched hills with rain.

This is where housewives from Lincoln, Sioux Falls, Topeka, Henderson, Marietta, from the Ohio Valley, from the Great Corn Belt, from what used to be called, "America's Heartland," when it was certain America had a heart; this is where they come because their husbands smoked three packs of Camels a day while repairing fences and milking the cows; worrying about government subsidies and the price of feed while the missus got the meals on time and made certain the kids washed behind their ears, said their prayers and memorized their lessons. This is where they come after their children have grown, served their country, married, moved closer to her folks, have children of their own and slowly lose consciousness. This is where they come because the air is clean and the winters aren't as brutal as back home. This is where they come to learn how to stoically sweep sidewinders from under their beds, how to crush scorpions, how not to fear flying cockroaches or lizards the size of a man's middle finger. They learn to walk slowly beneath the steel sun and how to reap more than heatweed and devilgrass from the parched caliché. This is where they'll become widows and spend their early morning hours playing any one of forty-three varieties of solitaire and listening to the same, self-repetitive, all-night talk show. (Crack, blurp, whistle. "I think we ought to be thankful and proud of what we got and those creeps should be strung up and shot. The president knows what he's doing; got special inform . . ." "Sorry sir, but your time is up. We'll have our next caller after an **important** word from Arizona Mortuary. Arizona Mortuary's been in business since blank, sputter, zzzziiinnncccc, dignity, zzzzzzzzz . . . limo zine past your house . . . . . plink wwwwwoooowwwww . . . and remember, at Arizona Mortuary, we never let you down . . . flutter flutter . . .) Listening, listening for voices when all else is quiet.

2

It isn't only the elderly who come here, but the youthfully optimistic also find their way. Some move here to attend a university far from the threshholds of their dominated childhoods. Here they come to study because the weather's fine, the women are ravishing, the men ride something larger than Hondas, the desert at night has magic, Mexico is sixty-eight miles away, grass is half the price it is on either coast, the political intensity has evolved to the level experienced at Berserkley in the early sixties, (in other words; a good place to roost until the smoke clears), the sheriff has been arrested for running a string of massage parlors and the mayor returned hastily from Washington, D.C. when the newspapers reported that he'd lost his wallet while falling out of a cab and, somewhere along the debacle, His Honor had bitten a woman "above the knee", and, and . . . . In spite of this (or because of it) many find themselves dissatisfied with the university, with the system, with the weather, with the traffic, with the letters from home, with this and with that. They leave to set up communes in the desert or in one of the three ranges surrounding the city. They work only when it's clear that heaven won't provide; then they truck back into the city, getting transient jobs in leather shops, in candle shops or jewelry shops where they learn to weld turquoise into silver settings.

A few move further into the desert to become apostles in Sufism, Ananda Marga, Karma Yoga, or become masters in the most ancient of all arts; supplying the demand. They become dealers who learn how to fly kilos from Puerto Vallarta; how to ride cocaine in from Ciudad Juarez. They learn how to pick peyote in Brownsville at night; how to process Columbian weed into THC butter. They learn they learn, and dream dreams, and their dreams dream they are dreaming, thinking they are sleeping when they are awake.

3

This is Birch Country. (To let you know where it's at and where it sat; May 24th is set aside, by Governor's degree, as John Birch Day.) The final outpost where the old grasp at the beliefs they perhaps no longer believe in, but fear the emptiness waiting below once they acknowledge the only thing they ever believed in was fear. **O Lord, Most Merciful Heavenly Father of the Great Curve called Universe, in whom we do not really believe, take hold and lead us through.**

In taverns men suck in their bay windows and talk about the battle of the Pacific; about the coming Yellow Peril, and how MacArthur himself had said, "Good Morning," just as they were unloading bodies from the Missouri; and how until her death, bless her soul, the old lady used to keep the ration books in the top dresser drawer, just in case. Eyes squinting across the shuffleboard; one hand raises a beer as though it was a trophy, or a trumpet. Across the dark room, rolling across an emerald lawn beneath a cabled moon, striped and solid — multi-colored planets kiss, then danced away.

"I don't care what you say. I tell you Ole Mac never laid foot on no Missouri. Too busy preening for the newsboys."

The sharp click from the pool table is heard above the whushing sound of the leaden disc sliding across the shuffleboard, too close to the edge.

"I tell you I know what I seen. I was there!" On and on it goes until the building shifts and the floor starts turning, turning softly through dark space.

4

Tucson is so many things: A tourist trap, a drug depot, a waiting room for the debilitated, a hang-out for the employable old and the disinterested young. So many things. Some will tell you the desert has only two seasons; hot and scalding. Don't believe them. When winter begins to freeze the pipes in the northeast, the wealthy pilgrims come here from the ankle-deep slush and don't awaken from their arid lethargy until the hot summer winds spool across the flat dusty frontier streets. Then they pack and leave for their cozy Greenwich bungalows or their South Hampton beach-front cottages. Around early June students start to filter home and the hardhats begin spending more time swelling the sides of beer joints as they pull their transparent tee-shirts away from their sweat-streaked bodies. Once in a while a mountain lion or two will leave the drought-ridden hills and wander into the city; tongues waving like flags. The police and the black-garbed sheriffs are quick to act. This heap of concrete and clay, which once belonged to the wildlife of the desert, now belongs to the realtors, who cut it and slice it like hot pie; anything that runs free must be eliminated.

5

Tucson is one other thing. It's the cradle of superstition. The mountains are opulent with legends; stories of wolf-children, of Indians twelve feet tall who carry off the young women of the unwary. **The only thing known about the mountains is that they built themselves and now sleep under their labors.** But one doesn't have to travel to the back country to find mystics and soothsayers. All one needs to do is stand in one place long enough and understand that nothing is left behind or ever forgotten. Here Romany Gypsies run antique book shops specializing in texts on the occult. Practitioners of white and black magic can be found sitting in the parks reading the Freep, standing in Gayatri's on a Friday night, rummaging through new interpretations of the Tarot. **We never know what guises the gods and demons will deceive us with.** We never know who they are or where we'll find them. Those who show their hand have nothing to reveal.

Gerald Locklin

cochise county

has two of the most imposing
desert mountain ranges in the country:

cochise holed up in one
and geronimo surrendered in the other,
just in time for that picture of him with the rifle
that you see in nearly every beer bar in california.

but what truly distinguishes the settlers of this region
is their versatility in place-names:

cochise city, cochise highway, cochise wells, and cochise cheese;
cochise laundry, cochise funeral parlor, cochise underwear and,

believe it or not, the tourist center in willcox, arizona,
is not known as the willcox tourist center,
it is known as the cochise tourist center.

don't ask me what the fuck geronimo did
to get on their shit-list.

perspectives

once a bright young student of mine
was thinking of getting his ph.d.
at the university of arizona.
he asked me how i'd liked it there
and i said i'd loved it.
there was enough to do in tucson
when you really needed a break,
but you weren't overstimulated
when you should be studying.

but i'd come west from rochester, new york,
while he was bearing east from l.a.

in a year in tucson he earned zero credits,
had two heart attacks,
and turned queer.

Paul Galos

RATTLER

(i)

the child stands before a "snake pit" of a road side show
the walls of the booth form a circle
the floor is coiled solid with muscle
rippling like a carcass fat with worm
no one animal is distinguished
any head on a hundred different tails

the "trainer" stands in center,
a medusa hidden by shadow,
he hooks and milks one dark stiletto after another
the venom is thick and rich as cream
each drop takes an eternity to fall
shiny underbellies flash out of control
as they wrap around his arm

he asks for a volunteer and points to me
I cannot stop my feet
I smell of prey
I move slowly toward the center
the flesh under foot
gives like water and covers my shoes

the man raises his head
he has the face of a snake
his tongue   slips out from armor gold scale lips
signals an explosion of reptile
as the walls collapse in fury
the mass of heads bite aimless at heat
at each other   even turning on themselves

only the first bite hurts
the others tickle, shooting sparks
into the cool effortless midnight
that glides across my eyes

(ii)

Make the hills home
keep to high ground mostly
to goat path and rock

290

that leave no trace of my steps
and climb when I can . . .

my foot gives under loose stone
I become avalanche
and everything grabbed moves too
until one hand feels the strength of root
jerk stop caught on chance
on greasewood brush

there is a whirlpool of sound
of cellophane and pine on fire
sharp/chatter/crackling/shake
spin fast around my ears
a rattler disturbed by falling rock
spits bad noise at my feet
his voice in spasms
stutters then terribly is quiet
I recognize the face of my dream
that same triangle chisel of skull
each of us waits for the other to act
stiff in the burn of his color
as light breaks off in rainbow
his skin is spanish treasure
out of a hollow in the side of earth
the force of his beauty draws me
but my arms refuse
and the sun is too hot

in spite of my stare he vanishes
slip side through cold black holes in granite
leaving me restless in the faint howl of mountain wind

Sandy McKinney

BENSON COWBOY

Down in Benson, Arizona
all the cowboys wear a frown,
and their jeans are worn down to their jockeys
from too much sitting down.

Ride 'em, ride 'em, Benson cowboy,
have another beer.
The wind blows holes in your hatband
and there ain't no hookers here.

Down in Benson, Arizona
to get a cheap motel
you have to have a haircut
and toll the wedding bell.

Ride 'em, ride 'em, Benson cowboy,
have another beer.
Our streets run straight for the homefolks
and there ain't no hippies here.

Ray Quintanar

VIGNETTE

My Tío Conrado
lives all by himself
except for my Tío Chico.
He plants corn   at night
            wheat in the fall
            chile   when the moon is ripe
and he has an old mule
who takes him into town,
San Lorenzo, to buy   mescál
                        sugar
and sometimes   cigarettes

and he smokes, even after my abuela died,
right in the kitchen.
When my Tío Chico nailed Se Prohibe Fumar
on the wall, he banged so hard
he dislodged a snake
sleeping in the canes
the dogs took to the figs to hide
and the nopales dropped more of their share
of fruit.
After we had killed the snake
and stretched it as a warning
for other snakes
my Tío Conrado pulled up a chair
and lit the cigarette
that had started it all in the first place.

Alberto Ríos

Bracero

A slatted pickup truck is piled
with nuns of men in cotton white
who wait for dawn again, that light,
that day-long whipping of a child.

A child become at once a man,
who did the work of men whose pain
he sweat, who listened for the name
they kept with spittle in a can.

This can was in a hall we saw
as children waiting for the sight
of what emerged into the night
in tears, that thing we called papá.

It was American disease
that weakened men whose callouses
could speak, could make them all say yes,
we'll work as certain deportees.

Nani

Sitting at her table, she serves
the sopa de arroz to me
instinctively, and I watch her,
the absolute mamá, and eat words
I might have had to say more
out of embarrassment. To speak,
now-foreign words I used to speak,
too, dribble down her mouth as she serves
me albondigas. No more
than a third are easy to me.
By the stove she does something with words
and looks at me only with her
back. I am full. I tell her
I taste the mint, and watch her speak
smiles at the stove. All my words
make her smile. Nani never serves
herself, she only watches me
with her skin, her hair. I ask for more.

I watch the mamá warming more
tortillas for me. I watch her
fingers in the flame for me.
Near her mouth, I see a wrinkle speak
of a man whose body serves
the ants like she serves me, then more words
from more wrinkles about children, words
about this and that, flowing more
easily from these other mouths. Each serves
as a tremendous string around her,
holding her together. They speak
nani was this and that to me
and I wonder just how much of me
will die with her, what were the words
I could have been, was. Her insides speak
through a hundred wrinkles, now, more
than she can bear, steel around her,
shouting, then, What is this thing she serves?

She asks me if I want more.
I own no words to stop her.
Even before I speak, she serves.

Hisaye Yamamoto DeSoto

The Pleasure of Plain Rice

I know an Italian doctor in New York who has changed his name from something like Malacci to Malarkey, and another New Yorker, a Polish distributor of soft drinks who was born Keliovski but who now goes by the name of Kelly. Strangely enough, these two — I don't know whether they are even acquainted with one another — resemble each other physically, both being tall, large-boned men who could easily pass for brothers. Here in Los Angeles, I know of a Mexican physician who has changed his name to one that is strikingly Jewish. All these name changes are rather hard for me to understand, since I don't quite see that being considered a Wop or Polack or Spic are much different from being considered a Mick or Kike. But the discrimination these three men encountered under their childhood names no doubt resulted in their decision to give their children, as well as themselves, a better chance in this strange country. The two who have chosen to be from the auld sod have probably never been to Cambridge, Massachusetts, as I have, and been invited to a delightful supper of waffles and bacon on the Summer terrace and listened to this cultured and gracious Quaker family discuss the Irish politicians who have the city of Boston in their greedy and relentless grasp.

Then there is my former dentist hereabouts, a Jew, who several years ago sent out notices to his patients that he was changing his name from Lewinstein to Lewis. Since I no longer live near that neighborhood — it was a charming place to me, with its open pickle barrels, its bakeries featuring delectable cheesecakes, its slightly Red bookshop (you could buy the old **New Masses** there, as well as anything by Howard Fast, and the last time I went by, **The Ecstasy of Owen Muir** was being given a big window display), and the uninhibited sidewalk conversations carried on in Yiddish —, I go to another dentist, Dr. Kawamoto, but sometimes we drive by that corner where big neon letters advertise **Dr. Lewis, Formerly Lewinstein,** and I admire this frank admission of what America has done to him.

Once, after finishing school, I did housework for one week (homesickness drove me back to my family) for a Jewish family who did not conform physically to the racial stereotype and who even bore a neutral name. There, during one bridge session, I was called over to the game and asked to spell out and pronounce my name, Hisaye, and my ample blonde employer said triumphantly to her three companions, "See . . . !," and I gathered that it was because my name was similar to a Jewish name or word. This lady spoke Yiddish freely to her bridgemates and over the telephone; the husband once pleaded with the son to come along to attend some special service at the synagogue, so that (he said) his friends could see what a fine son he had. Yet the two teen-age children, fair-haired and delicate-featured went out of their way to inform me that their origin was Canadian, nothing else.

As for me, with my ineradicable Oriental characteristics, name-changing would have served no purpose, although in my childhood I once longed to be named Martha (we were studying George Washington at the time) and there was a later period when I would not answer my brothers unless they called me Nicky (someone at school began calling me Nicky, short for Nicotine, because of my short stature, but I thought that whatever the derivation, the resultant Nicky was rather pretty).

However, as one Jew once wrote in an article which deserves to be better known (it appeared in Frank Chodorov's **analysis**), I do not **feel** any particular Japaneseness. I feel, most of the time, like a human being and look upon other people, most of the time, as fellow human beings. The only qualifications are that when I have to yell at my children sometimes, I feel mighty like a monster, and sometimes I see my fellow human beings acting like monsters — such as the time one white streetcar conductor here got into a hassle with a Negro one and shouted at him, in front of everybody, right there at First and Broadway, "Why you black bastard!" How I felt for the Negro conductor then; I cringed inwardly with him; how I admired his **endurance** (and I understood what William Faulkner has said over and over again, that this Negro ability **to endure,** learned painfully by generation after generation, is what will count on that day, that day of wrath, when we shall be judged by the same measure that we have applied to others) when he quietly climbed back into the streetcar and into the driver's seat and proceeded with his day's work.

Because I don't recall that I have ever been called a yellow Jap to my face. But in grammar school, I was once laughed at because I wore my Japan-made shoes to school and they, manufactured of white rubber and covered with blue velveteen, looked just like bedroom slippers to the teacher and my schoolmates.

Of course, there was the war, when our family, along with some one hundred thousand other Japanese, was moved inland "for security reasons," and spent about three years in Camp I, Poston, Arizona. This made me bitter at first, but it was no Dachau, no Buchenwald. There was a benevolent Great White Father looking after our needs, and since I was young then and full of the joy of living and learning, I came to see beyond the monotony of the black tar-papered barracks and to appreciate, after a fashion, that wide expanse of blue, blue sky; the surrounding mesquite trees from which hung, festooned, the silver-grey parasitic holly which we gathered for Christmas: the green tamarisk

296

trees which turned bright orange towards Autumn; and, most of all, I treasured the friendships begun then which continue to this day, held together at least in part by the common cement of that enforced evacuation and relocation (the government shied away from brass tacks and preferred these euphemisms, even though, in those first days, we came across more than one discarded carton stencilled with the address (PARKER JAP CONCENTRATION CAMP).

During the relocation phase, two of my brothers and I decided to go to Boston, Massachusetts, where the War Relocation Authority had an office. It was principally my decision, because I was the eldest, and I had always been fascinated by New England, and I also was hungry for the sight of an ocean, any ocean. This enforced inland living had caused in me a sense of being marooned, for I was born in Redondo Beach, California, and when we were removed, it was from Oceanside, which now is only a suburb of Camp Pendleton, but which in those days, on the very site of the Marine camp, we dwelt amidst strawberry farms on lovely and peaceful Stewart Mesa, from where we could see the Pacific every day and where occasional blobs of white fog would drift in during the day to hover here and there over the sunlit strawberry patches. Alas, the only glimpse of the Atlantic we got that trip was from a window high up somewhere in the Boston post-office building, where the WRA office was located, and that one glimpse of small craft tied to the wharves reminded me of an etching of San Pedro Harbor by Lionel Barrymore. But it served me right, for I was also moved to my decision by the mercenary fact that since the government was paying our way, it might as well pay up to the hilt, and Boston was the farthest east we could officially go.

We travelled on old sooty trains that left us covered with filth by the time we arrived in Chicago, where most of the rest were relocating, and then we transferred to the train going to New England. Since then I have loved this country from coast-to-coast (and I have crossed it four times in all, twice by train and twice by Greyhound), particularly those small Middlewestern towns like Elkhart, Indiana, which Mr. Wilkie never should have left; Galesburg, Illinois, which Mr. Sandburg has celebrated; and Emporia, Kansas, which the White family has made notable. I only saw these towns from the antiquated depots where the train stopped, since we were not permitted to get off just anywhere, but it seemed to me that those quiet, tree-lined streets, those white frame houses, those little freckle-faced boys (who stared curiously at the foreigners on the train) represented all that was best in America, that in these villages there would be, above all, the orderly procession of days and nights, the constant stars, the renewal of Spring.

On the New England train, I had with me just the right book, **The Education of Henry Adams,** and as we went by the thick woods interspersed with ferns and little shaded streams that ran along the railroad tracks, everything seemed so cool and green (it was the middle of Summer), that I was delighted to come upon a passage which fit so aptly the landscape we were passing: "Hot pine woods and sweet fern in the scorching summer noon; of new mown hay; of ploughed earth, of boxhedges . . . of stables, barns, cowyards . . ." But, unfortunately, one of my brothers, Jemo, suffered an acute case of homesickness after we left all our Japanese friends at Chicago and refused to eat a thing. He got constipated, too, and turned a pale green, and the pleasures of seeing America first turned rather flat as I worried about his condition and my decision.

As it turned out, the WRA sent Jemo and me to Springfield, Massachusetts, to work as butler and cook for an extremely wealthy widow, heiress to a factory which turns out an ineffectual but well-advertised remedy for athlete's foot. The War Manpower Commission had deprived her of all her household help as well as her chauffeur, so we were arriving to the rescue. Our younger brother, Yuke, had a ball; he was selected to join an interracial Summer camp which was being held in the Berkshires. This was in the early days of the well-known Springfield Plan, which was supposed to resolve all the city's racial conflicts. In fact, Yuke so enjoyed the experience that he returned to Springfield several years later, married a blonde girl, maiden name Whitney, of Scotch-French-Indian background, became a Catholic convert, and continues to reside there today, with his wife and two lovely daughters, the eldest of whom, at a very tender age, has already appeared in Summer stock musicals like **The King and I, South Pacific,** and **Teahouse of the August Moon.** And Yuke himself has become quite well known in local sports because God gave him a pretty good left arm for pitching, and we understand he was recently elected to serve a four-year term on the Springfield City Committee.

So, anyway, Yuke never knew what Jemo and I went through. I had asked for work on a farm, as that was about all I knew for practical purposes, but this twenty-room mansion, most of its rooms covered and draped with unbleached muslin and closed for the duration, was the best the government could do for us at the time. We hated it, and Jemo, especially, when we learned that he would have to wear two sets of monkey-suits, one for everyday and one for serving guests when the lady of the house gave one of her parties. I could cook up a good pot of rice and turn out an edible country-style Japanese meal, but that was the extent of my culinary ability, so I assiduously studied Mrs. Rombauer's **The Joy of Cooking** in my free time. But I was properly taken down a peg when the man of the house, an uncle of our employer (we were given to understand that he had once been an operatic basso, but that he had given up all music after a nervous breakdown) said, coming down the stairs to the kitchen one time and catching me leafing through Mrs. Rombauer, "You don't use that very much, do you?" I did not reply, as I could have, that it was not of much help because his asthmatic niece was restricted by her doctor to vegetables cooked in non-aluminum utensils, but — oh, well.

But one evening the lady of the house gave a Japanese supper (she had not only a cellarful of staples and canned goods, just in case, but a pantryful of exotic viands from S.S. Pierce in Boston), and what I remember most from that occasion was that the guests, instead of eating it plain, drowned their rice in soy sauce, to such an extent that there was soy sauce floating on the otherwise empty plates when they were through. To me, this was rather barbaric, but I now have a husband and children who are similar barbarians, and it just makes me a little sad to know that they will never know the pleasure of plain rice.

Then, helping with some vacuuming in my employer's beautiful bedroom, we were chatting of this and that (her basement contained 40-odd trunks, collected during her extensive travels around the world as wife to more than one Army officer), and she said casually, "we've always loved the Japanese people, you know. They're so (she paused for an instant to find the **mot juste**) — so quaint."

Seething inwardly (My God, what availed that ornate writing room, its wide four walls flush to the high ceiling with books; was this all she had learned on those several journeys around the world?), I finished what I was supposed to be doing and reported these tidings to Jemo. He was highly indignant. "Boy, some of the guys back in camp would have beat her up for that!"

Later — I think it was one morning after she came down and reproached us for eating too much bread —, I managed to get in a small lick. "It hasn't always been fun, being a Japanese in America, but it's always been interesting." And I can say the word **interesting** in a most annihilating way, thanks to a high school teacher of English who gave an "A" to anyone for the day if he could catch someone else in the class pronouncing **interesting** as it is written. This left my employer speechless, so I was quite satisfied.

But when, after a month in her employ, we learned of the death in Europe of our brother; and our father, still in Poston, insisted we return to camp to share our grief in common, we were relieved to have a valid excuse to go. Yet, the silver-haired, palsied Irish seamstress whom we loved and who came in daily to do such chores as rinsing out 98 pairs of nylon stockings — patiently tying each pair together first, in order to keep the various shades separate — had told us that our youth had transformed the household. Why, even the uncle (who got very angry when we used the fascinating, circular front stairway and told us to confine ourselves to the rear stairs) had sat down at the piano in the music room on some evenings and run through a few scales in a deep, rich voice that was very moving. She said he had never done such a thing in all the years since he had come to live with his niece.

Too, our loss made them kind, so that the lady of the house took me aside to recall her own several losses, and I felt then that she was finally looking upon me as a fellow human, instead of a quaint Japanese. My employer herself had, at least in part, a Scotch background. One well-known Scotch ancestor had helped improve the steam engine, and the British government had sent over for safekeeping in her house an enormous, wall-sized painting which celebrated his achievements.

As we left that splendid mansion forever, in a cab, the driver confided that he had once sparked this lady in their youth. But that six million dollars, he said, who could overcome the barrier of six million dollars? So, as we drove away, I knew I had learned another lesson, that while black and white and yellow may be alike, the rich are, indeed, as Scott Fitzgerald once tried to tell Ernest Hemingway, **different.** I had become different myself, picking up, among other things, a taste for fresh blueberries in season and for that expensive Connecticut-baked stone-ground bread, which remains with me to this day.

On the bus trip back to the concentration camp, it was Yuke who was sullen because he had not wanted to leave the Summer camp at all. In fact, the Episcopalian minister (Yuke had become an Episcopalian during the month) who phoned from the Berkshires to intercede for him, even went so far as to protest, "I don't see any sense in him going back for such a sentimental reason."

This statement infuriated me, coming on top of the information from the Japanese minister from New York, who had been sent by the WRA to dissuade us from returning, that the lady with the Boston WRA office (she had a Ph.D. in psychology, so I suppose she couldn't help herself) had come to the conclusion that I was straight out of Freud, with my two brothers knotted to my apron strings, that I had kept them close to starvation on the way to Massachusetts so that we would have enough money to make a go of it when we got to our destination. I almost lost my manners and was tempted to ask, "And just how large do you suppose that congregation of yours would be, without this thing you call sentiment?" However, I managed to retain a semblance of calm and to insist on Yuke accompanying us. He was 15, irresponsible. (Later events, when he was 18 and alone back in Springfield, bore me out. On his own, he discovered the Springfield Plan to be sadly wanting, as far as he was concerned. He was forever between jobs and writing home for money; his landlady even found it necessary to write me that he wasn't "the type to break his leg to keep a job . . . if he oversleeps, he just takes the whole day off." And once he wrote pathetically of his loneliness, of riding buses to the end of the line just to kill time. He confessed later, after he had married and settled down, that he had spent most of his free time, and he had gobs of it, drinking beer in bars.)

Anyway, when we arrived in Phoenix, we found we would have to stay overnight in order to transfer to the small bus which would take us to Parker. There was no room at any inn, it seemed, but we finally found a shabby upstairs hotel which accepted us. From Parker we had to take the taxi to the Military Police station which inspected all traffic into and out of the relocation center. The MP on duty could not allow us in until someone from camp came after us. So we waited there wearily, in the warm early dawn, sitting on our suitcases, and the tired MP, whose accent placed him as a Southerner, did not even bother to inspect our luggage as he was supposed to do.

"I would, if I thought you had some whiskey in there," he said.

"No whiskey," we said.

"Why didn't you buy some in Parker?" he asked.

"They've got **No Japs Wanted** signs all over the place," we reminded him.

"Oh, them guys in Parker don't know from nuthin," he consoled us.

Then he shared with us a lukewarm cantaloupe which he brought out of the MP booth. As we ate, he grew nostalgic over the good old days before the war when the Army was really the Army. He was one of those who had chosen the Army as a career. On one occasion, he remembered, he had been part of a special guard assigned to accompany President Roosevelt.

"We had to have everything just so in those days. We had to shine all our buttons, our belt buckles, and we could use our shoes for mirrors — that's how bright we had to keep them shined. Nowadays, nobody gives a damn."

The sun was beginning to come up. In an hour or so, it would be blazing hot again. A jeep drove up, with another MP to relieve our friend. And soon a truck came to pick us up, to take us back to our father and home.

WITH A PRISON WORK GANG

— Near Coolidge, Arizona

Working the embankment
our distance grows
from what goes by.
Days ease out from under their rocks
reaching for the morning sun.
They stretch themselves, winding slowly down the years.
And all of them the same after a while,
with no signs we recognize.
Sometimes the wind shuffling through an underpass
makes us look up from our shovels and stare,
as if an old friend were coming down the road.

RAIN

In the desert is a toad
which appears full-born and bawling
for the spring Caesarian of earth.
It joins with others.
They form a congregation,
a choir of lambs in the night
like a tent revival.
In the morning there are tadpoles
thick as spermatozoa
whipping across the water with
thin, motile tails.

The sun drinks like Navajo cattle,
greedily, in great shuddering gulps.
Then the earth closes up like a wound
and a dry tongue licks it smooth and deep.
The desert is quiet, the air still,
as if nothing happened
or ever will happen again.

Ray Gonzalez

THE BRIDGE, GILA BEND, ARIZONA

what I want is to understand
the rotting wood I walk upon.
bubbles in the water below
flicker like matchsticks.
the mill upstream
burned down years ago.
its foundation leans
into the water,
the stones a castle
for hidden things.

I watch surrounding vines
embrace everything,
believe their power
cannot be tamed.
I lean on the bridge,
feel splinters in my arms.
tiny grains of black and red
impose into my skin.

I wish I could rub
the whole bridge down
with my hands,
clean it of decay,
build it again.
in the distance, thunderclouds
rumble, startle me
back to the edge.

I pound my feet hard
against the planks,
wait for the bridge
to collapse, for my
body to fall through.
I pound again and again.
long into the evening,
I wait.

Thomas Cobb

January

for Richard Shelton

The black birds have returned
from wherever they nest.
They cover the trees
and speak to one another
of winter and another place
where it is even colder.

We use these birds
to mark our seasons
and to give thanks to our fathers
who came this way from a cold place,
looking for warmth and solitude.
When they mistook prairie grass
and mesquite for salvation,
they stopped here.

We are the sons of good men
who refused to discover California.
Living here, with our winter birds
and cold wind, we are content,
suffering no more than we must.

Breaking the Drought

The spadefoot toads sense it first,
the warm air rising
higher and higher each day.
They come from deep underground.
Called by the rising air;
they begin to sing,
their voices growing from the desert.
At night, everything slows
We listen to the toads;
they are never wrong.

On the second day of the toads
it begins. Dark clouds build to the south,
each day they cross further
over the mountains. On the fourth
day, at sunset, we hear first thunder.

It will not rain tonight.
This is ritual, ceremony
begun long before; the toads
understand how it began.
Late afternoon of the sixth day
the rain comes; it rains all afternoon
and through the night. The morning
dawns clear, but this is allowed for.
It will rain for weeks, afternoon
and night, until our faith, like the prickly pear,
swells and grows for another year.

On the seventh day, we sit out to watch.
It rains slowly at first, with the voice
of women; later the lightning ignites
our lives. We watch for hours,
relearning the smell of rain.
All over the world, honest men
sit on porches, drinking whiskey.

William Pitt Root

AT THE FOOT OF A HOLY MOUNTAIN

Nothing seems more still
than this desert at night,
late, after the breezes
of twilight
establish themselves
in the chaparral.

The crickets are quiet
and the moon is silent
as a sailboat
in a childrens' book
here where each incarnate scrap
hunts for another,
cold glass eyes
fired by night hunger.

Webbed feet and scaled bellies
scour the rocks and sand
while wings overhead
cross and recross
the scarred face of the moon
and all the idiots of appetite
pursue each other blindly
by the jeweled light of their jeweled eyes.

Mount Lemmon

Drummond Hadley

SONG OF THE BORDER

Or where it flows where the washes of Silver Creek,
   and the Guadalupe and the Agua Verde
   come together to make the San Bernadino River,
where John Slaughter's veranda'd ranch house sits
   by the boundary line of Mexico,
where Ira Glenn watched Slaughter quietly pull back the bed tarp
   on two Mexicans camped under a mesquite
and shoot them as they lay there.
   Walk up the river, walk up the river . . .

MARVIN
   "Slaughter hired my dad to pitch hay and drive the hay wagon."

BILL BRYAN
   "Ira could look at a bunch of cows and guess their weight
      closer than any man I ever met."

One day a man rode up from the South while Ira was shoeing a horse
   and Slaughter was sitting in the shade under a tree,
   and they could see the man coming a long way off.
And Slaughter told Ira who was just a big-footed kid,
   'Tell him I've gone somewhere and you don't know
   when I'll be back.'
And when the man came up he asked Ira where Slaughter was,
   and Ira said he'd gone and wouldn't be back for a couple of days.
And the man left, and Slaughter never said anything about it,
   and Ira never knew who the stranger was
   or what had passed between them.

Gerald Haslam

Medicine

First time I ever seen Lonnie he was drunker'n hell, and a might onery. It was a Saturday night right after I'd took that job at Bob Manhart's ranch, and I was at the Buckhorn just outside Fillmore, me and other boys that worked ranches round there, givin them town gals a twirl and drinkin a little tonsil varnish just to stay loose.

Anyways, a bunch of us boys had went outside to watch two fellers have a pissin contest, when up roars this old Ford with one door open; it throwed gravel all over us whenever it stopped. Well I started to go whip the driver after I seen he wasn't nothin but a wrinkled Old Indin, but Johnny Johns, this wrangler, he grabbed me. "Wes," he hissed in my ear, "don't tangle with old Lonnie less'n your insurance is up-to-date." That's all he said, but it was enough.

That old Indin climbed out of his Ford, then swayed there, his eyes little and red like a boar's, mean lookin, him watching them two boys try to pee farther than one another. Finally he whipped out his own pecker and shot a stream clean over the hood of his car, scatterin spectators right smart. I never seen nothin like it before. Then he grunted: "I win. Who buys beer."

Well, Johnny Johns he was laughin to beat hell, and he sang out that he was buyin. When Lonnie walked up to him, Johnny asked: "Where's Dorothy?"

Lonnie rocked on his heels for a minute, looked around, then staggered back to his car. He walked slowly around it, stoppin next to the open door on the passenger side. "God damn," he said, "Dorothy he fall out." Then Lonnie walked into the Buckhorn for his beer.

We was all standin at the bar next to the door, listenin to Johnny tell stories about Lonnie, the dancers still cuttin a purty mean rug on the floor, when the front door busted open and in wandered the damnest specimen of a Indin woman, all beat up, scraped and scratched, dirty like she rolled in a ditch. She walked right up to Lonnie, and Lonnie said: "God damn Dorothy. Where you been?"

"Fall out," Dorothy answered.

Lonnie pushed a cowpoke aside at the bar to make room for Dorothy. "God damn," he said.

It got to where I seen Lonnie regular after that, him ridin with us at spring roundup, workin at Manhart's sugar beet spread down in the valley when he wasn't up at the ranch. He was one hell of a worker, I'll tell you; I never seen nothin like it before. He'd work any three hands into the ground. And tough too. Whenever the Navajos come North to thin the sugar beets, Lonnie took to whippin em one by one till he worked his way through the whole crew. And, hell, he must've been sixty-years-old then.

Him and Dorothy they had em three boys: Elmer, he was about my age; Charley, he was around twenty; and Millard, he was just a kid, maybe fourteen. They was top hands, hard workers, and the young one was doing real good in the county high school.

Well, Elmer he taken sick. Lonnie and Dorothy they tried doctorin him, but he just got weaker and weaker. I recollect how Elmer kept sayin his head hurt, then he finally just passed out. Finally, old Bob Manhart got wind of what was happenin, and he had Doc come out from Fillmore to check Elmer, but Doc said he couldn't tell right off what was wrong with him. They carried Elmer clean up to Salt Lake to the big hospital so's they could run some tests, but before they could get started, he died. I never did hear what killed him.

One day not long after they buried Elmer, I was drinkin Ripple after work with Lonnie and Dorothy in their Ford; we was parked in front of the Kanosh store just in case we needed to buy us some more. Anyways, this queer-lookin Indin come walkin up the street. He seen the Ford settin there, so's he made for it. Lonnie he seen him comin, and he said somethin real fast in Ute to Dorothy. I couldn't savvy it, but he sounded hot.

This Indin walked right up to Lonnie, and I seen he had what the boys call flat eyes; the kind that don't show no white, all darkness like burned holes, so his face looked like a mask with a animal lurkin behind it. He barked somethin in the window at Lonnie, him talkin Ute of course. Dorothy tensed right up, and I seen Lonnie's face turn all chalky. Lonnie looked away from the queer-lookin Indin, shakin his head no, then that other Indin he turned around and walked away.

Soon as he was gone, I asked Lonnie who that was. He never answered for a long time, pullin long and hard on the Ripple. Finally, he told me: "Name Coyote. Medicine man."

I waited, but that's all he said. "What did he want?" I asked.

"Money."

"Money?"

"Money."

"For what?"

"You nosey bastard," Lonnie said, so I took the hint and climbed out of his car. I walked into the store and bought my own Ripple, then walked back to where my pick-up was parked. Lonnie stood there waiting for me, and I was afraid I'd have to fight him.

Soon as I got close, though, Lonnie said: "When Elmer sick, Dorothy he call medicine man. Medicine man he say give five hundred dollars and Elmer get well. I tell him go hell."

"Is he still tryin to get the five hundred for Elmer?"

Lonnie shook his head. "Naw. He say give five hundred dollars or Charley get sick."

"And you told him no?"

Lonnie nodded.

"Well, old Charley's healthy as a fresh-serviced mare," I said, but Lonnie's eyes was uncertain.

"And sure enough, not more than a week later Charley took sick. It was the same thing that got Elmer, headaches and feelin weak, so Bob Manhart he had Doc rush right out and they got Charley to the hospital before he lost consciousness. But it didn't do no good. He died anyways.

Lonnie slowed down some after that. He never hit the Buckhorn no more, and didn't talk hardly at all. He still worked like a whole crew, but he was gettin darker, lookin more and more like he didn't give a damn for nothin. I never seen nothin like it before. It was just my luck that I was to their cabin when things come to a head.

Dorothy she used to make buckskin gloves and shirts that all the boys at the ranch bought; they was twice as good as you could buy in a store and cheaper. So one afternoon I drove out to their cabin to buy me some new gloves and maybe swap tales. When I got there, I walked right in the kitchen door like always. Lonnie he set at the little table drinkin whiskey. "What hell you want?" he asked, and I could tell he was gettin mean drunk. I told him what I wanted, and he just grunted, his eyes little and red.

"What's wrong, Lonnie?"

He glared at me. "Go hell," he said.

"I ain't takin no shit off you, Lonnie," I told him, knowin good and well he could whip me.

He stood up, reached for the bottle like he was gonna belt me with it, then handed it to me. "Drink," he ordered. I drank and it was awful stuff, Thrifty Drug Store special. He finally said: "Millard he sick like Elmer and Charley." Then I savvied why Lonnie was sore.

"Oh Jesus," I said. "I'll go get Doc."

But Lonnie shook his head. "Doc he no good," he told me. "Medicine Man come."

Dorothy come shufflin into the kitchen, lookin all shriveled and sad. She touched my shoulder; "Come," she said. Dorothy led me into the little room where the boys all had slept, and there was Millard on his bunk, pale, his breath shallow and ragged. I figured him for a goner. I never seen nothin like it before, all three of them boys took sick the same way. "He's gotta see Doc," I told Dorothy.

She just shook her head. "My boys good boys," she said as much to the room as me.

"I 'preciate that, Dorothy," I answered, "but Millard's lookin bad. He better see Doc."

She sighed and, without lookin toward me, said: "No. Lonnie call Coyote. Lonnie make medicine with Coyote."

"You mean Lonnie's got five hundred dollars?" I asked, remembering what Lonnie'd said about the medicine man before, and knowing his fortune hadn't changed between then and now. I couldn't figure how Lonnie could pay. Me, I had three hundred, maybe three-fifty, stashed away; I was saving for a Mexican saddle. But lookin at that kid laying there on his bunk more dead than alive, it seemed like I didn't need a new saddle too bad. It wouldn't be much to pay for a kid's life. "Let me drive back to the ranch," I told Dorothy. "I'll scare up a little money."

I run out the front door to my pickup, and I'd just opened the truck's door when I heard a scream, pullin and suckin at my brain like a wild animal's cry, but it was a guy's voice alright, and he sounded desperate. I stood froze for a minute tryin to figure where the sound come from; when the scream cut loose one more time, I knew. I busted to the kitchen door and flew in.

Lonnie knelt on that medicine man's chest, hands white around his throat; Coyote's flat eyes wide and dark, he gurgled a little, that's all; his legs jerked and his arms flailed in slow motion. Then they stopped flailin at all. Lonnie held on for another long minute, my heart poundin like crazy; key-rist, I just seen him kill a man.

When he let go, Lonnie done somethin I'll never forget: he reached down and, one at a time, pulled both the medicine man's eyes out, them murky in Lonnie's hands, and he called Dorothy in Ute. She come scuttlin in, steppin over Coyote's body like it was a sleepin dog, and took the lid off a pot that held boiling water. Lonnie dropped the eyes in.

Then he turned to me, and I noticed he was breathin heavy, but his own eyes was clear and untroubled. He sounded relaxed when he told me to grab Coyote's feet. For some silly reason I done just that, and we toted him out and tossed him in the bed of my pickup. "Drive up Kanosh Canyon," Lonnie said, and I did, my belly tight, my eyes wanderin to the rear-view mirror.

Lonnie set like a statue next to me as we wound up the dirt track alongside the creek, his eyes readin the land. Right after we forded the second time, he pointed up the stream; "Stop!" he grunted. I eased the pickup to a wide spot off the dirt road, not wanting it clobbered by some drunk hunter buzzin back toward town. Don't ask me why, but I slipped the .30-.30 from the rack behind the seat, and slung it over my shoulder before me and Lonnie commenced totin Coyote. Lonnie led the way.

We huffed up a side canyon, then a draw — a place I'd never even saw before — then all of a sudden the draw just opened up into the damndest meadow. Lonnie stopped and dropped Coyote, the Medicine man stiffenin up a little so it was like droppin lumber. "You stop," Lonnie ordered. Since he'd already dropped his end of the body, I could either stop or plow a row with Coyote's nose. I stopped.

"Now go," he ordered.

"Why?"

"You go!"

"Why?" I asked again, comfortable with that loaded .30-.30 on my shoulder.

Lonnie's eyes narrowed. "I shove rifle up ass," he said.

Well, I'd just saw old Lonnie kill a man with his bare hands, and that .30-.30 didn't look like it'd fit very comfortable, so I walked back down the draw and waited at the pickup.

After a spell — it was dark by then — down come Lonnie, his face hid but his eyes just glowin. He climbed into the cab and said: "Go." We went.

When we got back to the cabin, I naturally let Lonnie lead the way, and lead he did. We hurried right through the kitchen door, steamed through the kitchen to Millard's room. Dorothy was next to the bunk, spoonin some kind of broth into Millard's mouth, and Millard he was awake, his cheeks already colorin up. By damn! He'd been most dead when we left.

"Millard drink eyes?" Lonnie asked, and I liked to shit.

Dorothy nodded.

"Drink eyes?" I asked. I didn't mind killin some bastard, and totin his body off, but drinkin his eyes? Jesus, it was uncivilized. I stood stunned for a minute. Then my own fears busted out; I couldn't stop em. "Jesus, Lonnie," I said, "what if the sheriff finds the body?"

"Coyote in tribal earth," he said.

"I'm hungry," said Millard.

Dorothy laughed.

Me, I just went for the kitchen door, but when I got there Lonnie was with me. He grabbed my sleeve. "Stop," he ordered. He picked up a spoon from the boilin pot, raised it up in front of his face with both hands like I seen a preacher do in meetin one time; he blowed on the steamin broth, and sipped. Then he nodded and smiled.

Just as I was fixin to turn and leave, he stuck that spoon in my face, and ordered: "Drink."

"Drink?"

"Drink," he repeated, lookin straight into me. Well what the hell, I'd did damn near ever' other crazy thing a man could that night, so I took me a sip. Lonnie he grinned and I had to grin back. It tasted a damn sight better'n that Thrifty Drug Store whiskey.

David Lee

Behold

And came forth like Venus from an ocean of
heat waves, morning in his pockets and the buckets in his hands
he emerged from the grey shed, tobacco and wind
pursed together in song from his tight lips he gathered day
and went out to cast wheat before swine. And in
his mind he sang songs and thought thoughts, images of clay
and heat, wind and sweat, dreams of silver and
visions of green earth twisting the cups of his mind
he crossed his fence of wire, the south Utah steppes
bending the air into corners of sky he entered
the yard to feed his swine. And his pigs, they came.

Leonard Bird

LONELY WOMAN AT TSAILE

You say no man sits on the floor
of your hogan now, and no man
lies with you under summer stars,
and some nights you cry in your sleep.

On the day you threw his saddle
outside the door six years ago,
he took with him, over the blue
mountains to his mother's people,
his sheep, his bootlegger's whiskey,
and drunken songs you sometimes miss.

Now there is no man at your side,
only uncles to sing old truths,
as your children sit in red dust
and watch the sun sink from the sky.

ABOVE ARCH CANYON

At sundown the wind's fingers slid
like ghosts through gnarled junipers.
    Even as we made camp within
    the rock bowl, I sensed their presence,
    unmassed atoms adrift in time.

Sit on one rock for hours.
Listen to the wind, and sense the change.
At first fear vibrates your spine:
    In this place I don't belong.
    Intruder. Even this pen,
    scratching across a soiled page,
    violates the canyon wind's hymn,
    silence felt within the heart's core.

But as you sit, feel the breeze along
your neck. Your veined feet root in red earth,
your blood becomes the stone, and the dust
along your arm whispers: This earth
    is all the home you'll ever know.

Silvia Scheibli

A Desert Storm

White moon sketches thunderheads.
White jimson weed blossoms begin to play.
White throat of poor-will expands.
White bark of fig tree crouches nearer.

Black mesa drags her long skirt of mud
over the canyon.

314

NAVAJO SANDSTONE

smooth faces without childhood
wrap the sky
in telephone wires
throw cement
into the canyon's eyes
press tourniquets
against sandstone ribs
carry off Anasazi paintings
to parlors
tape the moon-lily's song
edit it for bedrooms
bulldoze it under parking lots
lust for the Cottonwoods'
green bride
Escalante River
dark sleeve of rain

James L. White

An Eagle at the Saint Paul Zoo

Medicine bag beneath long feathers.
His arrow eyes look beyond us
to the sun.

He recognizes my necklace and screams.
I knew him once before:
old Joe Loloma along the road
back to Third Mesa.

Hopi Snake Dance

(for Otillie Loloma)

Chu, tiva

The Plaza stops.
Kiva gods appear
dark and suddenly,
men in brown ash.

Feet of earth,
they growl from
the ground's viscera.

The first snake is prayed and danced,
stretches cold against the sun,
then falls limp in the spirit's hand
and is told.

The kachinas circle the plaza slowly,
swaying with their cold and sacred snakes.
When their prayers ended
the white sky cracked rain.

Two Hopi men,
their arms full of messengers
ran deep into the desert.

Became tiny against the sand and rocks.
They ran past the mesas and canyons
to the holy place.

They ran and ran
smaller and smaller
to tell the universe . . .

will inman

s h a r d

shrunk to microcosmos   i stand
on the platen of an Hohokam shard — clay
sown with mica, earth spermed with stars:

o here once not on flat but in open round
of a vessel for water whether or for seeds or berries
a hand entered or lips brim-parted
or, since this one's marked with square spiral,
what voice chanted the sacred dance over
secret stuffs in
                    mingling spirits and people
with fresh be-whole
                    medicine.

those rhythms still work in this shard
between earthclot and rockshine vibrating
that shaman's living presence — that woman, that man:
gather   tote   work   share —
i hold this fragment under penalty of mojave rattler's
strike
        if i do not let its lifebeat
enter my hand, no, not with past, but with elemental
now
        is tribe woke with peril if not with terrible
trust:
        o earthgod and great spirit, grind
me with your clay and mica, mingle me savagely
joyous and whole
into one resonance of brothers and sisters!

that one who wrought this shard works me.

SIWLOKI

A fish in this desert!
Would you believe? he swims in sand,
cuts thru currents of igneous rock
with fierce fins, carries volcanic seeds
in his blunt jaws, wields a tornado
in his tailfin, sees thru mountains
with eyes amethyst or beryl or onyx,
and stores drought and monsoon
side by side in turquoise scales:
a mountain stream sounds its swift waters
cold always thru his deep porcelain gills.

(No, I cannot prove. A coyote told me.
You do not believe in coyotes?
All right. No one can force you.)

But once I heard an underwater laugh
near a dry cave with potsherds.
At once, a sand devil — Siwloki —
rose tall into a perfect blue sky,
whirled across the desert, churning
orange dust.
        I asked a Papago what it
meant. He looked at me with such eyes,
volcanoes that stayed under, as if I had
asked him to tell me about his mother's
body. Then he smiled, meditating yonder
towards the sacred mountain, Baboquivari.

"Go follow the Siwloki. Where it ceases
to whirl, you will find a rattlesnake,
coiled. Ask the rattlesnake. He
might tell you."

I'm still following the Siwloki:
I'm learning to swim thru sand:
a rattler coils under my tongue:
Baboquivari is a Wave of an Ocean that Knows.

L.D. Clark

Over Tall Mountain To Short Mountain

They pulled into the trading post at Wide Wash because they needed to ask directions and to squeeze another gallon or two of gas into the little bus before heading off for the back country. Ann said while John was doing all that she'd step in and find out what they had in the way of rugs: she might locate a Short Mountain **yei** right here, because it couldn't be that far from the area where they were made.

And so John went up to the man who looked like the one running the place and said, "Say, can you tell me how to get to Small Mountain?"

Ann was already halfway across the store, but not so far away she couldn't turn around and holler, "Short Mountain! Can't you keep anything straight?"

"Short Mountain, I mean," said John, a little louder than he needed to.

"Which way you headed?"

"West."

"You just passed the road, about a hundred yards back."

And after that the trader simply looked at him: like here was a couple of tourists already out of their element and sure to end up lost if they were fool enough to leave the blacktop.

John left the trader happy in his own opinion and walked back to see how Ann was making out. She was standing at a counter shaking her head, as she turned up corner after corner of the small pile of rugs, saying, "Nothing, nothing at all. Let alone a pattern I'd have. Ha! two hundred dollars for that piece of junk!"

So they left. Outside, once John had checked the rack on top of the bus to see what had been rattling since they left last night's campsite, they drove back and found the road to Short Mountain, which was nothing but a dirt track not half visible in places that trailed off across bare white ground towards a couple of hogans and, near them, a new tarpaper hut with a bright blue roof. Past these, the road dropped the bus into an arroyo and whipped it around through sand and sent it up the far bank astraddle of a ditch that looked like it had carried a lot of water into that arroyo. As they topped the bank John said, "It's gonna rain sure as piss."

"You always say that. We don't have to get more than two hundred yards from the blacktop for you to say that."

"Well, I reckon I like back roads as well as you do, and the Navajo Reservation is just as interesting to me as it is to you, but I don't see no use plunging into a flood if you can help it."

Though they hadn't come that much closer to the mountains, it seemed a lot closer now, when you looked up at them. The sky was still fresh blue from the rain two days back, and the heavy timbered mass of the range still cut a clean outline all the way along its crest, except for the highest point, and over that a cloud was bumping out strong and gray-shadowed and carving a burning line between itself and the mid-day sun.

Ann thought of rain, silently, and told herself not to be annoyed at John over so little, and since the **yei** were on her mind she pictured those Navajo gods as the tall gray columns of rain she had seen advancing across the Navajo deserts these past couple of weeks.

The road became merely a little arroyo headed for a bigger arroyo down there at the lowest of the rough terrain ahead. They tilted and bounced and came to the main wash, and John eased across as he puzzled whether the bus would climb the bank ahead, where some recent heavy flow of water had cut a sharp perpendicular slice.

He tried it. The front bumper kept digging into the ground, the back wheels clawed sand. He tried to back up. Stuck.

It took a while to dig out behind and back up to where there was a rock rib safe enough to swing into.

He backed into the spot and sat there, a little slumped, disgusted. Ann looked at him sympathetically and said nothing.

All of a sudden he jumped, startling her.

"Hey! Bath!"

"What's eating you? . . . Oh yes, bath."

Taking a bath this summer of camping meant finding a small flat isolated place open enough to catch the sun, on a still day like this. And around a sharp curve in this wash, as John had suspected, was just such a place.

Bath this summer, as for water, meant filling the two plastic dishpans and carrying them along with the two plastic washpans to the spot of concealment. And there, if you were lucky enough to find a warm rock to stand on, which today they were; and if you hadn't forgotten the towel, or the soap, you could begin at once. You could dip out the first washpanful, which was for washing, leaving the rest for the rinse.

Today they found not one warm rock, but two, side by side and rising just enough out of the gritty, sticky sand.

They faced the mountains as they swished and wrung and scrubbed.

"I wonder," said John, working on an armpit, "just which one of those is Short Mountain. Could it be behind the one with the cloud over it?"

Ann said, "If you ask me, it is. But the map's confusing. Anyhow, since we seem to be cut off from this side, maybe we should circle the range, on the blacktop, and see what we can pick up from the other side."

They mulled this over in silence. They'd forgotten that on the reservation a Navajo on a horse, or a whole pickup-load of Navajos might appear anywhere anytime. There came a noise, no special noise, just some unmistakable break in the quiet. And they'd no sooner sensed it than John realized he'd hung all towels and clothes on a salt bush a good twenty feet away, and towards the road at that.

Nothing but a raven flying over, it turned out, and he appeared before John made the sprint for the towels he was ready to make.

They laughed and went back to bathing. But Ann couldn't ignore, now, how vulnerable they were: "You better bring those things closer."

"Never mind."

"But what if somebody did come along?"

"Guess they'd see a couple of asses disappearing into the bushes, one round, one thin."

Ann laughed till she nearly shrieked over that, till John added, "Like a glimpse that maybe God had of Adam and Eve one time out of reach of their fig-leaf drawers."

Which made them both turn serious, and turned them back to looking at the mountains. The sun and the stillness descended in waves over them. The mountains stood high and dark and watchful. The cloud had risen so high it looked ready to send out the arching **yei** that live in Navajo clouds as rainbows live in clouds elsewhere.

Finally Ann said, in a calm voice, "Short Mountain has something to do with the **yei** besides rugs, and I've been trying to think what it is."

"Seems to me you're right, but I don't know what it is myself."

Clean and ready for anything, they skirted the whole range, and along in the afternoon they were speeding across a plain with no defense against the sky except bristling patches of rabbit bush and black sage. A new power line drew long and shining scallops over the plain, from tower to tower, and up through a barren pass. The towers were tall and thin, and crooked out infantile arms to grasp the cables. They descended the slope, these towers, and headed for the mountains like long line of skeletal **yei** striding along between two ropes they carried.

John and Ann found at the base of the mountains a cluster of new cement-block buildings and glittering house-trailers and a blinding aluminum-colored water tower: a BIA school. And when the only man they could find to ask there told them he was pretty sure that the road he pointed out led to Short Mountain, they snaked along up it and soon came to juniper and long ridges of clotted red sand.

John had made up his mind not to bring up rain anymore. Then he irked himself immensely by blurting out, "It's gonna rain sure as piss."

Ann only gave him a weary look and exhaled sharply.

The road went into steeper ups and downs and crawled into a canyon. Juniper and piñon gave way to pines, and the near heights rose to hide the mountaintops, rose against darkening and spreading clouds. Giant redrock cliffs towered out of the pines, or whole broken mountains of redrock appeared before them, now to this side, now to that. Narrow side canyons of redrock broke the cliffs and ran far in to become secret and strange. The number of shapes of redrock was past counting, but in a kind of rhythm of forms one appeared now and again as an enormous block with something like a slant of roof.

"Oh . . . . Oh . . . . I remember," said Ann. "This is the place of the hogan gods, the home gods."

"And what kin are they to the **yei,** I wonder?"

"I wonder."

Now the sunlight had gone from here. But for a moment, suddenly, it came back, and at the same time a fine wafting mist. The redrock shone, the pines glowed, the mist flung out points of light. Then thick clouds closed over, so black that heavy rain must soon fall on the road ahead.

A steep grade, sheltered from sunlight by an enormous cliff, jutted ahead. The road was clay here. The little bus slipped and slid. And halfway up it spun to a stop.

John backed gingerly down. And sat. "Oh shit, oh shit."

It was growing late in the afternoon. The trading posts always closed early. Rain, maybe storm, lay in wait. It would be tomorrow, at least, before they could check for a rug at Short Mountain.

Neither of them felt like saying a thing.

"What do you know, there's a hogan," said John abruptly, having turned his head by chance towards a side canyon broader than the rest.

Ann thought he meant a rock-form. "There are so many. Which one?"

"No, I mean a real hogan. Look."

It was a hundred yards or so off, on a flat place in among timber next to the canyon wall. A pair of ruts in fair shape led to it.

John had a sudden thought, but he shrugged as he passed it on to Ann, it was so unlikely: "The weavers that make the rugs live around here. One of them might live there, for all we know."

The exchange of a few hesitant words made it sound worthwhile. So they drove in.

The squat little building sat in an open spot of bare ground and scraggly grass among the pines. They could see the close-stacked timbers of the six walls and the round roof of very little pitch covered with sod. The one door, and the door facings, were of plank. The door was shut. As far as they could see, the hogan was vacant.

Only now did they notice there were other structures, right behind a broken screen of pines: a one-room frame hut roofed by asphalt shingles, and something half-seen beyond that could have been a heap of cast-off tin and boards and wire and hemp sacks and a couple of dry

322

sheepskins: but what it was, after all, was a sheep pen.

A man appeared, coming slowly from the hut, a tall heavy man in gray khakis and a hat with a wide curved brim: from a distance any resident of any Western ranch. The not-very-dark Indian face that soon materialized from under the hat brim was pleasant, reserved. And when the man stopped and waited a few feet from the car, he was neither welcoming nor hostile, only ready to learn who had arrived and why.

Although John had talked with many Navajos this summer, he was still disconcerted by this "You approached me, you tell me what you want" air. And it wouldn't do to ask flatly if they had rugs: the answer might be a flat "no."

So he said, "Is this the way to Short Mountain?"

The Navajo lowered his chin slightly, grinned and eyed the area all around John's head before looking at him straight again: "Short Mountain? You wanta go there?"

While John was trying to decide whether he could put a request for rugs into his answer, and Ann looked ready to burst out talking, the Navajo came out with, "Where you guys from?"

Ann spoke up: "Tucson."

The Navajo grinned some more, maybe cagey, maybe shy: "Tucson . . . . Short Mountain. I don't know . . . ."

A sort of panic struck John at the thought of the distance between Tucson and Short Mountain. This led him to try a direct assertion: "My name's John. My wife's name is Ann."

The Navajo answered readily, with a mouthful of hisses and glottal stops, and appeared to enjoy the incomprehension these met with. "Or John," he added. "John too. My other first name, she's too hard. Last name, that's easy: Begay."

Which around here, as John knew, was as common as Smith in Tucson.

John Begay blinked, looked pensive but kept a bit of his grin, and since he might be ready to say more, or he might not, John and Ann waited. It came at last: "You have to go over Tall Mountain, to get at Short Mountain, from here."

John felt more than ever that unreasoning fright, late in this mountain afternoon with black cloud, and now distant thunder, at the remoteness of Short Mountain. He was even afraid to ask, but he did: "Could we have got to Short Mountain, easier, from the other side?"

"No, that's bad road."

"And over Tall Mountain too, I guess," said Ann.

"Oh yes, over Tall Mountain too."

It was a smile, not a grin, that now covered John Begay's face. Except for that edge of Indian taciturnity, he might have been described, John thought, as beaming. And he was certainly exultant over the distance to Short Mountain. If he'd had another second to think John felt he could've found the right word to begin to know why the distance to Short Mountain was a matter of celebration to John Begay and of fear to himself. But Ann cut in:

"We're looking for a rug, Mr. Begay. You know about any? You know any weaver? What we want is a Short Mountain pattern: Short Mountain **yei**."

John winced, waited. How safe was it to throw the word for "gods" around? Ann was testing too, only more bluntly.

But John Begay, though silent for a few long seconds, only gazed mildly through his half-smile at them: "You like to wait?"

"Oh. Wait?" said Ann. "Yes. We'll wait."

But then as they did wait, after John Begay had gone back to the hut, they began to suspect he'd never return. Long minutes passed. When he appeared, at last, a woman walked with him, her head tied up in a bright scarf, a large-boned woman wearing the common blouse of purple velvet, a heavy naja-and-squash-blossom necklace dangling to her waist. Without making the slightest gesture towards her, as they walked up, John Begay said, "My wife she weaves."

"Oh," said Ann, shifting about, galvanized. "You weave. Do you? . . . . " She came to a standstill near the woman. . . . . "Do you have a Short Mountain . . . . " (smaller voice) . . . "**yei**?"

"Esta Begay."

"What? I don't understand."

"She gives you her name," said John Begay. "She can't talk no English."

"Well . . . . ," said Ann, letting her head drift from side to side, nonplussed.

John Begay laughed. "No. It's all right. Sure, of course. We'll show you."

It was the hogan he headed for, and not the hut, with Esta Begay close behind him. By delayed response John and Ann knew they must follow.

John Begay stood square before the door of the hogan attentive and nodding to a minute or more of directions from his wife, and when she stopped he only said, "You help me, John. You wait, Ann."

As the door to the hogan opened, John felt that hollow fright again. Why was it so far to Short Mountain? Why did you always have to go over Tall Mountain to get there? If there was only some way to settle that question before looking at the rug, some way that wouldn't make him look like a fool.

But he followed John Begay.

It was dark inside the hogan, and the sky was so dark outside that the smokehole at the roof's apex gave scarcely any light. John felt his hands guided to an upright stick with heavy strings taut around it: it was one side of a frame. As he saw the dim form of John Begay lifting from the other side, he too lifted. The thing wasn't heavy.

The clouded light met them at the door. Ann gave a little "Oh!", and John stumbled but recovered. When he could back away to look he saw that it was an upright loom, that a rug about four-by-six feet, three-quarters finished, hung there.

Inside a thin white border the whole background was a soft gray like the gray of clouds building for rain. The row of long and slender **yei,** their bodies red and green like rainbows unbent, lay horizontal in the upright frame: until John Begay tipped it over and held it nearly level for them to see the effect. On either side of the **yei,** from their tiny hands, hung strings of feathers, nearly to the ground.

John had some vague notion of shocking John Begay into telling him things. So he said: "If you just went by the shape, and not the color, you might think they look like the towers carrying the highline down there."

John Begay turned completely Navajo-impassive.

Which made John quickly add: "Or more like the **yei** standing in the clouds and letting the rain stream."

John Begay laughed, he almost snickered. He made his hands busy, straightened the loom, smoothed out the fabric of the rug, taking up slack.

John looked at Ann and thought he could tell by her look that she was about to ask the price of the rug. And he wanted to cry "Stop!" because he was just now prepared to ask about Short Mountain.

Thunder came tumbling down from the heights, a quick avalanche of sound.

Ann could see the mystery of Short Mountain in John's eyes. She spoke to John Begay: "You still haven't told us why you always have to go over Tall Mountain to reach Short Mountain."

"It's her rug," said John Begay. "She decides the price."

Ann thought, Oh no, he'll never tell us. John felt his voice harden in spite of himself.: "Okay. But you'll have to ask her. We can't."

Which John Begay apparently hadn't wanted to face: he almost squirmed, he looked in every direction, when addressing his wife, except at her, as if this were some curious pattern of bargaining behavior demanded by traders from widely separated lands. And it was quite a little time, with only Navajo issuing into the air, and another rumble of thunder, before John Begay reduced it all to simple English: "She says two hundred dollars."

John and Ann quickly nodded approval to each other, and John said, "All right. And how long will it take your wife to finish?"

He knew it would, and it did, take another lengthy conversation between John and Esta Begay, before: "Esta says three days."

"We're camping," said Ann. "We can come back. Yes, we can do that."

John felt it all fiercely: he was going to be defeated. He would never find out about Short Mountain. John Begay was cheating him. He had no right to sell him a rug, no matter how beautiful, without the explanation of the Short Mountain mystery in the bargain. But it was too late now. Negotiations were closed.

The sun must be setting. It was too dark for anything else, no matter how heavy the clouds. A far-off dazzle of lightning caught their eyes. They all waited for the arrival of the thunder. The seething of rain in the forest higher up came to their ears.

"Can we camp here tonight," John asked, indicating a spot under a big pine a little way back toward the road.

No conference in Navajo, though John had expected it; simply, from John Begay, "Yis."

So the two men carried the rug back into the hogan, and there followed hand-shaking all around, and then the Navajo couple returned to their cabin and the white couple took their little bus to the chosen campsite and set about preparing for the night.

It soon rained, hard, but not before John had stretched and staked the canopy of his own devising that served as a shelter attached to the side of the little bus. Still, the rain blew and swept so that it filled the space under the canopy with thick eddies of mist, and that made starting supper over the campstove inadvisable.

John unfolded the seats into the bed and they lay down under a blanket to wait the rain out.

John thought: The **yei** are marching over from Short Mountain. Over Tall Mountain they come. They carry long feather strings of rain. They move across the soft woven gray clouds that have the keen beauty of lightning in them, and the bands of rainbow. They dance as they come, from Short Mountain over Tall Mountain and on to John the Indian and John the white, and Ann and Esta.

Ann thought: The **yei** are coming to visit the hogan gods. They walk like the tall rain over Tall Mountain. I wish I could see them right now, walking between me and the sun, or is it on the other side of the sky from the sun, just so they'd be in the colors of our new rug.

They held each other close while they thought.

Along after dark, the rain quit. It was magnificent to step out under the high dark cover of the pine tree and look away to distant lightning burning this or that tuft of cloud and flashing great silhouettes of rock with towers and strange twisted excrescences: as if the hogan gods had changed their dwellings into weird forms to receive the visiting **yei**.

It was easy getting supper now, which Ann did while John set a big fire going in a horseshoe of stones he built between the trunk of the pine and the edge of the canopy.

They had just finished eating and sat down on their folding chairs, to keep the evening by the campfire, when John Begay stepped out of the shadows.

Neither John nor Ann moved. They were aware, but only just now, that they'd been expecting him.

He wouldn't take the chair John offered; he sat on a stone; he looked at the fire — and kept looking at the fire.

They waited until he had made up his mind about that, until he said, "That's a good fire."

"A fire is . . . .," John wanted to say "life" — what he said was, ... "lively."

"This fire is under the tree," said John Begay. "The lightning, that's fire up there. Over there the **yei** build their fire. The stars, out there, they burn. Fire you don't see burns in what the stars hide."

John felt a trembling over his flesh: it was such a long way, past fire, past lightning, past the stars, past region after region of the dark of space, from Tucson to Short Mountain.

"John," he said, "the **yei** live in that direction, do they?"

He motioned in what he took to be the direction of Short Mountain.

Which was a mistake: a terrible dumb mistake.

Or was it?

John Begay said, "Used to be a way to Short Mountain without going over Tall Mountain, but the bridge . . . ," he extended his hand as if setting something afloat . . . . "the water took it away."

"Bridge?" said John. "Now that's a bridge over there, is it, on that road we started up by Wide Wash? Not on this road, is it?"

"Road from far end, another road. Main road, used to be."

"And it wasn't rebuilt, the bridge? But that makes it so hard to get to the trading post, now."

"Oh, there's not no trading post, no more, at Short Mountain."

"No trading post!" Ann cried out. "But that's what we've been asking the way to, around at Wide Wash, at the BIA school down there. Why didn't somebody tell us? . . ." Not wanting to say, Why didn't you tell us?

But John Begay understood, and laughed. "You didn't say that. You didn't ask for any trading post. All you asked was Short Mountain."

John and Ann both admitted, but only in silence and chagrin, that nowhere had they specified a trading post as such. They had just assumed that if there was a rug pattern well enough known to be called "Short Mountain **yei**," there naturally had to be a trading post on hand to sell them, like at Two Gray Hills or wherever.

John Begay said, "That man died, the man that run Short Mountain. Nobody to keep it open nomore. Roads are paved down there, scoot along them. People leave Short Mountain alone now. Rugs, not many people make good ones now, just trash, sell it anywhere, make money."

John said, "Tell me, does anything take place, ever, at Short Mountain anymore?"

John Begay said, "You guys ever come here, to Navajo Reservation, in the wintertime?"

"We never have," said Ann. "We'd like to."

John Begay said, "You never see **yeibechai**?"

Both John and Ann knew that this was the dance, the "sing", in which the dancers impersonate the **yei**, one of the most sacred dances of the Navajo, a "sing" that could only be held in the winter season.

"Do you have a **yeibechai** at Short Mountain?" John said, his heart beating wildly.

"Yis," said John Begay. "Maybe you come."

"We will," said Ann. "Sure," said John, "this year."

They all looked at one another and laughed, strange and loud. John Begay got up and kicked a log on the fire and sent out a swirl of sparks. John got up and carried over a big pine-knot and placed it with great care in the flames.

Nia Francisco

With Endless Curved Walls

with endless curved walls of cedar logs,
the cool breeze touches our bare bodies
while curtains slowly move in rhythm
to the passing rain, silence moves
my curled lashes against your cheeks . . .
colors dance on the mohair blanket,
we had listened to round dance songs
echo from Kiowa albums . . .
my long hair a tangled display
on your sand hue skin . . .
smell of wet sage raining in . . .

iridescent child

    call me
        diné asdzaani

i am child of winter nights
       growing in rhythm of summer thaw
i am the one you will see walking before dawn
       and dancing after rain dew has dried

call me
       southwest child

recently Earth greeted me
   a hand shake an earth-tremor
near farmington NM and tsaile arizona
south of aneth utah and towaoc colorado
She says, "it's been years since
      i stretched and yawned" . . .

there is a rainbow surrounding
     encircles my stomping ground
     (like an embrace)
the entrance from the east, from dawn's step
the rainbow stands
a rainbow having a face and limbs
a rainbow   a proctor and my shield

call me
      decadent child

decades ago   and everyday   now   BIA
   devours my heart they ribbed out
of my ancestors a hundred years ago
leaving our blood spots as legal documents
of victory reflecting distorted faces
in the subtle-blue shadows the Sun never sees
that BIA and óólt'a' decapitates
      a thousand children
in the thickness of sage brush shrubs
leaving confused faces dusty on the ground

call me
        artifacted child

amongst native people
missionaries are trying to change
coyote stories to parables of recent times
but now indians are expected to act indian
        for the glamour and benignant donator
(it is foreign to be indian from india)
besides it is too dam expensive to buy
back our pawned jewelries
even our hand-made jewelries, moccasins
and clothes or to rob those museums
(50¢ to xerox one sheet!)

call me
        child-bearing child

i am a child of winter stories
        feet bundled with warmest rags
        born into a blizzard
named after surviving in a cradle board
now a grown woman touching
a man of experience
his experience of killing plants, animals
and vc people
his experience of raving
    about his male pride and manliness
    and i am making copies of him for him
    (carbon)
producing innocuous eyed males

call me
        incorrigible female

my body is curved and carefully carved
    at the touch of the wind
        sculptured like sexy mesas
            and red sand stone cliffs
my hair black like storm clouds
and you'll often see black birds
        flying through my thoughts
            and gestures

my breath in the rain essence
my finger nails are chips of abalone shell
   and i have a purple shadow
like a hedge-hog cactus
i have been cured   for centuries by the smoke
   of cedar bough . . .

Leslie Silko

SLIM MAN CANYON

       early summer Navajo Nation, 1972 for John

700 years ago
        people were living here
        water was running gently
        and the sun was warm
           on pumpkin flowers.
It was 700 years ago
        deep in this canyon
        with sandstone rising high above
The rock   the silence   tall sky and flowing water
        sunshine through cottonwood leaves
        the willow smell in the wind
               700 years.
The rhythm
        the horses feet moving strong through
                white deep sand.
Where I come from is like this
      the warmth, the fragrance, the silence.
Blue sky and rainclouds in the distance
        we ride together
           past cliffs with stories and songs
           painted on rock.
              700 years ago.

Simon J. Ortiz

Tsaile Rain, Late June 1976

I watched the downpulling gray currents of rain
coming from the west upon that flat stretch of sand
and stone miles north of Black Mountain, move into
the Chinle Valley, and head up into the dark line
of pinon and juniper on the Defiance Uplift. I
thought of my father singing. I thought of my
blood singing.

At this moment,
it comes —
the sound above,
the sound below.
At this moment,
the movement is with us,
with all things.

'You should have seen
it come, like rain curtains
into the Chinle Valley,'
I said to the woman
who is soon to be my wife.

Breathe so well
and tightly
to make sure
you are doing it right.

'I'm scared,'
my little daughter said.
No, do not be afraid,
it's the Rain.
The Shiwana.
The Shiwana.
They come, they come.

When I was a boy,
I would shiver
like the trembling lambs
I held tightly to me.
The first cracks
of thunder,

the blue distant lightning.

And then when it sprinkled
lightly at first,
the lambs would run,
back and forth,
back forth,
so excited,
and I would race
with them.
My heart pounding.
My heart pounding.

Haitah muumuu kah.
Haitah muumuu kah.
North, West, South, East,
from there
it is thundering.

Do not be afraid.
Do not be afraid.
You must take it into you.
It belongs inside of you
as well.

'Repression is always dangerous
to your mental and emotional health.
You must be able to see it
before you and within you.'

The lightning cracks
into the line of juniper
less than a mile away.
The terrific slash of electric force,
the blue furious spirit
that is physical,
and then the sudden so sudden
rending of sound.

It would be like an unknown
sudden wracking into you,
the power wrenching so quickly
that even the stone
that you are bursts
and you would settle

quietly into a vacuum
becoming part of it
all — you would know
without needing to know.

Soon, the electric field
has moved on to the east,
to Tsaile Peak, and from there
racing along the electrodes
of my blood, its motion reaches
so quickly into me.

It rains,
the strong gush
of Rain, Rain.
Shiwana, Shiwana.
Peh ehcha.
Peh ehcha.

Prayer:
I offer this for your notice.
Accept my humility
as I breathe into me your sustenance.
Do not let me forget my part.
I will remember I will remember.

I Need a Ride to Chinle

for Geri Keams

'That's my line.
I always need a ride to Chinle,'
she says.

Sunset, the hills, the clouds,
the far distant rain
beyond the evening line
of pinon and juniper.

'You come up sometimes.
It's easy to find,'
he says.
He draws me a map on a mimeod
theater program.

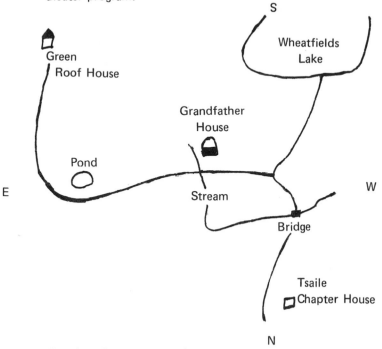

The directions are opposite
to those of the usual map,
but I know the pines around there,
the dark bright groves of oak,
the worn grass by Black Pinnacle.

His daughter plays by jumping
with her tenny shoes
into a pool of muddy water.
She squeals and smiles and smiles.

He is the Navajo father.
She is the Navajo daughter.

The Navajo woman says,
'Simon, why don't you write me a poem
called, 'I Need a Ride to Chinle.'

Okay, I say, 'Okay.'

Los Angeles is a hundred hick towns, a handful of righteously pissed favellas and a few hoity-toity sancta mixed together in a melting pot that does not melt but stays on its guard like a suspicious stew.

Oh, everybody mingles, everybody passes everybody else on the freeways, every man in his island, each with a finger meditatively in his nose, but that is about as close to neighborliness as anybody ever comes.

People are as wary as they are because Los Angeles is a frontier town. **Frontier:** it usually means terra incognita, unknown land. It is a term dipped in Romanticism — there no living soul has placed his moccasin and the eagle soars free. That kind of thing.

But a frontier is really the furthest extent of a country's settled region. So Los Angeles is the frontier. It is the furthest extent.

It is mighty congested for a frontier but Los Angeles is like the scene of an accident where people climb on other people to see what's happening.

The suburbs rear-end one another, the first row of tract homes in Peerless Hills smack up against the back row in Quintessential Acres.

That's where Los Angeles is, anyway, in the suburbs. The city itself is mostly high-rise/underground parking bullseyed among Monterey Park, Vernon, Beverly Hills. Then swooping around in a lovely logarithmic curve there is Hollywood, Alhambra, Montebello, Hawaiian Gardens, Lawndale, Bel Air. Some of these are concoctions of realtors sweating in their Buick Rivieras but some are real dream babies nursed all the way from plains and scrub pines and skies ominous as blackboards.

And it is in these suburbs with their sunny-side-of-the-street christenings that the people live who make Los Angeles what it is.

For the most part they are pilgrims who have come west because it is in their very cells, and as each cell dies and each nucleus passes on its megamysterious information it also transmits a longing and a direction that will satisfy that longing: West. Unhappy, restless people sleeping for years with their butts to the Atlantic, shading their eyes into setting sun after sun, every systole and diastole Go West   Go West   Go West.

Eventually they do. They go to Los Angeles where things are moving so fast there isn't even time to pronounce the ten letters and four syllables for fear of missing something, for fear of not being **there** when **it** happens.

So Los Angeles become L.A. and it might as well stand for Lovely Acceleration.

And it occurs to these sojourners as they stand on the shore at Santa Monica that this is as far as the country goes; they have come as far as they can in their pursuit of happiness: surely it must be nearby.

So they make figure eights, dihedrons, acute and obtuse angles as they roam the freeways. Not roads or lanes or pikes but free ways. Ways that cost nothing, that set you free, that lead to freedom.

And monumental disappointment. The California job is after all just another job, the kids are still Alcatraz, the old lady is just that.

But at least there is always something to do! At least you don't have to sit around and think about it!

There are so many things that the main pursuit here is pleonastic: Angelenos pursue pursuits and they pursue with a vengeance because nothing, no thing, job, home, stud or skating rink cutie could satisfy the expectations they brought with them across the Mojave, U-Hauls piled to the inversion layer with maybes.

So they buckle down and have a good time, indulging their puzzling off-spring, buying things they can't even pronounce, busting ass to Disneyland or Magic Mountain, lining up to drive the Tumbrel Dodge Em's or jumping onto the Perfidy Whirl but more thrilled, really, on the road again, going home with the scenery melting away on either side, probably within a few hundred yards of where they really want to be, some place that would soothe and satisfy forever, but not able to see it for the smog and broke, anyway, and glad, maybe, to just think about it out there and not have to find happiness finally and be disappointed in that, too.

— Ronald Koertge

338

Sandy McKinney

A TRIP TO CALIFORNIA

One night away from home
and the world tumbles like seaweed
streaming down forgotten bayous,
pulled oceanward
shoreward
the drift
of tides, magnetism
of memories/hiatus/the tendrils
cling like cotton candy
stuck to everything it touches.
Too many elements are mingled here,
the fire, the froth, and where
is home?

The wheels click on the rails.
We're leaning. We're pulling in.
The porter calls.
I've left my Tom Collins half finished in the club car
and the station calls, is called.

Home is where the rented car is,
the clean shirt, the neat packet
of travelers checks.
Home is Disneyland, Marineland, Safariland, Winter
Wonderland, Howard Johnson, Riverside
Parkway. Home is
finally, I suppose, in the lap of God,
Father
fathers, all the dacron-slacked
glassy-eyed, office-whitened, torn
all the wearied, harried, stroller-worn
fathers walking patiently through Disneyland
lost behind their sunglasses, their
ice cream, their
corndog, their anonymous
faces,
lost in the mish-mosh of the scrambled
genetic code
the computer forgot to sort out.

Michael C. Ford

PASADENA POEM

Alright, in the old song
birds really do fly
over the rainbow; but
where I come from, birds
chase the smog like raffle-
tickets on a Chrysler New Yorker,
& cancer slams up against
the San Gabriel Mts

A rage of poison now prevails
upon what used to be, for
example, a distress of silken
ladies; every night their patent-
leather spikes would cripple the
parking lot of the Black Cat Bar
& the kid who lived
over the Los Robles Laundry
lean'd out of windows
long after *The Lux Radio Theatre*

watching the vice busters,
hearing a whorl of sirens
        just like Fritzi Ritz
        screeching:

at enterprising Nancy
from a dog-ear'd copy
of *Tip Top Comics*
under the bed

If only the fading strains of Sibelius
on *I Love a Mystery* & Arch Oboler
konkt out the lights; a local vocal
by Monica Whalen, who sang about birds
flying over rainbows,
were able to put us to sleep again

It's impossible now, because by 1959
radio is dead; & birds fly
thru this cigar-ash of a city
that slams like Jack Benny's
vault door
for the last time
against lowering slopes of
the San Gabriel Mts

Bruce Severy

ON TOUR: EL SEGUNDO IN THE RAIN

Every four minutes a jet
Pours out over Playa del Rey.
A woman, or plea
Cuts into these,
"The Days of Our Lives,"
(Breaker nine?   Breaker nine?).

Continuous rain floods Main St.,
Fronting this house on stilts.
Before that: utter drought.

I brood.
It's not like L.A., these extremes,
More like soap opera,
Just removed.

The jets resume.
The rains continue.
I watch TV.
Like an unwanted child
I've come to love, this,
My life.
I must leave.

Nick Ranieri

Headquakes and Hunger

Sand man sand split popped blink, arm hung loose over edge of bed, fingers touching floor, Lenny saw sheet and crumpled corner of pillow, thinking: Awake. Light. Morning. Time. What time? Stuff! Have I got stuff to get up on? Think. Remember. No! Shot it all up. Gone. Wait! Beeper's pad. Beeper. Turned me on. Yeah. Got some in my pants. Okay. Gonna fix! Gonna fix right now! Green stuff gonna come up. Sick. Gettin' sick. Make it to the head.

Incentive enough to raise dead men, Lenny swung feet to floor, stood, reached for pants, thinking: Outfit's in the head, under the towels. Okay. Take it easy. Shakin'. My hands shakin'. Cool it now; just cool it.

Saw empty bed. Peeked around corner. Saw Doll wife bundled on couch, curled fetus, covers fallen half off, still, asleep, dead, forsaken.

In head, water tap running slow stream, sitting hunched on toilet seat, both hands busy, monster smack made its fist in Lenny's throat: Comin' on now. Yeah. Comin' on good. Don't never stop man. Okay now. Everything's okay now . . . Cellophane. What's this other shit? Last night. Hycine cactate Spino gimme. Save it. Outta stuff now. Maybe need it later. Spino said it's bad shit. Should be home . . . Fuck it. Get ready for work now. Doll. Gotta to'er. Just pretend last night didn't happen. See what she says.

Doll awake, heard soft sounds, movements, thinking: He's up already. Gotta fix'is breakfast. Get'im off to work. Jesus God can't talk about last night. Don't say anything. Please don't say anything.

Perky cat hungry, sprang to arm of couch, head cocked ace-deuce, stared, making urgent feline noises.

Lenny splashed water over face, washed easy with soap. Dried hands and face combed hair. Stepped into pants. Stashed outfit back under towels: Other fit's in my truck. Leave this one here.

Bathroom door cracked open. Lenny buttoned clean shirt, tucked tails, made everything fast with belt pulled tight: Didn't shit again. Three days now . . . Gotta shit soon. Get sick if I don't. Banshee babies gotta come. Put it off. Too much hassle.

Doll said: "Lenny you up? What time is it?" thinking: Don't say anything. Please don't say anything.

"Seven thirty."

"You want breakfast?" rising, finding slippers, Perky cat rubbing up on legs, looking up, pleading.

"Just coffee an' some toast. Should I feed the cat?" I ain't straight.

It's gone already. Can't feel shit. Gorilla's gettin' bad. Be sick by noon.

"There's a coupla cans left in the cupboard. Give'er liver. She loves the liver."

Perky cat stretched paws up side of sink, head turned back over shoulder, all triumph, all gloating, hearing Lenny open can.

Doll leaned against kitchen doorway, arms folded over chest, Lenny looking over shoulder, eyes meeting, motions stopping, quick, momentary, silent.

Doll said: "Sure you don't want somethin' else? I could make up some eggs and warm that chop."

"Naw, just some toast. You have it."

"We're early this morning."

"Yeah, I know. Didn't sleep too good. I'll get the paper."

Lenny met morning sounds outside front door. Sun shining bright in California sky. Rush hour traffic honked and droned on Imperial Highway: Gotta make my move today. Get things rollin'. All that stuff shit he's got under the dresser. Wish the fuck I had some of it now. Can't hit'im up. Freeze on my ass I go too far. Gotta hustle up some bread. Bad shape. Just fixed an' already I'm worryin'. Easy man. Everything'll be alright. Just take it easy. Gotta work out alright.

Toast popped, coffee pot rumbled, Doll spreading butter. Lenny sat, glanced at headlines, tried to read.

Doll said: "How 'bout some juice?"

"Yeah, sure," throwing paper off to side.

Doll brought coffee, plate of toast, sat.

Lenny said: "Doll . . . I'm sorry 'bout last night."

"Let's not talk about it."

"I'm sorry is all."

"Okay, you're sorry. So am I. Let's just drop it now . . . Drink your coffee."

"You wanna leave here Doll? You wanna go someplace else an' start over?"

"Where Lenny? Where could we go to start all over?"

"Anywhere. I'm thinkin' Chicago."

"Would it be any different there? Would it?"

"I don't know. I thought maybe a change of scene."

"Where we gonna get the money? How we gonna get there, walk?"

"That wouldn't be no sweat. We could always get up the bread."

"We're not taking any more money from your folks. That's out."

"No, not them; but the money wouldn't be any problem. I could take care of it. We wouldn't need a whole lot. They say it's easy to find a slave out there."

"You couldn't drive a truck. You don't know the city."

"I could take anything until I learned it. Keep up my union dues. It's an easy city to learn. Not half as hard as L.A."

"It takes a lot of money to make a move like that. Where we gonna get it? Two years we've been married and we haven't saved a dime. Where we gonna get the money?"

"I'll get it."

"What you gonna do — rob a bank? You get in trouble and nobody's gonna bail you out. No funny business."

"Just leave that part to me. Just leave it to me. How much you think we'd need?"

"Lenny, you're dreaming."

"You wanna go or not? Just tell me if you wanna go."

Silence. Doll played with sugar, lifting spoon, letting grains trickle back to bowl, said, "Lenny I'd go anywhere with you. You know that," thinking: Why do I say it? Where do the words come from?

Lenny said: "Okay then, start plannin' on it. Pretty soon Doll, pretty soon."

Perky cat finished with food, people, licking chops, up on easy chair for bath and nap.

Lenny took dregs from cup, clink on saucer, looked at clock.

"Want more coffee?"

"No; gotta go. Traffic's thick," eyes up, triple blinking, fingers drumming table top.

"You comin' home for lunch?"

"Yeah," up from table, hands checking pockets: wallet, comb, car keys, change.

"What time?"

"I'll call."

"I could have something hot ready."

"Doll?"

"What?"

Eyes from eyes averted, slow, Lenny saying: "Never mind; seeya later," closing door, thinking: Gotta cop today. Gotta cop right away. Be sick by noon.

Skin smarting lip, bitten in anger and frustration, Doll stifled urge to pummel wall and door. Alone in silence, standing still, hearing din of life outside, emptiness crushing, squeezing tears from gray green eyes, Doll put hand to under breast, felt for heart beat: I feel it. Stop this silly crying . . . Bastard!

Two quick steps, down on knees, saying: "Come on Perky, let's take our little nap," scooping warm perturbed bundle of fur into arms, humming tuneless tune, stepping lightly into bedroom, to flop on bed and doze, scratching cat ear, senses fading to sleep near thoughts of pimps and prostitution.

Lenny shifting gears, pumping pedals, watching road — Wait till ten then start making calls. Tony, Flaco, Leeroy, they'd all wanna score regular. Maybe a few more if need be. Know lots of hypes man. Good

344

stuff Beeper's got. Dynamite. Gotta get me some soon. Somehow. How much bread have I got? Lotta change and maybe four or five in bills. Almost outta gas. Gotta buy gas soon. Fuck! Gonna be sick by noontime. Gonna be runnin' sick by noon. Few minutes more I'll be to work. All those dudes. Have to rap to them dudes. Big day comin' up. How'm I gonna do it all? Gotta put in my eight, get all that shit together, make my move. What if nobody's around? Gotta cop. That's the first thing. Gotta cop right away.

Parked car in Company lot. Walked through gate into clanking roar of truck terminal. Activity all around. Movements, men, boxes, crates, dust in sunbeams, all astir, all in flux. Deep growling diesel motor sounds, raspy, warm. Shouts from dock hands loading vans: curses, laughter, insults. All around sickly stench of diesel fuel stung noses eyes and throats.

Punched time clock. Walked toward green two ton bobtail truck backed against dock.

"Hey Lenny, you ready for these?"

"Stay ready Arty. The kid stays ready."

"You ain't got but six deliveries."

"Lemme see the bills. All routed and loaded?"

"Yeah, all ready to go."

Lenny, looking at bills — Six deliveries, not bad, no big ones, oughtta be through delivering by noon. Hope there ain't too many pick ups. Gotta have an easy day today. Got bizz to take care of. Big time bizz. No time for hang ups.

Jumped off dock and two steps up to cab. Engine fired. Pulled away to clear spot out in yard. Flipped on two way radio. Static. Adjusted squelch. Voices crackled. Lenny waited for lull, pressed button on mike, spoke: "257 leavin' the yard Teddy. Got anything yet? Over."

"257 Lenny, U.S. Gypsum called. They're gonna have four grand for Phoenix today. One time Lenny, ten four?"

"On one Teddy. They give you a ready time? Over."

"They said okay for regular time."

"Okay Teddy, I'll get it."

Drove out of yard — Turn this fuckin' thing off now. Can't stand the racket. Twenty minutes to ten. It's twenty minutes to ten now.

Watched for break in traffic, gunned big Ford engine, turned, merging into slow moving line of wheels — Home for lunch is out. Have to work it out later. She'll keep. How much more can she take? Some day I'll come in the door and find an empty pad. Then what? Where would she go? She's got no place to go. Hates her mother's guts. That'd be out. Stepmother hates her guts. That's out too. Somethin' happens to me wouldn't be surprised she ended up with my people . . . What if I never saw'er again? Never heard'er voice again? Be alone with my gorilla? Alone with the monster? Sleep with'im? Eat with'im? Marry the bad mother fucker? No way. No. Need that bitch. That nothin' little bitch. Need'er. Can't let'er get away. Gotta make it up to'er. Stop fuckin' with'er mind. Get myself together. When? How? Where do I start? How do I get off? How the fuck does anybody ever get off without goin' nuts? Never met a reformed junky yet wasn't some kind of clown or fanatic. Not for me. Tell the whole fuckin' world about what a rotten dog you are? Ask for it like that? Bask in it like them dudes do? Them snitch rat motherfuckers gettin' people busted for their own good. All of'em snitches. Robbin' themselves of the only thing they got left that's worth anything. All the rest goes in the first year and you can't never get any of it back. It's gone for good man, all gone. Anybody tries get it back's a goddamn fool.

Rumble, wheels, Sway, springs. Rattle, hardware. Swirl, dust. Shine, sun. Burn. Sweat, brow. Curdle, stomach. Stretch, skin. Fray, nerves. Ripen, moment. Age.

Gotta concentrate now man; get these deliveries off. Traffic's bad. Chance a posted street? Don't want no ticket. It's gone man. I'm down. Completely down. Four hours and I'm through. No stuff. Nothin' left to it now but the dried up skin. Eleven o-clock. Call Beeper? He'd never come way out here to meet me. Can't hit on'im. Freeze on me. Go too far he'll freeze on me . . . PL 2-2776.

Red light stop. Idling engine. Racing plots.

Come on, change. Gotta get goin'. Gotta do something. Stuff's still in me. Can't get sick really till tomorrow. What am I gettin' all excited about? Easy. Work somethin' out. Need that needle man. Need it now.

Green go. Tore from signal, tearing blind, blind to all save Demon. Chasing Demon down city street and private walk.

Hycine cactate man. Got that shit right here in my pocket. Don't usually fuck with no synthetics. Spino said it's bad shit. Makes you do funny things. Should be home. Said it's like morph only stronger. Didn't even want his. Gave it all to Beeper for a little taste of smack. Must not be too good or he wouldn't've made a trade like that. Hycine cactate. Don't even like the sound of it. Put it off. Hold out. Make some other calls first. Set up some scores. Then call Beeper and I'll have business for'im. Earn me somethin'. Can't just call'im cold and hit for credit. I blow him I'm in trouble. Have to run the streets again. Cop different every day. Get busted sure. Ain't ready for jail yet. Get there sure someday, but not ready yet. Like dyin'. It's just like dyin'. Happens to everybody but you. Never be ready to fall . . . Put it off. Calls. Gotta make calls. Find a phone booth. Feelin' sick now. No bullshit. There ain't enough time for everything. Probably callin' me on the radio by now. Oughtta listen in. Gotta calm down. Pull over an' relax a minute.

Road sounds whizzed passed open window. Parked on shoulder, staring straight ahead. Turned key. Engine gave torquing shudder, died.

Gas station over there 'cross the road. No phone booth. Don't see any phone booth. Can't call'im anyway. Call others. No phone booth. Gotta have water over there. Take a little gheez of this cactate shit. Can't kill me. Gotta calm down. Gotta calm me down, got to. Like morph, Spino said, only stronger. PL 2-2776.

Took empty paper cup off floorboard. Opened door. Hopped two steps down to ground. Sized up traffic like wise old dog. Watched for break, sped balls of feet fast through empty corridor, momentary, churning arms, safe at other shoulder. Lone attendant busy with pump while Lenny filled cup with ice cold water from cooler outside office door. Last chance eye sweep of premises for familiar glass booth, furtive, unrewarded, Lenny thinking: What the fuck kinda gas station this ain't got no phone booth.

Pump man nodded Lenny passed.

Like sprinter on blocks, Lenny stood poised, watching speeding stream of noise and movement. Two way traffic solid — Gotta save at least an inch of this water. Need at least an inch to cook up with. Gimme a break people, just a little fuckin' break.

Avenue artery pumping, skipped a beat, Lenny off like slapstick, across, safe, holding dripping half full cup of warming water. Grinned. Held in evil urge to burst out laughing. Gauntlet run — Gonna fix! Gonna fix right now!

Back in cab, alone, doors locked, windows up gave Lenny sense of privacy in midst of public's way. Slid across slick brown leather seat to passenger side of cab. Reached under dash for outfit jammed tight between wires. Set water cup down on flat transmission hump. Paused to shake shakes gripping gut, traversing, wringing organs tight. Felt lump of sick anticipation swell in throat. Reset eyes, making sure of rear view mirror's scan — Hate to have some good hearted cop pull up to see if I'm broke down — Opened glove box down with bang: small, saintless altar ready for offering. Spread works and stripping off belt making snaps in loops. Breath coming short, opened cellophane, saw small white pills, like saccharine — How many? One? Two? Can't be quarter grain. Must be sixteenths. Two'll make a quarter grain. Fuck it man, can't kill me. Two. I'll go two — Rolled deuce into spoon. Made characteristic sigh cough to steady nerves. Took up water, cleared out works. Hand finger frenzy turned to artistry in motion — Coupla hours more I wouldn't be able to fix myself. Stop this shaking, blow my gheez — Struck match flare stink, acrid: Satan's sulphur spumed, turning spoon bottom carbon black — Fuckin' drug store stuff don't even need to cook it up. Just dissolves like that — Took chewed up end of belt between teeth like swashbuckler's blade. Squeezed off — Fuck it man, can't kill me — Heard air bubbles pass arm pit like pixie's hiccup. Waited. Heard breath through nose. Waited . . . Dam broke at core and rush of senses flowed, strong, like eagle's wings. Soaring fright, lungs frozen flash of blinking eye, perception driven inward, quick, like telescoping lenses — I got too much man . . . Goin' out.

Clunk of skull on dashboard.

Sun made slow graceful arc through sky, over apex hung, dove for sea in west, glowed through haze like fiery doubloon. First star.

Lenny moaned. Head came up off dash and rolled against seat back. Eyelids heavy fighting harsh perception. Dried blood clogged works on floor board. Belt around arm, dangling. Reflex leg jerk toppled dixie cup, water running into grit filled puddle. Down length of inside arm, from bow to middle finger tip, dark red pencil stripe of dried up cracking blood. Lenny's mind racing uncontrolled, like over revving engine: Gotta get U.S. Gypsum today sure, called in four grand for Phoenix, probably them fifty pound sacks, ready regular time, then I'll cut over down Mason street catch L.A. Chemical, most times they got somethin' over there, buncha chicano pill heads load my truck, talk spanish shit to'em they dig it laugh, bomb in drums, carbouys, fuckin' acid an' poison, drums, carbouys, man, what the fuck am I thinkin', can't see right, gettin' dark, after that, depends on how I make out in Paramount City, not too much out there I'll stop over at Superior Honey, always got freight over there, honey house gives us all their bay area freight, bay area freight, belt, blood on my arm, gotta shake it off, load them cartons on pallets, clover, sage, orange blossom, all different kinds man, load'em six tie on a pallet, run'em in sometimes get nine, ten grand, good account the honey house, trouble, I'm in some kinda trouble, gotta clean up, where's my outfit, trouble, can't move right, gotta clean up, sometimes don't get shit, time to kill, stop off the Hofbrau, sip a beer, watch that pretty bitch's legs behind the counter, kill time, you can't let them people know you ain't got nothin' to do. they find somethin', yeah, stick together, together, blurry, everything blurred, can't see right, move, gotta move, get moving, keep that radio on hear everybody rappin' cuttin' in on each other, tryin' get through, get back to the yard, air waves all full of voices crackin' an' carryin' on, nobody wants make that last pickup, everybody playin' games, tryin' come in the yard home free without stoppin' for the meat over in Vernon, gotta make them meat stops man, somebody, Vernon and Soto man, funky ass corner of Vernon and Soto, must be what a field smells like after the battle, so close to home, stinks like a million dead rats, an' trucks all over, backin' in, turnin' corners, cats yellin' an' screamin', blood all over the place, blood, dried blood on my arm, all the way down, must've went out, dizzy, it's almost dark out, have I been parked here all afternoon, I'm blithering to myself about something, weird, can't get moving, gotta get outta this truck, clean myself up, the door, move, can't move right, sight comin' clearer now, blaze of headlights blinding me, cover my eyes, try to snap, come out of it man, move, roll in the yard, gas up, back into the dock an' them lights in the night air, the noise an' racket, hear it for blocks around, everybody rushin' 'round tryin' get through, go home, clean up, dudes with lots of bills milkin' it off for more overtime, Ferraro pacin' back an' forth gettin' it all together, shit, what a scene, scene, I'm on a soapbox an' there's an audience listening to me blither about my slave, come down man, legs moving now, find my works, get rid of'em, ain't got much time, somebody's gotta be wonderin' about me, what happened to me, comin' back now, movements easier, smell again, I can smell, I smell the truck, works clogged, ruined, get rid of'em.

Spinning window knob let eve's damp air into cab, cool, refreshing. Lenny pitched works, belt, paper cup, cellophane, everything dirty, out of window, far as strength allowed — Clean now. Clean? Not sure. Radio. Try to raise base on the squawk box.

Turned on radio to scratching steady static beat — They're off the air. They split home already and a unit still out? They'll dump me sure after this. Didn't do shit all day. Lucky I'm alive. Hycine cactate. Threw it out. Fuckin' poison man. Remember now. Hit me like a bolt of lightning. Knocked me to my knees. Can I drive? Gotta get back the yard. Can't stay here forever.

White sedan company spotter car stopped and steady behind Lenny's truck. Idling engine. Night's smoke swirled in oblong headlight beams. Cricket's creaking hushed abruptly. Follow footsteps crunching rock. Moon. Lenny heard, watched in mirror, thinking: It's Ferraro. They've been out lookin'. I don't believe this shit.

Shouldered open door, half stumbled out of cab to one knee, back up quick.

Ferraro said: "What the hell happened Lenny?"

"Nothin' Frank, nothin'. I'm okay."

"Whataya mean nothin'. Where the hell you been all day? Your radio out? We been after you on the radio all day. Why haven't you called in?"

"I said I'm okay Frank. Can't you see I'm okay," arms out in beggars attitude.

Spotter car driver, boss man, joined group, outlined stark in eerie light, saying: "What's he sayin' Frank? What's he got to say?"

Lenny said: "I'm okay Grayson. Frank, tell'im I'm okay."

"You make any your stops Hart? Any at all?"

"I couldn't."

"Look at'is eyes Frank. He's drunk or crazy one. Look at'im."

"I ain't drunk Grayson."

"Frank, you drive the truck. I'll bring in Hart. You're through Mister. You're through with this company."

"I'm tellin' ya I ain't drunk."

Grayson said: "Frank, first go 'cross the road that gas station, call the office, tell'em we found Hart. We're comin' in. Get'n the car Hart. You're through drivin' for us."

Lenny said: "Frank, there ain't no phone booth in that station.
Tell'im there ain't no phone booth."

Gerald Locklin

A Traveller

He got off the freeway at the nearest ramp.
Fumbling in his pocket for change
he asked the porcelain attendant,
"How much you getting for a gallon these days?"
"A dollar-ten a pint," the other replied,
never once cracking a smile
"My God!" the man exclaimed,
only then remembering that there
was no longer any God, or even,
for that matter, any California.
He drove wildly from the station,
the standard man still grinning horribly
in the rear-view mirror.
Back on the freeway he pressed it to the floor
and searched the billboards for a familiar sign.
Why had he failed to notice it before —
every single phosphorescent square read:
"You Are Already There!"
except the last which grinned "Ha Ha."

And why were there no other cars on the road?
How long had he been on the road?
Had he ever been to California?
Why was the gas gauge rising to full?

low tide floodtime: winter **1969**

I go to watch the sunset from the seawall.
go alone, and others come alone.
we stand up high there, hands in pockets.
the wind comes head-first, hands in pockets.

I had forgotten california could be beautiful.
I'm glad you're not here with me, love; stay
home and sulk. I'm glad my kids aren't here.
I'm glad no young girl strikes up a conversatior

is this what we came to california for?
chromatics of a catalina sunburst?
bomb-burst? eye-burst? oil-lights upon
the bruised waters? a sound that laves?

this, and the midriffs of young girls, and to be
where it was happening. it happened
tonight it is too old for mermaids and
matrons. the sea is post-coital, blue.

the city lies a-light and preternatural.
from here, neither sailors nor storm-troopers.
only the lights of pensioners' chateaux,
the cyclone racer, battleships at rest.

the texture of wet sand is like the gooseflesh
of the surfers, hauling their boards along the long
beach. the red horse of the horizon ramps
to the burst of the black crust.

we are silhouettes upon the silhouetted
sandwall. the waves are
shadows on the wind, the eucalyptus on
the island, rock upon the sun,

the day within the darkness. we stand
with hands in pockets; one-by-one we go
away. we did not come here to commune.
we came, I think, for a last look.

Ronald Koertge

Bringing It All Back Home

While my wife sleeps I prowl the topless
bars, driving hundreds of miles a week to
find them like a mad motorist who does not
believe he is actually getting 2.4 miles
per gallon more than the car without twaddle.

By now I have seen it all, everything from
Three Breasted Annie in Culver City to Skin-
N-Bones Rosie in Bell Gardens, a girl who is
so thin it looks like she has only one.

God knows what I am looking for. It cannot
be only boobies because by actual count I
have seen over five hundred pairs of them.
Then what is it?

I swear I do not know. But sometimes after
the lonely miles between suburbs when I see
the moth-eaten lights of the inevitable bar,
hope swells me like a good Catholic bride.

Will there be inside such an amazing girl, an
off-spring of the gods placed there by some
cosmic opthalmological mistake, a girl who can
with one thrust of her Olympian breasts
obliterate the formlessness and utter chagrin
of my daily life?

The answer is always no, and after some bad beer
I am content to drive home. There my only
love is asleep, so I putter around, drinking
too much and watching Claude Rains movies.

The click comes at about the fifth stiff one,
and I think about the good girl upstairs and
shake my head at myself: my daydreams, my
dumb romanticism, my gasoline bill. And then
I'm go glad of a woman who loves me without
reasons that I write a poem for her and leave
it on the milk carton in the refrigerator.

It is not much of a poem, but it is as good
as many I write. It goes like this:

> the sky is blue
> i love you true

Dick Powell

I saw him in Hollywood yesterday and I asked
him why he even considered acting in those little
T.V. dramas where he was cast as a farmer and
some tow-headed little bastard who wanted to grow
up to be a potato called him Pa and he was too
old to ever get the creamy ingenue.

And whatever happened to the Dick Powell everybody
loved in "Gold Diggers of 1933" where Ruby Keeler
and Joan Blondell never wore bras but he was too
cool to fall for that because all he wanted to
do was tickle those ivories.

He didn't answer, of course, just stared
until I turned to leave. Then he came for me.

The police separated us eventually and I apologized
for being rude and he mumbled something about
unusual pressures.

But that was days ago and I should have forgotten
all about it but at night and sometimes in the
afternoons and even as I write this I can still
feel those cold, yellow teeth in my bones.

Paul Foreman

L.A., A LAMENT

L.A.
you long ago lost
the beauty of your Spanish name, La Puebla
de Nuestra Senora, La Reina de Los Angeles.
Fitting now, you, always referred to
as L.A., like the acronym
of some new American corporation,
But your products do not sell north
of the Tehachapis; this dense cloud
gathered about your head, reflects
a dirty yellow cast, rejects the sunlight.   L.A.,
a city cannot live without sunlight!
but mushrooms can,   and do . . . .
What takes place in these apartments
that look like motels.
Will the picture shows tell us?
True, the television landscapes
all resemble you; or is it crosswise?
Despite your aura of doom
I often hear in your streets
Mexican women singing to their children,
the music of Chinese talk and barter,
and rough, tender bark of Brooklyn jews.
In your lower depths, L.A.,
black men raise possums
and barbecue ribs, and beat the ancient
drums of their African homeland.
These people are holed up,
determined to survive your holocaust;
already, you appear a refried pancake,
flat,
utterly flat, without taste,
and crust burnt at the edges.
The Angels in soot-blackened St. Andrews
chapel sing, sometimes only to themselves,

    KYRIE ELEISON,
            CHRISTE ELEISON,
                      KYRIE ELEISON.

The Sensei

There's a story I'd like to tell. It's been a long time on my mind, changing form, eras, situations, characters, but I think there's only one way to tell this story: the way it happened.

It starts back at the beginning of World War II, maybe earlier, but for my purpose, this is where it starts. Beyond that I'll leave to the reader because I think audience participation is important: like those paintings artists do that leave interpretations to the critics. If you paint too much of the picture, it's not first-rate because that interferes with the evocation of emotions. I believe this, but I never made it as a painter either. You've never heard of Utako Morita, have you?

Well, when the United States and Japan entered into war, the Japanese and Japanese-Americans living on the West Coast were shunted off to various internment centers in the more isolated areas of the United States. For security reasons, they said. I went to Poston, Arizona with my family; I was 17 then, and though I was resentful that my loyalty was questioned, what could a girl of that age do? Yes, girl. I'm not a man. Lots of people think that. I write letters to magazines sometimes, and they answer: Dear Mr. Morita. I'll give you a clue about Japanese names: if there's a **ko** at the end of a first name, it's female. This doesn't mean there aren't women with male names or female names without **ko.**

I guess I write like a man too. I've always tried to be direct and I guess that's a sort of masculine trait. I have this thing about being sweet: all Japanese girls are sweet, ask anyone. And while I was growing up, it was so important for me to be different from every other Japanese girl, I made great effort to be honest and unsweet. Not that **sweet** and **honest** are opposites, but directness isn't a desirable trait among Japanese women. Sweetness is. Sometimes it really annoys my husband Jim, this directness of mine; he thinks women should work hard at being women. But this is the way I am; I can't help it — but I'm all woman otherwise — and 38. You wouldn't believe that either, would you? But there you are.

Inside this particular camp, as in the others, there were many political factions: ultra-Americans, ultra-Japanese, varied degrees of both, fence-sitters, indifferents, and at least one pacifist. There was quite a bit of internal tension; there were rumors of all sorts, black lists, beatings, and a pro-Japanese strike. I attended this; we stayed up all night in little groups of campfires, block standards waving in icy winds, Japanese military songs blaring over the loudspeaker. My girl friend (she was the pacifist) and I huddled together and sang ballads — very conspiratorial.

About this time, the Government decided to separate the pros from the cons. The way it was done: questionnaires were passed to all American citizens and somewhere in the middle of the list (number 18 or 19), there were two important questions: Would you renounce all ties with Japan, and would you volunteer your services to the United States, only worded more legal-like. On the basis of the answers, the young people were sorted. I answered yes-yes; I mean, after all, what did I know about Japan, and what branch of service would take me? But my brother Toshio was a no-no. It was very hard on the old folks; they were brought up in the spirit of Yamato: patriotism, filial piety, and Spartan, or rather, Japanese existence, and though they weren't required to answer the questionnaires, the Government offered to repatriate those that wanted to return to Japan. These people, repatriots, and no-no's and yes-no's were sent to Tule Lake, California to await transfer to Japan. Some repatriots went in entire clans, some left their young folk, and some young folk left their families. It was very hard on the old folks. My brother went alone.

There's where Toshio met Jim Morita, the man I was to marry later. Toshio used to write to me about life in Tule: 6:00 AM calisthenics, Japanese language classes, the friends he'd made, the Morita clan in particular who were so kind to him, the pressure groups, the extremists who shaved their heads **bozu** (that's bone-bald), **banzai** meetings (that's a kind of battle-cry; it means like Hurray! or Long Live the King!), beatings, and knifings. They stayed in Tule quite a while; there was a long waiting list and only one boat, the Swedish Gripsholm. Toshio wrote me about contingents who left for Japan, how they wept. I sent candy bars, cookies, and once I saved up my clothing allowance and sent him a sweater. It made me sad — you know, my brother's keeper.

By the time war ended, we in other camps had gradually been processed (investigated and cleared) into the mainstream of outside life. We scattered all over; Chicago, New York, Cincinnatti, Boston, but most of us returned to the West Coast. My family moved back to Los Angeles. There was a huge group left stranded in Tule; they too were processed and allowed to sift back. Toshio returned to us.

The Morita family went back to Walnut Creek in Northern California, where they'd farmed before. Only Jim came to Los Angeles to attend the University here. That's when I met him.

I wish I could tell you about our courtship — the joy, the pain — but that's not pertinent to my story. I'm glad we got married before we had sense enough not to. We're both from Buddhist families so we had a Buddhist wedding, and the priest said he was so happy to unite two Buddhist families. Suddenly the awesome responsibility of family — generations from my womb — scared me silly and I felt like bawling.

That's what I mean about getting married before I had sense enough. I wondered what Jim was thinking but we were like in separate rooms.

The first years were rough. We got a small basement apartment for keeping the yard mowed. I worked at a shower curtain factory hand-painting shower curtains; you've seen them — flamingoes, palm fronds, sailboats; and every four and a half months we scraped the barrel to meet non-resident fees at school. Jim's citizenship problem disqualified him as a resident. His major was international relations and his dream was to work in the reconstruction of Japan. Phoenix from the ashes.

We spent most of our weekends in our basement apartment playing penny-ante poker with Jim's colleagues who were also very needy. Sometimes he'd go to the House, one of the dormitories, for a big game. "I've got to make tuition," he'd say, and most of the time he'd get it. He's what they call a tight player. But Jim's very superstitious and he could never go to these games without a smile and kiss from me. Sometimes I simply couldn't do it, smile and kiss, and he'd say, "Well, I just won't go if you don't want me to. I'll just go on to bed." And he'd lie in bed next to me (I'd have retired by them, sulky) with his coat and shoes on. That would make me laugh and I'd smile and kiss him, and watch him go off like a kid running to catch the ice cream man. I said to myself, when we have money he will stop this. He needs the money.

Jim heard about Las Vegas from these boys at the House. They planned systems and worked out mathematical theories and laws of averages, and Jim would come home all excited and tell me about them: gambling around the clock, night lit up like day, money flowing like water, free drinks, free breakfasts. We had to go.

It was winter; I cashed my fifty-dollar bonus check and we agreed not to write checks or use the tuition money. I tucked an extra ten dollars in the secret compartment of my wallet. I'd also heard about Las Vegas; of people coming home broke and hungry and running out of gas the last mile home. We drove off to Vegas.

We lost most of our money at the gaudiest, plushest casino downtown, the Golden Nugget. There were only a few dollars left so we went across the street to the Boulder Club, where dime and quarter bets were allowed. The clientele differed there — some of them looked like grizzled prospectors, refugees from a TV western. I sat at the Keno seats and bought a quarter card and pretended to mark numbers; they won't let you sit down unless you're playing the game. In a little while Jim came along and jerked his head, let's go home.

While we were walking to the door, Jim pulled my arm and said, "Look at the man standing at the water fountain." I looked. He was a small thin man, Japanese, about 40 or more. His face kind of hung on his neck like a rag on a peg. He was deeply tanned with creases like gullies on his face, his hair was thinning, and his eyes were incredibly tired. His two-toned loafer jacket was faded and dirty; he looked like a strip of bent clay. "He asked me for money," Jim said.

"Did you give him any?" I asked.

"I didn't have any to give."

The man leaned over the fountain and took a long drink and from where I stood I could almost hear the cold water rushing into his empty gullet.

We were maybe five miles out of town, driving in the cold glare of the desert sun when Jim spoke, "I can't get over it. Imagine . . . a Japanese begging."

"Oh, Jim please," I said irritably. This whole trip had been one big pain to me: pain in the arches, the pocketbook, and the butt. "Who can be responsible for all the Japanese the world over; why there must be thousands of them begging in the streets of Tokyo, or Hongkong, or wherever. Besides, what could you do? You didn't have the money." The ten-dollar bill in my secret compartment lay very still.

"I can't help thinking about him," Jim said and pulled the car over to the side. He looked at his nails. "I know him," he said simply.

I was really shook up. "Why didn't you say so?" I demanded.

"Well, I don't exactly know him, but I've seen him around in Tule Lake. He was known as Kondo Sensei (sensei means master or teacher — sort of professorial), at that time he was a Buddhist priest. He was a powerful man in camp, feared and respected. He had a big following of fanatics; people called them his goon squad, thugs. They shaved their heads like the monks in Japan and they moved in bands and people were afraid of them. My blood was hot then and I envied that power but didn't have guts enough to join his band. Now look . . . begging . . . I can't believe it."

We turned back.

Jim found him at the Boulder Club still standing where we last saw him, leaning against the water fountain. We drove to a restaurant. I can't remember what we ate, but it was a two-fifty dinner, all three of them. While we waited for our order, he told how he hadn't eaten for three days, nor slept in that long except to doze on his feet. He said he hadn't bathed for two weeks, and I believed this. He explained how he was on his way to Denver and stopped off to change trains and had become so fascinated by this town and the abundance and glitter of its money that he was compelled to stop for a day to study the situation. That was a month ago, and all his possessions were now pawned and he had nothing, nothing, not even self-respect, and ah, how low must a man sink before his senses return. If God would permit him one last chance, to continue to Denver, he would never again falter in the face of temptation. All the while, he talked slowly with his eyes closed and seemed to catch small naps between phrases. During one of these lulls, Jim mentioned how he recognized him as Kondo Sensei of Tule Lake.

358

He didn't even open his eyes. "Yes, yes," he said, "and they are waiting for me in Denver." I wondered if it was the parish that waited, but it didn't seem proper to ask right then.

"Sensei," Jim said, "your family, the children and your wife must be quite worried about you . . ."

"Yes, yes, I must hurry on to Denver," he said, and, "so you were in Tule — ah yes, I remember the Moritas, fine people. Your father, yes, he was very active, was he not? He worked with the block council . . .?"

"Well," Jim said, "you're probably thinking of some other Morita. My father worked in the Block 12 kitchen." He gave a small laugh.

"That's right, that's right. A fine man." The Sensei dozed off again.

Jim left us to see about cashing a check and when he returned, he passed the Sensei some money and offered to drive him to the Greyhound depot and buy his ticket for him. "I know your family is waiting for you," Jim said.

The Sensei's hands fluttered like they'd drop off. "No, no, no," he said, "I wouldn't think of putting you to such trouble. You've done enough for me. When I get back to Denver among my friends, I shall repay this money. You've rescued me as sure as you'd plucked me from deep water. I shall never forget you, Mr. Morita. The bus depot is not far from here and walking will help keep me awake." There was a crystal tear in the mucus around his eyes.

Jim slipped him some more money. He bowed deeply and as we turned the corner, I saw him raise his arm in a forlorn salute. Jim asked me not to tell anyone about this encounter with the Sensei; I guess he couldn't bear the thought of people laughing over it, although he got a lot of laughs talking about **my** friends.

We went to Vegas quite often after the first taste of being so physically close to so much money. During one of these junkets Jim came rushing over to me. I was pumping the arm of one of those slot-machines. If you stay at one machine long enough, it seems to get into a sort of frenzy and starts paying off and sometimes hits a jack-pot. So seven dollars on a nickel machine — it gave me something to do. "Let's get out of here," Jim whispered. "The Sensei's here."

I didn't want to leave; I'd already dribbled two dixie cups of nickels into this particular machine — they give you paper cups to use; two dollars worth of nickels doesn't quite fill one of them, and I didn't want to leave. "Oh Jim," I was exasperated, "the Sensei won't see us." And still pumping, I asked, "Where is he?" Jim jerked his head toward the black-jack table.

The Sensei stood behind the seated players and appeared to observe the game. He kept his hands in his pockets and they moved as though impatiently fingering coins. He looked much better than when we first saw him, tidier, but his eyes still had that weary glaze. They say if you stare long enough, a person will feel it; well, the Sensei turned. Then he walked away. I was right; he didn't see us.

That was a number of years ago. We don't go to Vegas much now. If we were married in '48, and Jim went to school for four years, this Sensei thing happened along '49 and '52. All that time I was painting shower curtains. On, it wasn't that bad: I did other things. Once I took a course in ceramics; Jim even bought me a potter's wheel and would have bought a kiln, but we couldn't cart it home. I studied anthropology too. You pay two-fifty for registration and you can take as many courses as you can bear. But it wasn't that good either; there were some bitter quarrels. And once Jim said when he got through school he would no longer need me and he would shuck me like an old shoe. Machiavellian.

Jim got his B.A. and went to work for an importing firm — stock boy. After a while he was made foreman of the stock room and he had me quit my job. He said now I could paint anything I wanted. But you paint flamingoes and palm fronds and sailboats for four years and you hardly want to hold a paintbrush or remember the things you wanted to paint before. Something akin to spirit leaves you and you don't even remember that you once lay awake nights thinking and seeing color and form and space. Maybe that's part of growing up. Maybe that's what people mean when they say you've "matured": you've lost enthusiasm.

Jim got restless working in that stock room and after a couple of years, he opened a small record shop. He stayed three years with that and then sold out. It never seemed to work out with his taking all his buddies out to lunch so often. He said this wasn't true; he would have left the business sooner or later because he couldn't stand the noise. All those teenagers, you know, and never buying.

Right now, he's selling cars. It's been all right; he wears a suit and tie every day, and he usually has a pocket of money, and he's among men. That seems to be important; they go off for a drink now and then, and they play liar's poker. That's a game that two people on a desert island with a hatful of money must have invented. It has something to do with bluffing about the serial numbers on currency; and the good thing, you don't need a lot of equipment, just money. But it's got to be genuine government issue.

He seems to be happy at this job, and we always have a good model car to use. Evenings he's often busy with clients, or poker, or a staff meeting. And he loves cars. This business is seasonal, of course. Sometimes the money is plentiful, but there's a long dry spell that's pretty rough just before the new models come out. I try to look out for these bad days although there never seems to be enough surplus to tide us over in any but the most frugal kind of style. When things get too rough, we pack a bag and take a trip for a few days to Ventura where my brother Toshio now lives. He married a girl from there who didn't like Los Angeles.

I had just finished packing the old Gladstone for this trip to Ventura, and Jim was on the front room floor fastening the straps and we were laughing about the many times we'd packed this bag for Vegas and never opened it. We'd lose the money before nightfall. The front door was ajar because we'd been to and from the car. It was a soft September evening and a pale grey light came through the door. We heard a shuffle of feet on the rubber link mat we have outside. We only saw a silhouette, and believe it or not, I mean it had been seven or eight years, I knew who it was.

"Oh, Sensei," Jim said bowing before he quite got to his feet. "My, my . . ."

"Ah, Mr. Morita," the Sensei bowed, "I have never forgotten you. I see you're planning a trip. I don't want to detain you."

Jim glanced at his watch, "We have a few minutes, sir, please sit down." I turned on the lights.

The Sensei looked as if he had walked all the way from Vegas. His shoes were cracked and dusty and his hat and coat were stained with sweat. It was the same or similar two-toned coat he wore when we first saw him. He looked as though the desert sun had beat upon him for days, and he'd lived on those paper bags tossed out by motorists.

"Make a sandwich for Sensei, Utako," Jim said. "And a cup of tea."

The Sensei put out his hand, the same fluttering hand he used at us eight years ago. "No, no," he said, "you were just leaving for someplace. I won't detain you."

"We have a few minutes, Sensei," Jim said, "my wife will make a sandwich for you."

I could hear them from the kitchen. The Sensei asked Jim how things were with him. "Not bad," Jim replied, "I'm in the car business now, and I have to see a client in half an hour, then we plan to drive to Ventura." The Sensei almost purred. He said that fate had been kind to a most deserving individual: the beautiful car, the lovely house, and weekend motor trips. Jim didn't bother to protest the car was on loan, the house in mortgage and the furniture payments were in arrears. There was a painful pause and then Jim asked, "And how is it with you," Sensei?"

It came pouring out like dammed water; the troubles he'd had — the heartaches. Five, six years of bad, bad luck. He'd gone into business with a partner: produce in Anaheim. Yes, partnerships are bad — two bosses, two different ideals — no good. The debt, the incredible debt this unscrupulous man incurred — the lying, the cheating; yes, bankrupt, had to dissolve the business. The anxieties, the tension! Yes, even considered suicide; very seriously considered it. Oh yes, yes, a terrible sinful thought.

They both stopped talking when I walked in with the sandwich. I was glad because I could see that Jim was looking a little uncomfortable. I pushed the sandwich under the Sensei's long face.

"You should not have made it, Madam, you are too kind, far too kind for such a worthless fool," he swallowed the juices in his mouth. "I haven't eaten in over three days," he said, "and sleep," he passed a yearning look over our couch, "I haven't slept for as many nights. I have considered suicide."

I remembered that on our first encounter he said he had not eaten or slept for three days and nights, and I wondered how many other people had heard this story unchanged and unchanging throughout those miserable years of the Sensei's misfortune. I had the sympathy, but it was way deep inside of me, not ready to come out yet. "God forbid," I said.

Jim glanced at his watch. "Sensei," he said, "I don't like to rush you, but I have an appointment in a few minutes, may I drive you somewhere?"

"No, no,' the Sensei protested, "you have done too much already. I can catch a trolley. I came to Los Angeles to call on a friend but he wasn't home. I'll try him again later. He isn't home now. I'll be all right; excuse me for imposing my foolish self upon you."

"Still," Jim persisted, "we must leave in a few minutes; I have this appointment, you see. It won't take long; you can wait in the car with my wife until I'm through, then I'll drive you over to Japanese town. We call it "Little Tokyo"; I'm sure you'll see someone you know there. Everyone turns out on Saturday nights."

The Sensei sat quite still chewing his sandwich. He nodded slowly and his eyes moved once more to our couch before he surrendered to Jim.

While we sat in the dark car waiting for Jim, I asked the Sensei how he came to find us in this big city. We had moved several times since we gave our address many years ago.

"Telephone book," he answered sullenly. I thought he might be mad at me for being so unfeeling earlier, and I felt real bad.

I tried again: "I hear Las Vegas has really grown since we used to go there. I understand they've extended the strip with many more luxury hotels, and the shows they put on are really fabulous. It must be quite a town now."

He turned to life again. "Ah yes, yes," he said, "it's quite a town." He was still for a while, and as though he'd been shuffling through his files and had come to a final analysis, he said again, "Yes, it's quite a town."

Sometimes I could kick myself for talking when silence is required, but it's like when you're with a fat person and you want to avoid the word "fat" so everything comes out like elephant, or gargantuan, or monumental or something. So I kept right on going. "You know, if all the hopes and dreams of those many people who go to Las Vegas were converted to units of energy, imagine what could be accomplished." I don't know why I was talking that way, I didn't really want to moralize. But already I could see the Sensei sweating all week long at some miserable job to lose it all at the tables, and I knew the hopelessness he felt as the last of his money slipped away. All that energy.

"And all the tears that have stained the sleeves of men," the Sensei said. "Still I love Las Vegas." That made me feel good.

Jim came back and he asked, "I wasn't gone long, was I?" We both answered "no" together.

It was a short ride to Japanese town from there. We pointed out the landmarks: the Statler Hotel, the Water and Power building, City Hall, the new Police Station. The Sensei was polite in his attention. When we got to the fringe of Little Tokyo, he pressed Jim's shoulder and said, "Here, let me off here."

He got off the car and bowed carefully. "Thank you for your kindness," he said. He nearly stumbled on a piece of side-walk litter, and then walked on toward the lights of Little Tokyo. Ginza Club, Miyako Hotel, Mikawaya — green, red, yellow; alternating and blinking, the colors reflected themselves on the Sensei's soft shapeless hat. He stopped, waited for a light to change, then disappeared in the pedestrian traffic.

That was the last I saw of him.

Billie Jean James

HOMING

Having highways all alone
west and south I come
returning to stars
the sky had been too full of fog
but now the moon is near
the first joshua near Goldfield
stands like an old miner's ghost
welcoming me back to dust
drier and wider now the night
asks me remove my sweater and stay
the desert is home

THE MAGIC STONE REFLECTS THE PRAIRIE

Phantom antelope
graze in brown
grasses near
the freeway.
Cars who hurry
on to Utah
detect no white.
Pronghorns
speak gun wind
to the girl
with Wyoming eyes.
She shares
this presence
and feeds unseen.

Howard McCord

THE RIM OF THE GREAT BASIN

> *Q. What is the holy power of the wilderness?*
> *A. The holy power of the wilderness is innocence*
>   *of man.*
>
> > *The Catechism*

Darkness is another kind of light,
and stones are sweet as air to breathe.
The Anasazi, the old people, knew.
In the depths of canyons
for a thousand years, they unlocked
the rocks themselves and slipped
inside like bones fit into skin.
They watch as the bristlecone

pine signals from the ridge,
and know how flames leap from
flint and steel.
The bighorn desert sheep nests
like a bird above the falling land,
unseen by man, and mountain boomers
play their cylindric minds
on the silences which are wisdom.
Canopus hangs like a breathing eye
in the arms of the pine, and the long
interchange of their awareness
is the heart beating at the core of everything,
a music of smoke and crystal, an impenetrable
language shaped out of time and the graceful,
falling curve of space between them.

Stephen Shu Ning Liu

At the Enchanted Palace

La Vegas, ah Las Vegas,
entertaining me with naked girls,
charging me $3.50 for a drink, in the
frenzied jazz, in the agitating sparkles.

Through my Roentgen-ray eyeglasses,
I see a galaxy of skeletons tumbling on
the moonlit floor: they spur my flesh,
they kick out ashes into my face;

in a few hours I've idiotically hurled away
more dollars than my father gleaned for a
month down in the southern Nevada mines . . .
I can hear him flipping over in his sandy bed,

and as I drain my last cup, stagger out that
sepulchre-dark cabaret, my hair and my hands
smell nitric acid. The afternoon sun blinds me;
over my Puritan conscience I nauseously vomit.

365

Robert Joe Stout

The Wooden Elf

As she stepped inside the church, Kay stiffened. The air was thick, close; the walls dank; about them hung the waxy thickness of undiscovered ghosts. But despite the overcast sky outside, the chill wind skimming in from the north, the oblong, high-walled sanctuary was not dark. The stone floors gave a rather pleasant and carefree echo as Ruthford, her husband, and Brooks, their little boy, followed her towards the small, slightly elevated altar.

She was disappointed. At the same time she felt lightened, relieved. The deep, unnerving blackness, the obsidian core she had learned to associate with Mexicans, with religion, both attracted and repelled her. Its absence thrust her back to the surface of life. She laughed. "Oh look! Rud, look, over there, tucked in that corner!"

Her sandals clattered againt the stones as she swooped forward, longlimbed yet graceful, her dark hair swinging around her neck. At the base of the altar, where worn stairs connected the raised portion with the floor of the sanctuary, she knelt and dug from the dust, silt and cobwebs a small wooden figure. "What is it, Rud?"

He knelt and let Brooks crowd past to squint at the statuette Kay handed him. It was twelve or fourteen inches long, of soft wood; its body and face were contorted into a leering, embarrassed pain, as though it were constipated or had just been kicked in the testicles. "A devil, probably," he grunted, turning it over. Whoever had carved it had known what he was doing. The blade strokes were long and sure, and the separation between the bowed legs was neatly augured. "They make them for Day of the Dead. Why, I don't know. Somebody told me they break them up afterwards. Or burn them — I've forgotten. Maybe the priest uses it to scare the children."

"But it's not scary!" Kay laughed. The sounds floated toward the peaked rafters and heavy roof above them. Brooks crouched forward, his big eyes and clear, not-yet-freckled face giving him the puzzled innocence of a young calf. Behind them, in the church nave, their other child, Harriet, the baby, was slouched asleep in her stroller.

Rud propped the figure on the floor in front of them. "Yeah," he agreed, "like some ol' boy caught taking a crap. Still, I think it's a devil."

"I'll bet somebody hid it there as a joke!" Again her laughter climbed, floated, arousing a slight echo. Rud pushed himself to his feet. Seeing that he didn't quite understand, Kay continued — "To tease the priest, I mean. Look at his expression! Want to bet that one of the priests who says mass here has a nose just like that? He can't see the whatever-it-is from up there but the audience — you know, the congregation — could! Oh, wouldn't they laugh at him! Rud, I'm sure that's it."

He grunted. Kay always managed to find something to laugh at. To her, Mexicans — peons — were funny people. Not pathetic, trodden-under beasts-of-burden. Her voice, deeper than that of most women, bounded into their expressions, and they laughed with her, at themselves. And, strangely, loved her for her laughter while standing aloof from him.

"No, Brooks," she was telling the child, "put it back, we mustn't take it." But lifting it she hesitated. "Can we, Rud?"

"Take it, you mean?"

She nodded. Her eyes, large and almost perfectly elliptical, waited like traps, magnets, for him to turn, purse his lips, decide. For a moment, evading her, he remembered how he had disliked her voice, so slow and poised and sure of itself, the first time that he'd seen her. Then he had turned and met her gaze and, suddenly naked, suddenly elated, had leaped and swum in the feelings that had appeared between them. Walked, as it were, the marrow of a startling new possibility, a feeling that, later, he had called love.

"Why not?" he shrugged, "the priest doesn't want it."

Kay frowned. Her face, haughty but plain, a big-city, upper-middleclass coolness, congealed around her desire. She pressed her teeth together to resist the intrusion from within — a voice that spoke in syllables her mind couldn't grasp. But deep down, in her personal self, she understood. "No," she contradicted, her voice flat, unemotional, "it belongs here."

Rud snorted. "Like the gold? the jewels?" He waved his hand towards the dirty, chipped wood of the altar, his voice rising to fill the silence, fight the echoes that seemed to float down like bits of paper from the ceiling. But it was not the church in front of him that he described. Nor even the big, stately church in Yuma, 16 miles across the border. It was an abstraction. A caricature. To him it was monstrous, vivid, true. Brooks stared up at him, blinking; Kay bit her cheek and frowned. Intellectually she agreed with her husband: the dogma, the sterility, the imprisoning phrases, she could accept none of them. But the people . . .

"Still it belongs here," she insisted, lowering the carving. To Brooks more than to her husband, "We'll put it back where we found it. Here."

Rud stepped back, trying not to watch as she tucked the idol back into the crevice and patiently, in her concentration excluding even the awareness of his presence, rearranged the cobwebs around it. Twice his hand jerked as he started to shout to her to stop. **What does it matter?** a logical, more fatalistic voice insinuated. It was only a piece of wood, a crude, handcarved reminder of some medieval **indio** superstition; there were others like it in every shop between Mexicali and Juarez. A tremor ran through his shoulders. It was not the idol, it was Kay — Kay with her clear, decisive mind, her Eastern art-school education, kneeling at the altar in subservience to a shadow, a non-existence.

"Oh-for-Christ's-sake!" — the words a tumble as he pushed Brooks aside, his hand darting towards the hidingplace. Instinctively, Kay defended it. For a moment, combatants, they wrestled with each other, then Rud jerked away. "All right," he mumbled, "leave it, I don't care."

Kay crouched at his feet, her fists pressed against her thighs. She had won — she knew she had won — yet there was something indefinite, tentative, about her victory. Brooks, beside her, squatted with his feet flat against the stones, his tanned, chubby hands picking at the dust between the cracks. Slowly, Kay pushed herself erect. "I'm sorry," she whispered, "it's the way I feel." Then, more ironically, "Maybe I want them to laugh, Rud. If I took it, there wouldn't be anything . . . ."

Out of the church into the implacable gray streets of the village. The sand, also gray, and the sky, gray. His mood, gray, heavy. He pushed the stroller while Kay led Brooks by the hand. At a corner two blocks from the church, they turned to look at it, squat and massive, a darker gray than either the streets or the sky. Rud stiffened, constricted by a loathing he couldn't repress. It was as much an intruder as he and Kay. An anachronistic jumble, a huge, heavy fossil pushed out of Jerusalem, another gray land, and forced onto this land's consciousness. He spit. Kay bit her lip. "Somehow," she said, "however much one might detest it, it's beautiful, there, with the desert behind it, and the houses so small, and the sky . . . ."

"I don't see it!" Abruptly, almost spastically, he whirled to face her. "I, I see, goddamn it . . . . a prison, Yu-Yuma Prison over there across the river, it, I don't give a damn what kind of sunset's behind it, the men inside fed like animals, beaten, screwing each other, they're not beautiful! And that's what that church is, that's . . . ."

His hand, beating the air for emphasis, contorted around the thought. Kay, drawn inside her plain, placid face, fought him with her eyes. "No, no," she muttered while he still was talking, "that's not it, that's not it at all, I don't mean 'pretty,' it's not pretty, I know that. I, there . . . in beauty, real beauty, always there's a great deal of pain, always, and, and suffering, the beauty of . . . ."

"Suf-fer-ing i- . . . , is not . . . beautiful!"

The words came through his throat like stones. Kay bent her neck. Harriet, asleep but uncomfortable on the board seat of the stroller, twisted and tried to slide into a more recumbent position. Brooks hunched his shoulders and shielded the glance he lifted, hesitantly, towards his parents. For a moment, smiling, Kay did not answer. She loved this man, his staunchness, his belief in his ideals; she did not want to anger him. Yet it was partly his anger — so like his physical love, consuming, complete — that drew her towards him in admiration and desire. She loved him and could not leave the words he'd put between them standing there, obstructing. "Harriet, when Harriet was born, I, it hurt, Rud, God! how it hurt! and, beautiful, it was, Rud, it was!"

His hand went out, withdrew. He nodded. "That's not the same," he said slowly. "You wanted that, you were proud, happy." His gaze swung towards the church. "But they, when the people come there, to that church, they're coming like prisoners, they're not free, not happy, they're . . . dammit! they're cattle, dumb, blind, ignorant cattle! And they're kept that way on purpose! To satisfy . . . ."

She'd stopped listening. Her eyes drew his toward the church again. It seemed to resist his gaze as it resisted the sand, the sky. "I had no choice," Kay was whispering, "neither do they. Their faith is beautiful, even if it is misplaced. And the church is beautiful, like a tree or stone. Because it is. It doesn't matter what it stands for — really, it doesn't stand for anything, nothing does. Except in our minds. It's just rock and windows and a tilted roof. I think the people know more than the priests do. I think they go in sometimes just to get warm, or have something to look at, or make jokes. That's why I like them. I like the way they are. I know they're oppressed. That's part of it. I don't want them to be oppressed, to be, like you say, exploited, but I can't, I can't help it if I find them beautiful. If I like them. If I like their church. It's only the words that are so bad, the priest's words and the government's words and the rich Americans' words. What my eyes see I cannot be angry with, what my body feels. Is that so bad, Rud? Is that so cruel of me?"

He shook his head. At the end of the street the church sat like a fat toad digesting its midday meal. In the other direction the road converged with another, as dusty but wider. In front of the one cantina their almost-new Ford sat where they'd locked and left it while they explored the town. Beneath him, within reach of his fingers, were his two children. Beside him his wife, chanting in her deep, elocution-lesson voice. It annoyed him that she would not agree with him, that she had to remain herself, placidly stubborn, as unable to catch and trap in logic as the waters of a pond. It annoyed him, yet entwined with the annoyance was a desire for her, a thirst to fling himself upon her, fiercely. The more angry he got, the fiercer his love and the more of hers she returned. He shook his head. Someday the churches had to be torn down. He and Kay would celebrate by making love. In the church itself he would like to have made love. But Kay, he knew, wouldn't. Ghosts of old superstitions still shadowed her mind.

They drove slowly. Near the river the wind lifted fine sand into wrinkles that skimmed across the windshield in front of them. Kay fed Harriet a bottle; Brooks stood on the back seat. There wasn't a bridge across the river except at San Luis so they had to drive south, away from Yuma, in order to cross. Rud sat erect, both hands on the steering-wheel, his eyes caught up in the network of wrinkles that had begun to crease his features. He was thinking about the church, Kay knew, and about her insouciance.

As they pulled into San Luis, she suggested they stop and have supper. He pulled up to park in front of the only white-tablecloth restaurant. There were no curbs nor sidewalks; a few wooden, old-fashioned hitching rails ran the length of the block. Most of the cars angled against it had American license plates. He opened the door for her and swung Brooks to the ground. Between the restaurant and the adjacent store, half-a-dozen peons were crouched around a tamale vendor's butane stove. Several others had tourist goods — pottery, pinatas, brownsugar candy — spread out on blankets. Kay, with little Harriet cradled in her arms, stopped to peer at their offerings. Behind them, a block beyond the restaurant, the bells in a church steeple gonged with echoing, metallic dissonance. Rud straightened and frowned into the unpleasant sound. Kay bent closer to one of the vendors, a heavy, middle-aged woman with a flat, broad face who was selling candies stamped into the shape of Christian crosses. For a shawl she had a fragment of khaki wool wrapped around her shoulders; it looked like it might once have been a U.S. army blanket. Her hair, pulled away from her face and fastened tightly at the neck, was coarse but dull and brown-tinted. Her eyes did not pull away from Kay's examining curiosity. Instead, they pressed their weight against the American woman, a weight unexpectedly buoyant, empty, without substance of any kind, like a perception of autumn or awareness of an uninhabited room.

"**Que chulitas** . . ." Kay whispered, withdrawing slightly. Behind her she heard — sensed — the rasping of men's voices and the staccato retaliation of a woman's pain. Apparently, they were following an animal dragging itself along the unpaved walk. As she stepped back, seeking Rud and Brooks and tightening her grip around Harriet, her eyes flashed against a familiar impish face, and she gasped.

"Rud!" — her call instinctive as she pointed towards a tiny, bandy-legged twist of a man curled against the building's cornerpost. Propped between his knees was a wooden figure — not the same one they had seen in the church but one like it — with huge ears, a pointed chin, an expression of pained constipation. "Look!" Kay repeated, lifting her hand. The little man raised his eyes to her attention and bobbed forward extending the figure. But the crowd around the animal had pushed between them. From separate sides, she and Rud peered over hunched, twisting shoulders to see what was attracting attention.

It was not an animal. A young woman was groveling through the dust. Her right arm and right leg were lashed together with rawhide, her foot in front of her left leg, her hand behind it. Her pained, puzzled face had been battered and scraped, her lips were swollen and one eyelid was clotted with dried blood. In her free hand she clutched beads and a crucifix. An old woman with a face like knotted vines was crouched over her, moaning and making the sign of the cross. A man stepped forward and kicked the girl. She wallowed away from him, shaking her black, matted hair, and through her swollen lips whispered "**gracias, gracias.**"

"No! God- . . ! dammit! dammit!"

Rud shoved the cluster of onlookers aside. "Get away!" he shouted in English. "**Vete! vete!**" in Spanish. He grabbed the woman's ankle and tried to yank at the rawhide knot but she twisted away, "**No! por favor! por favor! no! no!**" in hurt, uncomprehending cadences. Again he tried to untie her, and again she twisted and struck at him with her free hand, her head, her teeth.

"Rud!"

Despite the baby in her arms, Kay shoved forward and clutched Rud's shirtsleeve. Some of the onlookers were laughing.

"The fools! the stupid fools!" Rud cursed as he backed away, fists clenched, mouth agape. "Oh! the fools!" But instead of sobs, laughter choked his throat and made his shoulders jerk, "fools! fools! fools!"

The girl rolled away and frightened, pained, propped herself on her hands next to the candy vendor. She looked like an animal spavined for slaughter. The vendor glanced down, blinked; she did not move her hands from her lap, but her eyes filled with tears, and she pulled her lips tight against her teeth. The little woodcarver elbowed in beside her, his carving pushed towards Kay's face. "**Lo compra usted? lo compra usted?**" in bouncy, birdlike syllables.

"No!" she heard Rud cry. The churchgongs were clanging again. Lifting her eyes to face her husband, Kay saw a contorted, angered man, fiercely virile, intensely proud, his strong blond face torn with frustration, with hate. His son, behind him, blinked with puzzled, frightened incognizance. In front, a woman, torn, bruised, beaten, inwardly unable to break whatever drove her to self-torture. And a woman blank, ungiving, so totally passive she could not lift her hand.

"Rud!" Kay called through noise that to her sounded like the cresting and pounding of waves, "take him away, it's true! it's true!" And with her white smooth fist she struck the little man's leering, hunchbacked elf. As it fell, it cracked one spindly leg and glared up at her, carved lips twisted into a grin of constipated lifelike humor, as though, in its wizened, wooden mockery, it saw something that neither she, nor her husband, ever would understand.

Barbara Mor

mustang ranch

his heavy back
& screendoor creak
of #2 van

in the middle of deserts
dusty time-center
where the sun
rides the sky / tight & hard
to break it

his thick back
white shirt
levis / wide belt
cowboy boots
cologne / hair still wet
from a shower

trucks in the corral
& silence everywhere
except the wind /
scratching sand
in the lizard noonlight

heavy man / square-back
flesh cinched too tight
threshold scrape
of #2 van
screendoor bang
in the middle / of nowhere

man / entering fuck
on the windswept range

* * * * *

the girls line up
present themselves
        i'm choo choo
        i'm darlene
        i'm sugar
        i'm china doll

wall-to-wall
wine-colored shag rug
black vinyl chair
for the customer

the girls in babydoll
nightgowns / or
tight pants & sweater
or dragon kimono

        i'm patti cake
        i'm lila
        i'm texas sue
        i'm tiger rose

& the girls call their sex
it / take me big man
i do it good

he chooses
tall blond sugar
follows along the knotty-pine
papered / corridor

no windows in the van
dim table lamps / day shut out
but the girls
can hear
wheels / pulling up outside

most clients / have
a regular shcedule

a radio wd carry
thru the bedroom walls
they read magazines / do nails
talk low /
dream of futures

well if he wants it
let him pay for it /
why should i
give it away free

choo choo swears

she always
enjoys it / sure its my job
but i get my kicks

& his heavy back
in the narrow doorway
of bedroom #4

sugar beyond / undressing
sweater over head

room a little bigger
than a double-bed
& the door shuts / with a metal click
like a train / compartment

& sometimes / the trailer rocks
in the big winds
from the range / beyond

                    *   *   *   *   *

all roads lead here
all xtian highways / all business
avenues /
all western routes

run to this target
a windswept desert
2 custom vans / where the girls wait
car corral / & office

motel-brothel
fucks on wheels
cunt-stop / in the wasteland
on the trail
of no tears

thirsty men /
eyes of blown sand
cowboys / at the end
of a dirty roundup

salesmen / travelling thru
with junk loads

& small-time winners
all time losers

feel wind wrap around
the tired body
like an arm / & maps
in the ditches /
lay them down

the skins despair
finds an answer
here / women
free of bodies

who can sell / their bodies
who can say /

it / & the lost world
never was

& the half-naked man
rides / his badlands
dream
boots & levis / on the shag rug

for a few minutes
for a few bucks /
& then walks out
into the all-cleansing / wind

the late noon-eye
glaring still
& grit / in his teeth

*   *   *   *   *

& the wind knows it
the wind / blows it
the wind wraps it
all around

desert-space / desert-time
the sun-spit sound /
of dust growing

& did you get it
did you get any
yeh i got it
yeh, yeh / its not bad

the god of wrath / & good deals
bites yr dollar / collects it
like yr scum
rings it up / on the wind

payment / on a life-loan
the whore thrown in
between men / 2 beers
wash it down

& the wind /
blows it all away
in the end / anyway / when the moon
on the desert / sucks

& the bones / lay on top
like dry straws
& the bitter-mouth taste
alone / is left

mans kiss /
on the barren flesh-range

& will you do it
sure i do it good
man / i dont give
it away / free

& the wind sees it
the wind has known / its touch
the wind grinds it down
& spreads it / far

& the wind whistles
it back /
& the wind / has moaned it
& the wind scours it /
on the tearless / sky

it
it
it
it /

el centro motel / heading east

el centro motel   10 a.m.
beige room / bed / tv / closed blinds
shower stall
95º in the shade / outside the door
& beyond that cars burn
in the melting lot / & beyond that
the suns desert highway
cactus posts / of tall heat
on the lizards trail

inside / no difference
between the room / & the morning
beige fan hum / & the tubes
dream / of women screaming
the game show mirage
thru electric desert air
in the tiled shower / rain
unreal as the skins cleansing

potato chips / soggy fries left
from the tired night before
predawn crash / on the anonymous bed
on the border /
of the suns flare
its solid style of rising
over the naked dust floor
like the eye / of the gila
the diamondbacks desire

& here / sipping cold water
in motel paper cups / & one glass
of childs milk
& munching chips / while the tv buzzer
rings / & the housewife squeals
& the red hot prize / is won
& won again
click dial / from channel to channel
& the mindless shrieking / is the same
& the kids whine / about the heat
that is not even yet / begun

& thru the blind slats /

50 false horizons
a maid in starched white / jangles keys
& vacuums the door mat
where wandering footsteps
as in sand / are crossed
& checked out / & crossed again
you will step out this door
to enter / the suns blood game
questions & hungers / in white veins
of real fire

& tonight the wind will shriek
in every channel / of the sand
& before that / yr eyes will melt
into blazed images
of the afternoon
face of the original desert / sun scream
& dried up dreams / of the rivers
passing across yr eyes film /
into the tortoise-calm crawl /
of the brain

into the old land
of the skins birth / the absolute challenge
of silent terrain
heat at dawn / & the nights nude coolness
the only prize /
that is won & won

Leonard Bird

THE MOURNING DOVE

for those who bow down
before the A.E.C.

1.

Yucca Flats: 3:20 AM. July 7, 1957:
Jury-rigged along a desert trench
half a mile long, loudspeakers growl:
"Break ranks. Enter the trench."
And eight hundred marines crawl down
into one trench, six feet deep, a grave
for innocence, dug by machines
designed to claw sewer lines.
We stand within the trench, stand and shiver,
stand and wait, for the word, for the dawn,
for seventy kilotons of fractured atoms.

2.

3:40 AM. Again the static-filled crackle:
"Gas masks in place. Breathe deep to check
the filter. Inspect the man behind."
3:45: "Down on one knee. Pull your jacket
over your mask. Cover your face.
Bury your face in your crossed arms."
And wait. For the word. For the dawn. For the bomb.

Wait for the demented twist of that magic
gift Prometheus stole for man. Wait for man
to untwine the Alpha and Omega
to render his brilliant apocalypse.
3:59. "One minute to detonation
and counting: 55, 54, 53 . . ."
Four thousand yards from ground zero,
from that Faustian tower about
to imitate the sun, our brains constrict.
Our energies condense to cold sweat.

"5, 4, 3, 2, 1 . . ." A split second
that lasts a thousand years. And then

379

the white light, brighter than the desert sun,
burns through jackets rolled across taut faces,
burns through smoke-gray eyes of grotesque masks,
burns through pink tissue squinted shut, and burns
a nightmare image on the retina.

3.

Again we wait. An eternity of silence
before the great KA-BOOM that rolls
across the buckling earth, a roll as slow
and deep as all the cannons of the world
massed for one last orgasm of war,
massed to celebrate the oft-prolonged
departure of a demented species.

We wait.. Again we wait, cowering
in that constricted pit that borders hell.
And then: an alien voice that jars minds
gone blank, the Titan voice growls: "Stand up and face
ground zero. Watch the fireball. Watch the fireball.
Watch the fireball. . . ."

We stand, eyes riveted upon
the orange-black cloud. We stare,
green automatons wired to the ball of dust
that mushrooms toward the stratosphere.
Slowly   like a great bubble of muck,
the fireball swells   and swells   and swells,
rises   bloated   through the torn sky.

And then the winds begin, triggered by
the great cloud of bile that personifies
the eons of man's progress around the circle
from cave to cave. Our mouths hang open.
Our eyes stare. Necks crane back until they
almost snap, as that orange mushroom obscures
the morning stars, blots out the sky,
then rains back upon the glowing earth
its man-concocted curse.

4.

And once again, down the labyrinth of time,
that torn ghost howls. And that speaker

still blares: "About face. Turn from the fireball.
Turn and leave the trench." That growl cracks
the stillness of hypnosis. The frozen line
breaks, and eight hundred pale marines
wriggle from the frothing trench.

I placed my hands upon the ledge and twisted
from the trench, just as the pale sun, not quite
obscured by a gray scrim of atomic dust,
rose above the far ridge. But as my head
rose above the rim, my outstretched hand grasped
the soft, spastic form. And as I touched, I saw
the bleeding dove, its feathers blasted by that
man made sun. A torn Mourning Dove flopped,
twitched from spasm to spasm, its wings singed black.

I smelled the stink of charred flesh, a stench
as old as life, but rendered fresh by the wrath
of Progress run amuck: Verdun, Warsaw,
Auschwitz, Hiroshima, Nagasaki,
and a hundred waiting towns whose tightly
woven strands of life our brilliant future
will too soon unwind.

5.

That dove's melted eyes oozed gray pus.
And from a throat that had sung men awake
since the dawn of time bubbled a faint
squeek   squeek   squeek.

That mangled dove still smoulders, radium
etched upon my brain. In my twisted dreams
that squeeking dove again becomes
the Holy Ghost, whose gray tears are shed
for man, for *Homo Ludens*, whose mad games
will some-day self destruct.

John Brandi

San Ignacio, 31 Dec.

from **Baja California Journals**

Old year ends in an oasis. Good omen. Figs, dates, olives, vegetables. Bougainvilleas leap over mud ovens. Thorn bramble fences outside a whitewashed village under the rising moon. Vultures soar in the twilight; cardinals & canaries sleep in villagers cages. People brush by me, hardly touching the ground. Plaza hung with colored bulbs. Man with beat-up saxophone in an adobe doorway. White geese, prussian-blue ponds. A burro goes Auuh-heee in the breeze. I think of Vincent, his olive orchards. How he demanded the **site;** to be there, to **feel** the vision, working directly on the spot; letting the landscape soak through. He thought the singular eye of the camera produced optical illusions. Wrote to his brother for more paints.

Calm night. Good for thinking back. Today a woman filled our truck with bluegreen gas from a glass-dome pump. This evening my brother asks me if I'm "against progress?" General question; it angers me at first. No safe answer. I think of the depleteable energy source that got us here; recall the flight of the vultures over San Ignacio, the air currents, the sunlight off desert stones. I ponder the romantic glow of kerosene lamps at home, the ugly fuel we burn. It all remains confusing, inbetween. A generation in transition. Did we learn from wood, whale oil, coal, gasoline? Now uranium; & strip-mine fed powerplants, useless in a few decades, that don't burn clean. I refer my brother to Emerson's essays on nature & say, yes, in an esoteric sense, I'm for "progress"; but that I'm wholly against the misuse of technology. Can't rely on what leaves us with unrecyclable wastes produced within systems of fast-profit at the expense of man/earth organisms. Don't understand government science which tears us away from nature, raping non-renewable resources at the price of global chaos, planetary imbalance. I'm against what gets in the way of our mammalian nature, what distracts & closes us off from our neighbor; whatever places inward/outward senses out of adjustment; whatever prohibits us from retaining "the spirit of infancy even into the era of manhood."

Few days back I uneasily faced the boundary: police, passports, customs. Nobody ever feels comfortable at borders. Even those that work them aren't sure what they're doing, protecting, defending; or which side is which. A sometimes exciting, often boring, easy paycheck, that's all. Plus the access to confiscated goods. Even though I knew it was coming, I was surprised at the "progress" the Mexican government had made on their side of the line. Huge new straight-line highway to LaPaz, cutting through the contour of the land at the expense of the innocent taxpayer. Barbed wire & all. Immediately I thought of myself as a kid, pulling up survey stakes in orange groves along what is now a maze of concrete. Why two roads where one would do; a trail replaced by high-speed killer asphalt when the former served equally well?

And now what? Blow up the roads? Pull up more stakes? Go back to my books & garden, utopian ideals centered within the false security of isolationist self-sufficiency? No solace, no answer. "Privacy" is a kind of mania that ends consuming itself to sustain itself. **—I don't give a damn about the outside world? I don't need anybody?—** Since when has the flower survived without the bee, man without flower, meat without leaf, the leaf without the energy output of a sunspot? Nothing can be dissected into one single self. On one level or another evolution implies co-operation, individual life-systems joined in social organisms, cells symbiotically associated, pooling intelligence, submitting new inventions for survival in the course of their relationship.

James Cody

NEEDLES

See America the old way.
Take a freight train.
Too hot to breathe in Needles, CA,
     facing another day in the desert,
the waitress said,
     "You'll burn up out there, just get in the shade."
Bus from Barstow to Needles
Greyhound man at Needles said,
     "I wouldn't take a check from my own father."
I said,
     "Jesus."
The temperature a hundred and ten at 9 p.m.
and breathing hard
       walked three miles in the sun today.

the sign said,
          "no freeway."
I turned back the other direction
went down a side street,
afraid to show my fear to passing cars,
          "I'm gonna die in the sun."
I looked down on my left
          saw a freight train moving along.
He came to a stop,
            as if to say,
            "Come on."
I walked that train a few blocks and   no box cars.
Then I saw a car hauling automobiles.
And remembered seein' an article somewhere that said,
          "that's the best way to ride a freight."
The first two cars I tried were locked,
and then I found one, a Chevy Vega,
          with the door open
Pulled my pack up off the ground
          and my brief case.
Didn't dare have train move without a place to hide.
I lay down waiting for the train to move
in 20 minutes I was rolling over the Rio Colorado   Rio Colorado!!!!

Clickety clack, clickety clack, Columbus brought a new mother back.
Swing out over the Mojave
          to Kingman, Seligman, Williams, Flagstaff
                    You can tell you're in Flagstaff.
                              Flagstaff is a wall of trees.
Too early for Albuquerk.
          "Comin' into Albuquerkee
          bringin' in a couple o' key"

                    to the world.
A bundle of *Wood Ibises, Desert Reviews, Huidobros.*
smuggled in by way of hardass country.
train stopped, birds sing in the field.
Winslow and the Little Colorado

                    Oraibi Wash
                    Canyon de Chelly

                    Painted Desert
                    Window Rock

                    Do I belong here?

384

Gallup
        two miles, El Morro
        "stay down there, boy.
        they'll gallup over you in Gallup."
"AnacondA Copper Co." in letters 100 ft. high. Dust and smoke
                boiling out of the mountains.
AnacondA strips the old ones
                in North America, too, Pablo.
Moving across the desert
I realize that you will always be los Estados Unidos
        afraid and hard.

Navajo woman, tending sheep
log hogan
cliffs well spaced
    sheep in between
I see an old Indian man out there
in the broad bowl of the earth
sitting on a rock.
drinking buckwheat honey
eating Matza and spam.
"Go Navy,"
says the sign to young desert Navajos and Hopi
buffalo grass.
GRANTS.

Albuquerque, 62 miles.
Albuquerk!
I figgered this'd be the right train.
Elevation and road right for Needles and Albuquerk.
                A preacher told an old Indian man that he
                was goin' to a place where there was sin and
                per-dition and did he know where that place
                was?
                        "Albuquerk."
Figgerd I'd make it.
Thought I might end up in Ogden, Utah or Phoenix
        Going home from San Francisco
        Go South.
        Going nowhere.
        From ....
or Mexico,
        or El Paso-
            that'd be all right.
But South, no North
now.

Mesas. Cattle.

A little rain.

Getting out and pissing on the side of the car.

                    in the day
                    hope nobody sees you.
woman who gave me a ride to Victorville
said,
                    "Mexico is a fantastic place to hitch."
She also said,
                    "Nobody ever gives a ride in the desert."
Seven mustangs.
Pueblos.

New Mexico has the most distinctive rainclouds in the world.
They move across the land, a curtain of water,
                    60 miles wide and three thousand feet up.
Rio Puerco.

Near Albuquerque the land thins out.
no towns, no refuse, no roads.
open plains, medium desert.
          High Country.

Looking down from the mesa we're on,
the desert wet, a pool.
Is water coming back to Aztlan?
Will the heron return?
In Texas, my home, more rain than any other year this century.
1100 years later,
will the old people come back?
Who are the *new* people?
Am I Viracocha?
Do I go home?

Ken McKeon

SMUDGING

1.

Going on to get some rest.
Not so, always the man
            with the marking words
to challenge the finest weather.
Not even winter cleanly escapes,
ice only on the highest ridges,
Ground frozen rarely if at all
here in the orchards.
But now, we smudge:
twenty men up all night
with the oil rising into fire,
tramping back home after dawn;
boots in the corner, wife with the children,
sleep till noon if it's Sunday.

2.

You bastards, blossoms
moist white balls squeezed into petals,
stamen tipped by gold,
all set on a waxed green
    bunch of leaves.
Rip your goddamned birth
out of the land,
smoke you out for houses,
give Florida the business.

Jane Kopp

L.A.

Here you are, your famous
acrid air
brown
as toilet water

your grinding freeways
freaky, ostrich
palms
loud, vulgar
(and I will say, irresistible)
bargains

beaches at Venice
acrawl
with your angry poor
afros
like Rorschach blots
promenading

one old hotel
its brick still white
or barely golden

delicate
terra cotta flowers
above each window

(that such a touch here
ever seemed right)

for four days
on your sidewalks
dodging
your young men strangely old

your Mansons
careening on skateboards
("We kill" chalked
on all your beach walls)

what a beauty

I keep thinking

you must have been

just the sight of you
tears springing
to the eyes

your shore itself and the sea
still entirely young
still divine

Leslie Silko

PRAYER TO THE PACIFIC

1

I traveled to the ocean
                distant
                        from my southwest land of sandrock
                        to the moving blue water
                Big as the myth of origin.

                2
        Pale
        pale water in the yellow-white light of
                                sun   floating west
                                        to China
                                where ocean herself was born
Clouds that blow across the sand are wet.

                3

Squat in the wet sand and speak to Ocean:
        I return to you   turquoise   the red coral you sent us,
                        sister spirit of Earth.
Four round stones in my pocket   I carry back the ocean
                to suck and to taste.

4

Thirty thousand years ago
        Indians came riding across the ocean
        carried by giant sea-turtles.
Waves were high that day
        great sea turtles waded   slowly   out
           from the grey sundown sea.
Grandfather Turtle rolled in the sand   four times
        and disappeared
           swimming into the sun.

5

And so   from that time
        immemorial
           as the old people say
rainclouds drift from the west
        gift from the ocean.

6

Green leaves in the wind
Wet earth on my feet
        swallowing raindrops
           clear from China.

The Southwest and its spirit are not defined by state lines, for geography, climate, and the human experiences bound up with them elude such things. We present, therefore, a *Coda* to our southwestern offerings, a natural opening-out from an ancient part of earth that knows no rigid boundaries, so long as there are men and women conscious to comprehend and love it.

William Matthews

Above the Aquarius Mine, Ward, Colorado

for Rich Jörgensen

My dog clatters up a talus pile. Is there a keystone, that when he steps on it will organize a slide?
The thin air hasn't got to him yet. He pranks down
toward us, stiff in his forelegs but his head's not back,
it's jutted toward us and his tail goes in circles like
a pump-handle, he's dancing as if there'll always be
enough water, enough air.
    We trudge up a swale, happy, 9500 feet. Locusts
clack past. One makes its first stroke just as it passes
my ear: it sounds like a bowstring let go.
    As we near the ridge the view drops away. We go out
onto a promontory and stare over the trough. Just as I
turn to go back down, a locust, going the other way, loops
over my shoulder, over the edge. My dog's so tired he
slinks back down. He looks as if he's claimed this place
in the name of something he's ashamed of, now that he's
done it, but he's only tired and keeping close to the
ground, wherever it goes.

Glenna Luschei

from THE BLACK HILLS

1.   Landmark

Eyes dark circles
Hubcaps   thermos bottles

The Thoen Stone,
South Dakota:

Came to these hills in
1833 seven of us
all ded
but me

I have lost my gun
and nothing to
eat and indians
hunting me

My kids are yelling from the car.
The horizon reels like a telephone wire.

Victor Contoski

PRAIRIE WIND

Spirit over the land

hot breath
bending the wheat

filling the sails
of prairie schooners

huge empty ships
of the kingdom of nothing

the Pinta
the Nina
the Santa Maria

driven far out into space
by great solar winds
and the rush of blood
in the ears of the captain.

Robert Peterson

Wingwalking in Oregon

Last Sunday petrified
on Bridal Veil, a beginner's climb,
trail no wider than a carton of Kents.
Nice cliff & Eiffel view
for families
fresh from church. But
goosed by heights, how can I
embrace the sublime
without a priest
& no goddam fence?

And now
Saddle Mountain,
called benign.
Trail this time
half a loaf of bread
& the scenery true
until I find
I'm looking over the edge
of Oregon
into the depths of Idaho & potatoes,
breadcrumbs, birds & diseases of birds,
starch in the blood, playground donkeys,
slides, songs & other conveyances
of my childhood
& if somehow
I let go
& spider down
concentrated & green
what should I, if alive but above all
safe, remember, & to whom
will I complain?

Les Standiford

Making Sheriff

You are the sheriff. You are L.C. Bodie, the sheriff of Cherkin County, and you spend most of your time in the seat of Cherkin County, which is Bullfish. There are not many people in the county and fewer in Bullfish, 700 in the last census, and nobody questioned the count. You sometimes wonder if there will ever be very many people in the town, knowing for sure there won't, but you wonder anyway, sometimes thinking about what Bullfish would be like big, eight or ten thousand, and sometimes you think about what could ever bring very many people up to a bare-ass corner of North Dakota in the first place.

Too far from the cities to get a factory. No more ranch land. No way to make it farming, and that wouldn't bring many besides. No freeway, no airport, no railroad close enough. Recreation? Not likely. Everybody drives fifty miles just to swim in the summer, and there's no cover for anything bigger than jackrabbits in the whole county. Maybe an oil strike, or a gold mine . . . but there just ain't no way, and there's no chamber of commerce in Bullfish.

There is one farmer's oil and gasoline co-op north on the main street, one farm implement dealership south toward the town line where you either turn the cruiser for another swing through town or park and wait for drunk Indians on the nights just after welfare goes out, and there's a store between them that sells staple items like overalls, gloves, groceries, and carry-out beer.

On the east side of the street there are two beer bars and one combination restaurant, liquor bar, and hotel. The hotel part does the least business, the restaurant a little more, and the bar does more than both put together and added to the tractor outfit, general store with its gas pumps, beer bars, and grain storage elevators down by the tracks. The liquor bar is the only one in a thirty mile radius and the reservation being so close doesn't hurt. You sometimes wonder what those Indians would do if they didn't drink, but you don't worry about it much because they're harmless for the most part, drunk or not.

Except for the one time Ken Two-Sheep drove his pickup through the side of the church of a Saturday night. And nobody really got upset about that, seeing as how Ken and some of his boys came in and fixed the hole in time for the next Sunday. The Lutherans sent a letter of thanks to the Bureau of Indian Affairs, not mentioning the crack in one stained glass window near the hole, and everybody forgot the incident. Ken didn't come around for a long time after, you remember.

And, you come to think of it, that's the only trouble you've had with the Indians in ten months as the sheriff. Furthermore, that's just fine with you. They leave you alone, you'll leave them alone, which is just about the guiding philosophy for the general way you handle the sheriff's job. Which in this part of the country is the way folks like it. That's what they told you when you took the job for $550 a month and legitimate expenses, not as much as cruiser duty pulls in Grand Forks, but a far sight better than beating up dust on 100 acres of long gone prairie farm. Not so bad for two years of police science in Minot.

And there's more about you, sure, a lot you don't even know yourself, and some you'll find out as time passes, but right now what you know for sure is that spring is taking its good old time coming to North Dakota, your breath is still hanging in the evening air, and your hands are warmer in your jeans than they are in the sheepskin jacket. Spitting on the macadam by the general store pumps, you think you'll get in the car and drive out toward the reservation.

Gone to St. Paul, Minnesota, just to get away from Minot and a college he never liked, Sheriff-in-training on-vacation L.C. Bodie lifts his head off the floor and spits a slug of blood from the back of his mouth. His lips, puffed and rubbery from the hardest punch he's ever been hit, flatten out with the force, and the blood and spit spray over his pearl button shirt, his powder-blue levis, his high lift boots, the unfamiliar beer and ashes floor. His tongue runs over numb teeth, checking for a gap, and settles back, no spaces, no ragged edges. If there is anything he ever wanted to do, it is lay back down. He does not feel from his forehead to his chin. Someone has rebuilt his face with cement. It must look bad. The girl with silver hair rigid around her head looks with a grimace and turns back to the bar. The bartender watches over her shoulder, frowning. He will wait for this cowboy to get up before he calls the police.

L.C. Bodie is no quitter. He puts his right hand palm down on the floor and shifts his weight to that side. He is slowly pushing himself off the floor, his muscles knotting in reflex. His face is numb, dentist-shot, and his eyes do not answer to the job at hand. They stray, drawn to the silver helmeted girl who grabs her purse; she is running already. The bartender has thrown down his towel and is lifting the phone to a scowling face. His mouth twists even as he dials. The juke box does not play, but its rainbow riff runs up and down the mirror; there was a movie like those colors once in Bullfish — Walt Disney, maybe.

He sees the narrow square toe of the boot, a pointed toe had it run on another inch, sees it lift past his eyes even before he feels the shock at the square of his chin. In that instant of weightlessness that means his brain has left its mounts at the bottom of his skull and is shooting toward the ceiling, straining all its ties at the base, he sees the boot sail on, up into the black sky, cold and empty, a bit of flesh on the tip of the boot, the moon rushing, a pinpoint of light at first, growing as it comes,

398

the size of a quarter, a plate, spreading, covering his face in a bath, shooting through him, leaving him black, empty.

Now the back of his head roaring, rubbing, tiny stabs of pain there, his feet in the air, his arms dragging the floor above his bouncing, rumbling head, gathering splinters, his shirt bunching tighter under his armpits, his chin, as they pull him out. The cold air runs down his legs as his feet enter the night, a jolt crossing the jamb on his back, the neon above his face in narrow profile against a strange eastern sky, the stars are washed out.

On the cement there by the gutter his head soaks up the cold. The cars cover him with a soft whir, a gentle fog of burning gasoline and oil, dust of rubber, asbestos. Someone has puked beside his head, he can smell if fresh. Sucking it back down when he breathes, he knows it is himself. Far above, soft grey felt against the black sky, his hat is spinning, turning over and over now like a tumbleweed bouncing off a rock in the prairie wind, soaring on, out of sight, into the street. There is a soft sound of landing; it lulls him. He sees boots pause by his head, hesitate, then step into the street. Now his hat rests like a pet on his chest. He is wondering if the man hit him for the silver capped girl. He never saw his face.

He remembers now his open fly, she had introduced herself. Wondering if his fly is open, he moves his hand from the glittering cement to his belt. Working up the leather to the silver cow's head of ruby eyes, slowly, feeling down, it is open. He lifts his head to see and turns out the lights.

L.C. Bodie, nine years old and youngest of three brothers, rides on the back of a farm wagon, legs dangling, sounds of the tractor behind him sailing in bursts over his head and toward the house like the field swallows that rush out of sight at the yellow edge of the plain where it gives to the sky. As he watches, squinting into the cloudless light, the dark house bounces its second story above the horizon once, twice, then is gone, a small dot swallowed by the rising hill.

His brothers lie stretched in the sun at the head of the wagon, hayseed dancing around the long thin bodies in the vibration of the springless platform. Jerry is home after four years fighting a war in the Pacific Ocean, the rippling scar on his shoulder a deeper red in the sun. He has not mentioned the war to L.C. Middle brother Danny has not asked either. He was the family exemption, graduated from high school last spring. L.C. is nine, and he sits far at the back of the wagon on his way to the last of the baled hay.

His father drives the tractor steadily, without haste. Haying is not a hurry-up job, it only breaks your back when you start thinking you will ever get it all done. L.C., though spared the heaviest of the labor, remembers his father's advice every day of this last week of sun and heat. The sun is higher on this second trip of the day, but a good afternoon's work means the end of it, the rest of Saturday and Sunday without stacks of hay that never end, stretching off to blend into the yellow fields and the heat and the sun.

His brothers show a tan on their backs as deep as the burn on their father's neck. L.C. wears a t-shirt everyday, and his arms and neck are circled with tan that leaves his chest and back whiter in contrast. The wagon rumbles on and L.C. picks up a splinter in his bottom as he slowly vibrates toward the edge of the wagon. He shifts his weight on his hands.

A mile or so to the east he sees the power line poles that mark the path of the road to the house. The poles lie black on the bleached backdrop, the hills that rise slowly beyond the fence there. At the crest of the highest rise, a line of scrub cedar silhouette against the sky like a string of camels stationary on the ridge. L.C. thinks of the wise men and their journey through the desert. In the heat the camels move back and forth, restless in the waves of heat rising from the fields.

The tractor pauses, then drops a gear and L.C. throws his hands palm down to brace himself. The field rises here and the tractor crawls up the incline. The nails in the wagon bed burn cold in his palms and he lifts his hands to his thighs. He squints into the white light and wipes drops of sweat from his hairline. The dry yellow field drops steadily behind him.

Now the house climbs onto the horizon above the last swell, a dot that gathers and fades on the blurred edge of the sky. So far away it seems more an idea, the memory of shade and water, a sense of ease. L.C. finds it hard to picture the house for a moment. He thinks of boards faded to a grey-tinged yellow, a pile of sandstone for the unfinished walk — and then the flash of light from the speck on the dancing line between sky and dry field, a beam that closes the distance as if the house itself had sprung up on the rise just past. It is the sun bouncing from the galvanized porch roof, firing the picture in L.C.'s mind, somehow like the television he's never seen, the house stark on the plain, two stories and a slate roof, a rare frame house in a land without trees, every window an eye on that flat land, watchful from the first light, waiting, like a cat by a knothole. Porch with glider and rocker and dusty, burred-up dog. The sandstone walk leading five steps into the brittle grass. The twin chimneys on either end holding the house between, smoke rising from the stack to the south, fed from the kitchen. Clothes are boiling today.

The flash again, but not brilliant, more like a mirror or a rifle, the field dips and levels, and now the speck is gone. L.C. falls back on the shifting platform, the grain of the wood searing outside the short coolness his shadow had cast. The nailheads burn at his shoulder blades and he rocks from side to side until he can stand it, the light burning through his closed eyelids first red, and yellow, now white.

He is a prisoner of the sun and the heat, he cannot rise or roll; he cannot speak, open his mouth. The sweat forms a line splitting his chest and stomach, dives under his belt; it trickles from the point of his chin, and branching, circles his neck; it sprouts and chills in his armpits. He tries to turn his hand, but the palm refuses, locked with the rough grain of the heaving planks.

He hears the curse, senses the motion of the wagon even after it has stopped. He lurches up, drunkenly, dazed with the heat that flops automatically on the stationary wagon. The sound of the dying motor rolls slowly away toward the hills. L.C. slips to the ground. His t-shirt catches on a splinter and gathers tightly under his arms as his stomach meets the sun. The shirt rips as he pulls from the bed. The field pulses with the heat, swelling at the edges toward the sky. It is his head, slowly cooking.

"Damn!" His father's second curse, heavy, loathful, skids over the yellow field. The older boys stare at him bent over the tongue where the wagon grasps the machine. His father raises slowly, shaking his head from side to side as deliberately as he drove to that spot.

He looks up at the sky, pausing. "And did I bring my tools?" The older boys turn away from the old man with the grey stubble, his mouth twisting under the brim of the yellow straw hat. It wasn't a question for them. "Damn me to hell, NO, I didn't!"

L.C. turns from the ground at his feet. They are all staring at him, eyes inflamed, red and yellow from the heat, sweat dripping, mouths bent by the weight of the sun. He knows before his father works up the words.

"What do you want me to get?" He speaks to the baking ground by the wagon, wipes his hands on the front of the clinging t-shirt.

Sheriff L.C. Bodie, parked a mile or so on the Bullfish side of the reservation now, looks up from his magazine as the pickup whines by. The straining engine catches him, pulling twenty over, easy. He watches the taillights fade, swaying, down the black road as he turns the key. The big engine rumbles and shakes the cruiser like a dog waking up, too many horses for just any Biscayne Standard without the special handling package — heavy-duty shock absorbers, thick springs, torsion bars to hold the curves, an axle to take the torque of the oversized engine and fast starts off gravel shoulders — just like any other kid's car, Bodie thinks. In twenty seconds he has passed 100 and the wind does not sound at all, the engine has leveled out, comfortable at this speed, and Bodie watches as the lights of the pickup swim steadily toward him, red eyes in the ocean. He cruises silently at one hundred and ten miles an hour, pushing through the dark, a big fish.

Before his lights catch the pickup, Bodie eases back, and the car groans, dropping through the warp again into the rush of air, the sounds of machine doing eighty. The red dots of light grow steady in front of him and Bodie checks the speedometer. Sold only to peace officers, the gauge is accurate to plus or minus two miles per hour at speeds between zero and one hundred. Bodie is holding at eighty-two. A jackrabbit kicks out of the brush and commas himself across the road in the lights of the cruiser. Bodie does not hesitate and the faint shock comes to his hands.

At the training school he ran over a dozen or more, purposely driven under his wheels, until he learned to ignore them. One man told him they used dogs the year he drove the course, but Bodie wasn't sure. Cows and sheep he learned to stop for. Men had ridden in feet first covered with parts of range steer. The deer he simply hopes to miss. If not he will lose another front plate and two weeks while they build the front end back on his car.

Bodie decides it is time and presses the accelerator; in a few seconds he switches the flasher. The siren isn't necessary. He sees the broad rimmed hat bob, and watches the white truck as it slows in embarrassment, bouncing into the sandy strip of shoulder, still moving too fast. The dust boils up and the truck is a rolling cloud. Bodie eases in behind as the Indian moves carefully down from the cab.

When Bodie asks for the license, the man is careful to speak away from the officer's face. Still the smell of whiskey blossoms into the dry desert air like the promise of rain. Bodie reminds him that his license expires in less than a month. The man, grasping at straws, thanks him, eyes shining, assures Bodie he will see to it.

"You were doing eighty in a fifty-five mile zone back there, Victor."

"Waaal," the Indian draws out his syllable but offers no other excuse. While the officer walks back to his cruiser, the Indian leans against the idling truck, hands at the top of the bed; and, hat brim pointed toward the ground, he drops a ball of spit between his boots.

Bodie knows that the ticket will cost the Indian twenty-five dollars, maybe even his license. He remembers Victor from before, but forgets just how many times in the past two years. He gives the ticket to the Indian as if it were something dropped on the street, and the Indian, covering his mouth with his hand, thanks him.

A mile or so up the road, Bodie swings the cruiser across the narrow blacktop and stops on a gravel turnout with a trash can at its head. He kills the engine and switches on the light to finish his article. The fading engine sounds spread over the scrub and a bird explodes into the night. The author describes American youth as men of the year. Off in the flat a canyon owl calls and the mice scatter nervously through the sand. Bodie drops the magazine and turns off the light. There is a faint glow over Bullfish, fifteen miles to the south. Another twenty miles behind him he senses the impounded lake, calm and cold against its dam, marking the northern limit of his authority. He steps outside and closes the door softly. There is a stirring in the dry sage behind the car and he listens while the animal moves quickly away from the road. Two hours, more or less; maybe he will have a beer at the hotel. The night has settled. He can see every star in the sky.

Walking back to the house in the yellow heat of haying season, L.C. Bodie, nine years old, watches the top of the rise as it dances in his eyes. Slowly, dipping away at first, then steady, the house grows from the stubbled field. Sweat molds his t-shirt to his back and chest, and the chaff gathers in the folds of his neck, his inner arms. His nose is packed with dust and he works his nostrils rabbit-like sniffing and snorting to clear the way.

Clearing the rise, he sees the house sharply now, a few hundred yards away. He wipes his forehead with a grainy arm and watches the old shepherd lumber through the dry field toward him. The dog circles him, nose high and bobbing, then settles into a slow gait just behind, panting and hacking in the dry heat. His coat looks unbearable to L.C. and he tries to hurry away from the dog.

His mother looks with surprise when he rounds the back of the house where she is hanging the clothes.

"What's the matter?"

"I have to get Dad's tools." L.C. does not feel like wasting time. If he sits down he will not want to go back. His back itches from the chaff. He paces behind his mother.

She reaches for another pin to fasten the shirt she holds by one shoulder. She notices that the first of the shirts to hang is nearly dry. The boy paces behind her.

"Now sit down a minute. What's wrong?" The boy turns away, kicking at the dust as he walks. He does not look at her. She takes him by the arm and leads him toward the shed in surrender. She lifts the peg latch he cannot reach and the boy rushes into the dark stifling place. The tin roof draws the heat like a stove top.

Inside the boy scrambles through the wooden boxes, scattering the tools like a robber looking for the cash box. His mother stands by the door, watching. She brushes a stray band of greying hair back from her damp cheek. A breeze seems a fairy tale ending. The boy closes his fingers around the warm, thick handle of the hammer and he runs outside, sucking for good air.

His mother puts a hand to his sweating head and he ducks away. Her touch is uncomfortable in the heat. The dog dances haltingly in the dust, drool matting the hair on his chest and throat.

"Stay, Roger," L.C. says, and the dog slinks off to the shade of the porch.

"Glass of water?" his mother asks. L.C. hesitates, but thinks of his father and brothers sitting under the wagon, and shakes his head. He hurries around the house and his mother closes the door to the shed, replaces the peg, catches a splinter in her rough hand, puckered and softened by the water.

Walking down the side of the last dip, L.C. sees the wagon just across the trough, pinned to the scorched field by the sun. He flips the hammer in the air as he walks, catching the spinning handle as it bucks toward the ground. He sees the three forms stir under the wagon and as the rise blocks them out, his feet move into a trot down the last of the hill and across the bottom to the rising side.

As he climbs, a strength returns from somewhere and the fire on his skin subsides. His strides lengthen, take on spring, and when he clears the last rise, he is flipping the hammer twice over, the whip of the handle solid in his palm after every toss.

A hundred yards away, the three men rise as one and their shouts mingle senselessly as L.C. approaches. He smiles. They are cheering him in.

". . . Iver, Iver, Iver." The strange shouts wing over his head. As he walks, spinning the hammer, he feels it rolling toward him a little before he understands, like the storm water sounding down a dry wash. Suddenly it is on him. He stiffens and grips the hammer. The sun catches him again, puffs his flesh, drowns his eyes. The hay chaff digs into his arms, burns under his belt. He wants to lie down in the shade. Their arms are raised, fists clenched. The shouts are clear, angry. He slows his pace and the three advance, his father leading.

With the closing distance he sees the fury in his father's face. At the speed the man walks, he could not live a half-mile in this heat. L.C. stops and his father takes the last steps, his lips moving, searching for the words. His face is deeply red, sweat bursts in white blotches along his brow. His eyes are wild with the deep pressure. The brothers stand behind, mouths tight in disgust. They shake their heads.

L.C. holds the hammer like something dead and his father snatches it in a rush. He tilts his hat back with his free hand, showing the white band on his forehead, and he shakes the hammer in the boy's face. He breathes long, incredible breaths, the air rushing in and out his nose, straining, and finally he speaks, low, hatefully.

"I said screwdriver. **Screwdriver!**" He is losing control. "There's a thousand rocks out here for a hammer. I could have used your thick skull." The brothers fight a laugh, but the old man has not finished. He shifts his feet in agitation, crushing the stubble in a helpless fury, looks at their sheepish eyes, and turns back to the boy. The sweat, miraculously, has disappeared from the old man's head. The line of tan on his forehead is not so clear. The boy waits. The sun has him here.

With a quick motion the old man raises the hammer by its head and brings the hickory handle down sharply on the boy's head, easing up at

404

the last instant, so that the split opens only an inch or so, the blood trickles just a little, the boy does not even flinch it happens so quickly. The old man lets the last of his breath out in a snort, and turns back to the wagon. L.C. looks up but loses his father in the glare. He brushes his forehead with his grainy arm, sees that the blood is dry already and turns with sudden sea legs for home, tacking long angles across the yellow fields, head swelling now, a little blinded by the sun.

The two beer bars in Bullfish, North Dakota close early on week nights, trade usually falling off by ten. It is eleven-thirty now, and the low buildings are dark as L.C. Bodie circles them, his last official act of the night. He has written two tickets, read a magazine, and now he will have a beer at the hotel. Rounding the back corner of the second tavern, the cruiser lights wash over a sandy cat with wrapping paper in its jaws, and the animal dives into the weeds. Bodie drives on, stopping the car on the strip of dust between the asphalt highway and hotel porch, and leans to sign the log — L.C. Bodie — in a loose circling script, at the bottom of the page. Pulling the rasping felt pen from the paper, his hand brushes the thick wooden riot stick nestled in the seam of the seat by the open notebook. Dust thrown up by the wheels of the cruiser drifts through the window and fogs the air. Bodie works his nose against the cloud, and thinking of haying season, adds "—SHERIFF" to his name.

Diane Hueter

Josie's Poem

Mother
wash your face
let loose your hair
and come with me to the meadow

Up the hill to the pond
We could take off
all our clothes
glide like snakes
through the water
We could sit on our haunches
like frogs in muddy shallows
and trap the tiny ones
between our fingers

Mother
wash your face
take the tired knots
from your hair
now before the sun
goes down
we must see the cornfields
sparkle
one final wave of green

Judith Moffett

FOR WILLA CATHER

Now whatever I glimpse qualifies the vast
disc whose rim is the horizon. Past
cornfields rumpling to the world's edge
and over, past haystacks shaped into

great coarse-grained breadloaves,
I am driving alone across Nebraska. I
in my midget car am the circle's moving
center, the whole horizon slides west

with me as the highway slides under,
soil off a moldboard. Bicycle pince-nez
glinting, one aluminum camper after
another swings around me, outrageously

exceeding the dream-slow fuel-poor downward-
adjusted speed limit. My car, blue dot
humming through the trackless mirage-slow
sea of grass's memory, steadily

exceeds the/speed limit by so little
no cop could possibly care, and passes only
the fixed things I-80 ruts and gouges
itself among: wheatfields; beetfields;

old homesteads the first sodbusters built
soon as they could pay for lumber
hauled overland from the Missouri,
each house, barn, outbuilding

in its cottonwood windbreak rooted
against the right hunch of land long calm
decades before the Federal plowboy
leaned to his task. Their fitness here seems

absolute, but the contoured concrete furrow
curves at the doorstep now. I know, I always
know, that when I kill my pounding engine
at every halt for tea, the perpetual

wind, blind and baffled, too ancient
to change her ways, still will be ruffling
the highway's beautiful shoulder-length
thatch of blond weeds.

John R. Milton

THE LOVING HAWK

The eye sees only this: two planes

one glacial-faulted,
grassed by greening rains,
rippled in new winds;

one blue, half-arched
in polar curvature
lightly on distant rims.

Between, a lonely tree
resisting summer gusts
gropes rustling skyward,

grain elevators probe the sky,
mooring posts in search
of fattening clouds,

distant puffs of dust
hold a running horse
between quotation marks.

And this dimly:

one fieldmouse braving the blue air
brief-clawed and lifted
by its loving hawk.

AUGUST IS ABSTRACT IN THE NORTH

August flattens, like no other month,
Sprawled in geometry across the plains,

Yellowed, like a Mondrian, in ripening wheat
And dying grass. The mottled and muddied green

Of weeds fuzzes through like memory welling weakly
From the consciousness of May, a frightened rain

That dwindled in the dust. Therefore this mindless
Place lies hotly on the canvas, the earthy skin

Stretched taut between horizons blued in age
And distance far beyond the painter's summer brush.

And yet, this is a painter's place, whose abstract shape
Dries hard and tense before the sunburnt eye,
Inviting the imposition of redemptive form.

THE PROMISE OF A PLACE

The flatness need not prove
that the world is not round.
Stand at the junction of
wire fences and see the spokes
of an unseen wheel; it
is there; it circles in
the mind and it is real.

The emptiness does not
make us barren. Indian
bones have floated in old
trees reaching beyond the
shield of sky; farmers rest
beneath boulders they could
not move; with coyotes and
hawks relics are everywhere.

The land is bright and the
land is dark; unshaded
suns expose new poets
and old plows; trees drink at
rivers, Indian women
string their traders beads, and
once each year the promise
of snow is unbroken.

CONTRIBUTORS

PAULA GUNN ALLEN — poet, Lebanese-Sioux-Laguna; poems in *Four Indian Poets* (Dakota Press); book, *The Blind Lion* (Thorp Springs Press); native New Mexican, lives in Albuquerque.

BERT ALMON — poet; books, *The Return and Other Poems* (San Marcos Press) and *Taking Possession* (Solo Press); born in Port Arthur, Texas; has lived in New Mexico and in El Paso.

RUDOLFO A. ANAYA — writer; novels, *Bless Me, Ultima* (Tonatiuh International Publications) and *Heart of Aztlan* (Editorial Justa Publications, Inc.); native New Mexican, lives in Albuquerque.

VIRGINIA BALTZELL — poet; born in Rising Star, Texas, 1905; adaptations of oriental poetic forms to Southwestern subjects published in various magazines; lives in Stephenville, Texas.

JIM BARNES — poet, co-editor of *The Chariton Review*, anthologized in *Carriers of the Dream Wheel* (Harper and Row); part-Choctaw; lives in Kirksville, Missouri.

WILLIAM D. BARNEY — poet; books, *Kneel From the Stone* and *Permitted Proof* (Kaleidograph) and *The Killdeer Crying* (Prickly Pear Press); born in Tulsa, has lived in Fort Worth from the age of 12.

CHARLES BEHLEN — poet, co-editor of *Chawed Rawzin*; poems in *The Smith, Blackbird Circle, TAWTE,* and *Texas Portfolio*; anthologized in *Travois* and *The New Breed*; book, *Perdition's Keepsake* due from Prickly Pear Press; born in Slaton, Texas; paints houses in Lubbock.

MEI-MEI BERSSENBRUGGE — poet; chapbook, *Fish Souls* (Greenwood Press); book, *Summits Move With the Tide* (Greenfield Review Press); born in Peking, China; grew up in Cambridge and Framingham, Mass.; has lived in El Rito, New Mexico.

LEONARD BIRD — poet, editor of *Rocky Mountain Review*; book, *River of Lost Souls* (Tooth of Time Press); lives in Durango, Colorado, where he teaches at Fort Lewis College.

RODGER C. BIRT — photographer, teacher, scholar; photographic shows in Beirut, London, San Francisco; photographs in textbooks and magazines; widely traveled in the American Southwest and in Mexico; lives in San Francisco.

ROBERT BONAZZI — poet, prose-writer, co-editor of Latitudes Press; books include *Living the Borrowed Life* (New Rivers) and, with Carlos Isla and C.W. Truesdale, *Domingo* (Latitudes Press); raised in Houston, lives now in Austin.

JON BRACKER — poet; books, *Constellations of Clover* (Prickly Pear Press) and *Duplicate Keys* (Thorp Springs Press); grew up in Louisiana and Texas (Houston and Austin); lives in San Francisco.

HALDEEN BRADDY — prose-writer, scholar; books include *Cock of the Walk, Legends of Pancho Villa; Mexico and the Old Southwest; Pancho Villa Rides Again;* Stories in numerous magazines and journals. Born in Fairlie, Texas, and lives in El Paso where he is a professor of English at UTEP.

JOHN BRANDI — poet, writer, editor of Tooth of Time Press; books include *The Phoenix Gas Slam* (Nail Press) and *Narrowgauge to Riobamba* (Christopher's Books); widely published and traveled, lives in Guadalupita, New Mexico.

BESMILR BRIGHAM — poet, prose-writer; books, *Heaved From the Earth* (Alfred A. Knopf) and *Agony Dance: Death of the Dancing Dolls* (Prensa de Lagar/Wine Press); anthologized in *31 New American Poets, From the Belly of the Shark, Rising Tides,* and *I Hear My Sisters Saying*; lives in Horatio, Arkansas.

SUSAN BRIGHT — poet; chapbook, *Containers* (numenon publications); poems in *Travois, Interstate, Quartet, Hyperion, Lake Superior Review*; lives in Austin.

ROBERT BURLINGAME — poet; "I was born in Kansas. I drifted west and south. I went to school at the University of Arizona, the University of New Mexico, Brown University, and (Fulbright) the University of London. I live most vividly in the Southwest. I teach at the U. of Texas (El Paso) — mainly comparative literature and modern poetry . . ."

DUANE CARR — novelist, poet; novel, *The Bough of Summer* (Endeavors in Humanity

Press); lives in El Paso with his writer-wife and four children.

PAT M. CARR — prose-writer; novel, *The Grass Creek Chronicle* (Endeavors in Humanity Press); stories, *From Beneath the Hill of the Three Crosses* (South and West); recipient of the Iowa Short Fiction Award for 1977; lives in El Paso.

JOHANNA CINADER — poet; her first published poems in *New Mexico Magazine* and in this anthology; a native of The Netherlands, divides her time between New York City and New Mexico (Albuquerque and Taos).

L.D. CLARK — novelist, story-writer, scholar; novel, *The Dove Tree* (Doubleday); critical study of D.H. Lawrence, *Dark Night of the Body* (University of Texas Press); a native Texan, lives in Tucson where he is professor of English at the University of Arizona.

LAVERNE HARRELL CLARK — writer, photographer, editor; book, *They Sang for Horses* (University of Arizona Press); co-editor, with Mary MacArthur, of *The Face of Poetry* (Gallimaufry); a native Texan, lives in Tucson.

NAOMI CLARK — poet; book, *Burglaries and Celebrations* (Oyez Press); grew up in Texas, has lived in New Mexico and Colorado; presently teaches creative writing at San Jose State University.

DENISE CHÁVEZ — poet, prose-writer, playwright; born in Las Cruces, N.M.; now an instructor in Theatre Arts and English Literature at the Northern Branch College of the University of New Mexico at Espanola.

THOMAS COBB — poet; book, *We Shall Curse the Dead* (Desert First Works Press); born in Chicago, raised in Tucson where he owns and operates a bookstore.

JAMES CODY — poet, editor of *Wood Ibis*; books, *Colorado River* (San Marcos Press) and *Return* (Place of Herons Press); born in Springfield, Mo., has lived in Texas since 1956.

BETSY F. COLQUITT — poet, editor of *Descant*; poems in numerous magazines; a native Texan, lives in Fort Worth where she is professor of English and creative writing at Texas Christian University.

JOSEPH L. CONCHA — poet, artist, native American (Taos Pueblo); books, *Lonely Deer* (Red Willow Society) and *Chokecherry Hunters and Other Poems* (The Sunstone Press); lives in Taos.

VICTOR CONTOSKI — poet, translator; books, *Four Contemporary Polish Poets* (Quixote); *Astronomers, Madonnas, and Prophecies* (Juniper Press), *Broken Treaties* (New Rivers); born in Minneapolis, lives and teaches in Lawrence, Kansas.

KATHLEEN DALE — poet; poetry in *13th Moon, Kansas Quarterly, Lakes and Prairies*; from Kansas, has traveled in northern New Mexico; lives in Milwaukee.

HISAYE YAMAMOTO DESOTO — writer; stories in *Partisan Review, Kenyon Review, Harper's Bazaar, Arizona Quarterly, Carleton Miscellany*; anthologized in *Asian-American Heritage* (Washington Square Press) and *Speaking For Ourselves* (Scott, Foresman); lives with her husband and family in Los Angeles.

SUSAN DEWITT — poet, co-editor of *La Confluencia*; "Tsankawi" in this anthology is her first published poem; a native of Seattle, has lived in Albuquerque and Santa Fe since 1968.

R.P. DICKEY — poet, writer; books include *A Concise History of Lead River Mo.* (Black Bear Press); lives in Tucson.

FRANZ DOUSKEY — poet; most recent book, *Indecent Exposure* (New Quarto Editions); anthologized in *For Neruda, For Chile, Poetry of the Desert Southwest, New American Poets*; born in New Haven, Conn., has lived and taught in Arizona.

CHRIS ELLERY — poet, prose-writer; born and raised in southwestern Arkansas; a graduate student in English at the University of Arkansas.

LAWRENCE S. FALLIS — poet; book, *Geronimo* (Blue Cloud Abbey Press); lives in Las Cruces. N.M.

DOUG FLAHERTY — poet; books, *Near the Bone* (Pentagram Press), *To Keep the Blood from Drowning* (Second Coming Press), and *Love-Tangle of Roots* (Ithaca House); anthologized in *From the Belly of the Shark* and *Heartland II*; lives in Oshkosh, Wisconsin.

411

MICHAEL C. FORD — poet, co-editor of *The Mt. Alverno Review*; chapbooks, *Sheet Music, Lawn Swing*, and *Rounding Third* (Permanent Press); lives in Ocean Park, Calif.

PAUL FOREMAN — poet, prose-writer, co-editor of *TAWTE, Hyperion,* and Thorp Springs Press; books, *Redwing Blackbird* (The Headstone Press) and *Texas Liveoak* (Thorp Springs Press); a native of Granbury, Texas, lives in Berkeley, California.

NIA FRANCISCO — poet; poems in *Cafe Solo, New America, Southwest Women's Poetry Exchange.* "i am a full-blooded Diné — Navajo. i am born for the Salt Clan and i am of the red-sideburns clan of red bottom clan. i am blessed with two children."

GENE FRUMKIN — poet, co-editor of *San Marcos Review*; books, *The Hawk & The Lizard* (Swallow Press), *The Rainbow Walker* (Grasshopper Press), *Dostoevsky & Other Nature Poems* (Solo Press), *Locust Cry: Poems 1958-1965* (San Marcos Press), and *The Mystic Writing-Pad* (Red Hill Press); raised in Los Angeles, has lived in Albuquerque since 1966.

DWIGHT FULLINGIM — poet, editor of *Texas Portfolio*, co-editor of *Poetry * Texas*; chapbook, *Ya Shouldna Died Ya Hair That Color 'Cause Now It's Growin' Out and It's a Two-Toned Mess* (Poetry * Texas); born "into a Texas preacher's family," lives in Texas City.

PAUL GALOS — poet; book, *Lycanthropy* (Moth Press); born in Chicago, raised in Las Cruces, N.M.; presently in the Northwest "for graduate study and unemployment."

RITA GARITANO — poet; book, *We Do What We Can* (Desert First Works Press); teaches for the Arizona Commission on the Arts and Humanities, and at Sahuaro High School in Tucson.

RAY GONZALEZ — poet; poems in *The Huron Review, Cyclo-Flame, Travois, The Remington Review, Cafe Solo, Rocky Mountain Review, Mango*; born in El Paso.

FRANCIS IRBY GWALTNEY — novelist, native Arkansawyer; nine novels, the most recent *Idols and Axle Grease* (Bobbs-Merrill); teaches English and creative writing at Arkansas Polytechnic College, in Russellville.

DRUMMOND HADLEY — poet; his most recent book, *Strands of Rawhide* (Goliards-Grossman); lives and works at the Guadalupe Ranch, near Douglas, Arizona.

JOY HARJO — poet, part native American (Creek); chapbook, *The Last Song* (Puerto del Sol Press); anthologized in *Passing Through, Settling America,* and *Traveling America with Today's Poets*; a native of Oklahoma, has lived in Albuquerque, and is now a graduate student in the writing program at the University of Iowa.

GERALD HASLAM — novelist, fiction-writer, poet; novel, *Masks: A Novel* (Old Adobe Press); short fiction, *Okies* (Peregrine Smith); born in Oildale, Calif., "worked as farm laborer, roughneck on a drilling rig, ranch hand in Utah, now a teacher at Cal. State, Sonoma."

GERALD HAUSMAN — poet, editor; books, *New Marlboro Stage* (Giligia Press and Bookstore Press), *Circle Meadow* (Bookstore Press), *The Boy With the Sun Tree Bow* (Berkshire Traveller Press), *Sitting on the Blue-Eyed Bear: Navajo Myths and Legends* (Laurence Hill & Company); lives in Monterey, Mass.

ARN HENDERSON — poet, architect; books, *Document for an Anonymous Indian* and *The Surgeon General's Collection* (Point Riders Press); born in Shawnee, Oklahoma, has lived in Japan, Mexico and New York City; lives now in Norman, Oklahoma.

GEARLD HOBSON — poet, prose-writer; poems and prose in *Sun Tracks, Greenfield Review, Yardbird Reader, New America, La Confluencia, Drum*; from Desha County, Arkansas; has lived in Albuquerque since 1970; part native-American (Cherokee/Chickasaw).

MICHAEL HOGAN — poet, translator; books, *Letters for my Son* (Unicorn), *If You Ever Get There* (Emerald City), and *Soon It Will Be Morning* (Cold Mountain); lives in Tucson.

DIANE HUETER — poet; poems in *Cottonwood Review* and other little magazines; native of Seattle; a senior (American History) at the University of Kansas.

WILL INMAN — poet; book, *A Generation of Heights* (Goliards Press); anthologized in *Where is Vietnam?, In a Time of Revolution,* and *For Neruda, For Chile*; edited *Kauri* poetry magazine, 1964-1971; born in Wilimington, N.C.; has lived in Tucson since 1973.

BILLIE JEAN JAMES — poet; poems in *Ghost Dance, Wind, Hyperion, Rocky Mountain Review, Poem*, and *Blue Cloud Quarterly*; a native of Wyoming, lives in Las Vegas, Nevada.

DAVID JOHNSON — poet, co-editor of *San Marcos Review*; book, *Pilgrim Country* (San Marcos Press); teaches in the creative writing program at the University of New Mexico.

KARL KEMPTON — poet, artist, editor and publisher of *rainbow resin*, co-editor of *Open Ring*; books, *Mandala for the Wind* and *Rune*; poems and visual poems in numerous magazines; lives in Shell Beach, California.

JOHN F. KERR — poet; widely published in poetry journals; "born and raised on a cotton farm in the flatlands of Northeast Arkansas, near Monette. As a teenager I traveled with carnivals, lived with Gypsies, and served in the U.S. Marines." He is currently a professor of English and Chairman of Graduate Studies at California Polytechnic State University, San Luis Obispo.

DAVID KHERDIAN — poet, writer, editor; books include *Looking Over Hills, Homage to Adana*, and *On The Death of My Father and Other Poems* (Giligia Press), *The Nonny Poems* (Macmillan); editor of several anthologies, including *Settling America* and *Traveling America With Today's Poets* (Macmillan); has lived in California and New Mexico; lives now in Oregon.

RONALD KOERTGE — poet; books, *Meat* and *The Hired Nose* (MAG Press), *The Father Poems* (Sumac Press), *My Summer Vacation* (VPC Press); teaches at Pasadena City College.

JANE KOPP — poet; poems in *Quartet, The Smith, Rhode Islander*; anthologized in *Travois* and in *Survivors of the Invention*; born in El Paso, lives in Albuquerque.

KARL KOPP — poet; books, *Tarot Poems* and *Yell County Machine Shop* (Three Herons Press), *Yarbrough Mountain* (The Baleen Press); born in Maryland, has lived in the Arkansas Ozarks and in Albuquerque.

REX LAMBERT — poet; poems in little magazines and in *Poetry of the Desert Southwest*; working in Houston "on an ARAMCO facility due to be constructed soon in Saudi Arabia."

DAVID LEE — poet; book, *For Jan, With Love* (Copper Canyon); born in Texas, lives in Paragonah, Utah "where I'm looking for ground to start another pig farm."

STEPHEN SHU-NING LIU — poet; poems in *The Texas Quarterly, Wascana Review, Chelsea Review, Perspective, Mundus Artium*, and *University of Windsor Review*; came to America from Chungking, China, in 1952; lives in Las Vegas, Nevada.

GERALD LOCKLIN — poet, prose-writer; books, *Poop* and *Son of Poop* (MAG Press), *The Toad Poems* and *Toad's Europe* (Venice Poetry Company), *The Chase* (Duck Down Press), and *The Criminal Mentality* (Red Hill Press); teaches creative writing and contemporary literature at California State University/Long Beach.

ROBERT LLOYD — poet; book, *Homage/Image* (San Marcos Press); lives in Albuquerque.

GLENNA LUSCHEI — poet, editor of Solo Press; book, *Back Into My Body* (Thorp Springs Press); director of Solo Flight, San Luis Obispo, Califronia.

J. MACKIE — poet; book, *Passages* (A Press); came to New Mexico in 1967 from London, England; lives in Albuquerque.

CAROLYN MAISEL — poet; book, *Witnessing* (L'Epervier Press); anthologized in *The New Breed, Intro #2, Voices From the Rio Grande*, and *I Hear My Sisters Saying*; a native of Grove, Texas; lives now in Albuquerque.

CAROLYNNE MALCOLM — poet, type-setter; from Yuma, Arizona; has lived in New Mexico since 1960.

E.A. MARES — poet; poems in *Sunstone Review, New Mexico Magazine, El Cuaderno, San Marcos Review*; anthologized in *Metaforas Verdes* and in *Festival de Flor y Canto*; born in Albuquerque, lives presently in Las Vegas, New Mexico.

RAMÓN MARTINEZ — poet; native Southwesterner; poems in *From the Belly of the Shark*; lives in Phoenix.

WILLIAM MATTHEWS — poet; books include *Sleek for the Long Flight* (Random House), *Sticks & Stones* (Pentagram), "and various pamphlets"; ". . . a persistent traveller carries a layered sense of home wherever he goes."

CARL MAYFIELD — poet, editor of *The Margarine Maypole Orangoutang Express* (Albuquerque); book, with Baker Morrow, *Circling the Garden* (The Anonymous Owl Press); lives in Albuquerque.

HOWARD McCORD — poet; many books and pamphlets, including *The Spanish Dark and Other Poems* (Washington State University Press), *Longjaunes His Periplus*, and *Maps* (Kayak Books), and *The Selected Poems of Howard McCord 1955-1971* (The Crossing Press); born in El Paso, lives and teaches in Bowling Green, Ohio.

KENNETH D. McCULLOUGH — poet; poems in a plethora of little magazines; has lived and traveled in several Western states; currently working for ETV in Columbia, South Carolina.

MARY McGINNIS — counselor, feminist, poet; moved from Philadelphia to Santa Fe to Albuquerque; poems in *Painted Bride Quarterly, Womansmith, Best Friends, New America*; anthologized in *Women in Transition*; lives now in Farmington, N.M.

WILLIAM McGLOTHING — poet; poems in *Blue Moon* and *Bottomfish*; born in Missouri, has lived in Colorado and Oregon; truck-driver, house-painter; lives now in Albuquerque.

KEN McKEON — poet; book, *Winter Man* (Thorp Springs Press); has lived in Southern California and the Pacific Northwest; lives now in Berkeley, California.

SANDY McKINNEY — poet; poems in *AMOTFA: A Magazine of the Fine Arts, The Naked Ear*, and *Best Friends*; born in Baton Rouge, Louisiana; has lived throughout the South and the Southwest; has worked "as clinical lab technician, cocktail waitress, TV and magazine copywriter, editor and woodcrafter . . ."

KAREN McKINNON — poet, prose-writer, instructor in modern dance and yoga; book, *Stereoscopic* (Solo Press); resident poet (1976-1977) New Mexico Poets in the Schools Program; has lived in Albuquerque since 1950.

CAROL S. MERRILL — poet, editor of *Southwest Women's Poetry Exchange*; chapbook, with Susan Kilgore and Julie Ryner, *Early Light* (Albuquerque, 1976); poems in *New America, Nimrod, Best Friends*; a native of Oklahoma, lives in Albuquerque.

MIKE MILLER — photographer; photographic shows in Albuquerque; has traveled throughout the United States and Mexico; lives in Tijeras Canyon, New Mexico.

JOHN R. MILTON — poet, prose-writer, editor of *South Dakota Review*; books include *A Tree of Bones* (Dakota Press) and *The Blue Belly of the World* (Spirit Mound Press); has lived in New Mexico, but lives now in Vermillion, South Dakota.

BOB MINICK — writer; stories in *The Hills of Home* (The Scrimshaw Press); native of the Arkansas Ozarks; lives in San Bernardino, California.

JUDITH MOFFETT — poet; book, *Keeping Time* (L.S.U. Press); spending 1977 in Sweden and England; born in Louisville, Ky., and has lived until recently in Denver.

BARBARA MOR — poet; book, *Mother Tongue* (Athena Press); fromer editor of *The Greater Golden Hills Poetry Express*, in San Diego; is from San Diego, lives now in Taos with her two children.

JANE P. MORELAND — poet; poems in *Inscape, Puget Soundings, Ataraxia, Pequod, The Texas Quarterly*, and *Travois*; born and raised in Beaumont, Texas; lives in Houston.

HARVEY MUDD — poet; book, *Soulscot* (Second Porcupine Press); born in L.A., has lived in New Mexico since 1967 — in Taos and Santa Fe.

JOSEPH COLIN MURPHEY — poet; book, *A Return to the Landscape* (Prickly Pear Press); born in Lufkin, Texas; former poetry editor of *Quartet, Southwest Review*, and *Stone Drum*; lives in Dumas, Texas.

AL NEELY — poet; "took refuge" in New Mexico from California in 1969. "N.M. attracts me because it is very ancient & also unfinished — like my best idea of me." Lives in Peña Blanca, N.M.

DAVE NICHOLS — poet, short story writer; poems in *Lynx, Yellow Brick Road, Salt River*

Anthology, Cloud Chamber; an Oklahoma Poet-in-the-Schools.

STANLEY NOYES — poet, editor, novelist; two novels, *No Flowers for a Clown* and *Shadowbox* (Macmillan); book of poems, *Faces and Spirits* (The Sunstone Press); poetry editor of *New Mexico Magazine*; a native of San Francisco, has lived in southern France, and in Santa Fe since 1964.

WILLIAM OANDASAN — poet, editor of A Press; booklets, *Earth and Sky* and *Taking Off* (A Press); born in Santa Rosa, California, lives in Bernalillo, New Mexico.

DAVE OLIPHANT — poet, translator, editor of Prickly Pear Press; books, *Brands* (Road Runner Press), *Taking Stock* (Prickly Pear Press), *Lines & Mounds* (Thorp Springs Press); edited *The New Breed: An Anthology of Texas Poets*; a native Texan, lives in Austin.

ANICK O'MEARA — poet, co-editor of *Road Apple Review*; book, *Birth-Water* (Road Runner Press); born in Ireland, lives in Oshkosh, Wisconsin.

SIMON J. ORTIZ — poet; native-American (Acoma Pueblo); books include *Naked in the Wind* (Quetzal-Vhio Press) and *Going For the Rain* (Harper & Row); presently lives in San Francisco.

FRANK PARMAN — poet, playwright, editor; book, *Daybook of Western Heroes* (Point Riders Press); plays performed in numerous theaters; a native of Oklahoma, lives in Norman, where he is co-founder of The Cottonwood Arts Foundation.

GEORGE PERREAULT — poet; poems in *New Mexico Magazine, Road Apple Review, Stuffed Crocodile, Puerto del Sol* and *Albireo*; born in Lowell, Mass., has lived in New Mexico since 1974 — in Jemez and Albuquerque.

ROBERT PETERSON — poet; books, *The Binnacle* (Lillabulero Press), *Wondering Where You Are* (Kayak), *Under Sealed Orders* (Cloud-Marauder Press); lives in Ranchos de Taos, N.M.

ANTONIA QUINTANA PIGNO — poet; poems in *Encore, Rocky Mountain Review*, and *El Fuego de Aztlan*; a native of Albuquerque; directs the Minority Resources and Research Center at Kansas State University.

LEROY V. QUINTANA — poet, editor; chapbook, *Hijo del Pueblo* (Puerto del Sol Press); anthologized in *Passing Through*; editor of *Metaforas Verdes* (The Baleen Press); a native New Mexican, Vietnam vet, teaches English and creative writing at El Paso Community College.

RAY QUINTANAR — poet, co-editor of Maguey Press; born in Nogales, Arizona; poems in *Windowrock* and *The Mountain Newsreel*; graduate student at the University of Arizona.

NICK RANIERI — novelist, story writer; novel, *Tracks*, featured in Latitudes Press anthology *Extreme Unctions and Other Last Rites*; shorter fiction in *Gallimaufry* and *Arx*; presently working on his third novel, *Leading Ladies*, and working as a waiter in Austin, Texas.

DAVID RAY — poet, editor ; books, *X-Rays* and *Dragging the Main* (Cornell University Press), *A Hill in Oklahoma* (BkMk Press), *Gathering Firewood* (Wesleyan University Press); edits *New Letters*, in Kansas City, Missouri.

DAVID REMLEY — writer; book, *Crooked Road: The Story of the Alaska Highway* (McGraw-Hill); born in southern California, grew up in Indiana and in Alaska in the days before statehood; teaches Southwestern Literature at the University of New Mexico.

STAN RENFRO — poet; pamphlets, "Earth" and "White Pueblo"; native New Mexican; walks in the mountains, lives in Albuquerque.

FRANCINE RINGOLD — poet, fiction writer, playwright, editor of *Nimrod*; poems in *The Texas Quarterly, Laurel Review, Poem*, and *Southwest Review*; born in New York City; has lived in Tulsa for the past 19 years — where she teaches creative writing and modern literature at the University of Tulsa.

ALBERTO RÍOS — poet; born in Nogales, Arizona; student in creative writing MFA program at University of Arizona; these poems are "his first in a long line of major publications"; has never been east of El Paso.

MARINA RIVERA — poet; poems in little magazines steadily since 1972 (under the names of "Silvia Ortiz" and "Marina Rivera"); chapbook, *Mestiza* (Grilled Flowers); a native Arizonan, lives in Tucson.

FOSTER ROBERTSON — poet, translator, co-editor of *Hyperion* and Thorp Springs Press); books, *Soundings* (San Marcos Press) and *The Wood Path* (Thorp Springs Press); a native of Virginia, lives in Berkeley, Calif.

LEO ROMERO — poet, artist; poems in *Puerto del Sol, New Mexico Magazine, De Colores, South Dakota Review,* and *Beloit Poetry Journal;* "born in a small valley in the Sangre de Cristo mountains . . . great sweep of sky, thrust of mountains, the heart cries out like a meadowlark in the evening."

ORLANDO ROMERO — writer, santero, sculptor; novel, *Nambe Year One* (Tonatiuh International, Inc.); a native New Mexican, born in Santa Fe, lives in Nambe.

WILLIAM PITT ROOT — poet; books include *Striking the Dark Air for Music* (Atheneum); widely published; has lived all over the Southwest; presently lives in Lafayette, Louisianna.

JIM RUPPERT — poet; poems in *Rocky Mountain Review, The Mouth, Spectrum, Margarine Maypole Orangoutang Express;* from Buffalo, N.Y., has lived in Albuquerque since 1971.

NORMAN H. RUSSELL — poet, botanist, part-Cherokee; many books and chapbooks, including *Open the Flower* (The Perishable Press) and *Indian Thoughts: I Am Old* (San Marcos Press); over 2500 poems in magazines and 11 books since he began submitting his poetry in 1966; lives in Edmond, Oklahoma.

SILVIA SCHEIBLI — poet, translator; book, *The Moon Rises in the Rattlesnake's Mouth* (Bitter Oleander Press); a native of Germany, spent several years in the Providence Mountains south of Death Valley, lives now in Half Moon Bay, California.

SUSAN SCHMIDT — poet, ceramacist, artist; book, *Grating the Cheese* (Contemporary Arts Foundation, Oklahoma City); from Port Arthur, Texas, to Oklahoma, to California, to Albuquerque.

JAN SEALE — poet; poems in *The Student, The Forge, Haiku Highlights, Nitty Gritty, Gray Sky Review;* a native Texan, lives in McAllen, Texas.

BRUCE SEVERY — poet; most recent book, *Jackrabbit, North Dakota* [*Chawed Rawzin*]; anthologized in *Voices from Wah-Kon-Tah* and in *Heartland: Poetry of the Midwest;* born in Los Angeles, currently en route.

RICHARD SHELTON — poet; books, *The Tattooed Desert, Of All the Dirty Words,* and *You Can't Have Everything* (University of Pittsburgh Press); chapbooks, *Calendar* (The Baleen Press) and *Chosen Place* (Best Cellar Press); professor of English at the University of Arizona, Tucson.

NAOMI SHIHAB — poet; chapbook, *Tattooed Feet* (Texas Portfolio); anthologized in *Travois* and *Survivors of the Invention;* a Texan since 1967, born in St. Louis; songwriter, singer; lives in San Antonio.

LESLIE MARMON SILKO — writer, poet, Laguna Pueblo; novel, *Ceremony* (Viking); poems, *Laguna Woman* (Greenfield Review Press); story anthologized in *The Man to Send Rainclouds* (Viking); lives in Laguna, N.M.

PATRICIA CLARK SMITH — poet; poems in *Best Friends, Cafe Solo, South Dakota Review, New America, La Confluencia, Blue Moon;* a native of Maine, has lived in Albuquerque since 1971.

JOSEPH SOMOZA — poet; chapbook, *Greyhound* (Grande Ronde Press); book, *Olive Women* (San Marcos Press); anthologized in *Passing Through* and in *Metaforas Verdes;* a native of Spain, lives and teaches in Las Cruces, N.M.

BART L. STAFFORD — prose-writer, poet, editor, critic; book of poems, *Too Many Sparrows* (Endeavors in Humanity Press); editor of 19 publications since 1933; statistician, book-reviewer; lives in El Paso.

LES STANDIFORD — writer, poet; stories, poems, articles in numerous publications; anthologized in *The Bicentennial Collection of Texas Short Stories* and in *New and Experimental Writing;* directs the Creative Writing Program at the University of Texas/El

Paso.

CATHERINE STETSON — poet; poems in many magazines, including *The Nation, New Mexico Magazine, Cairn,* and *Sunstone*; teaches Chicano Literature and Journalism at the National College of Business, in Albuquerque.

LEON STOKESBURY — poet; book, *Often in Different Landscapes* (University of Texas Press); anthologized in *Eating the Menu: A Contemporary American Poetry, New Voices in American Poetry,* and in *The New Breed*; born in Oklahoma City, lives in Austin.

ROBERT JOE STOUT — novelist, writer, poet; novel, *Miss Sally* (Bobbs-Merrill); poetry chapbooks, *Moving Out* (Road Runner Press), *Trained Bears on Hoops*(Thorp Springs Press), *Camping Out* (Samisdat Press), *The Trick* (Juniper Press), *Swallowing Dust* (Red Hill Press); a native Southwesterner, lives now in Chico, California.

LYNN STRONGIN — poet; three chapbooks; poems in numerous magazines; book, *Nightmare of the Mouse* (L'Epervier Press); born and raised in New York City, moved to New Mexico in 1971 from the Bay Area; NEA Creative Writing Grant, 1972.

CHESTER L. SULLIVAN — novelist, writer; novel, *Alligator Gar* (Crown); "Fish or Cut Bait," his story in this anthology, is the first in a series of planned stories set in a secret place, eighteen miles from Mineola, Texas." A native of Mississippi, has lived many years in Texas, now teaches creative writing at the University of Kansas.

ARTHUR SZE — poet, translator; books, *Willow Wind* and *Two Ravens* (Tooth of Time Press); lives in Santa Fe.

JAMES S. TAYLOR — poet, counselor (in Alcohol Abuse and Prevention, and in Family Counseling and Education in Alcoholism), member of A.A.; poems in many magazines; former editor of *The Black Bear Review*, in Taos; lives in Twin Falls, Idaho.

DENO TRAKAS — poet, translator; poems in *Kansas Quarterly* and *Poetry View*; born in North Carolina, teaches Spanish at the University of Tulsa.

ROBERTA TSANG — photographer, artist; a native of San Francisco.

H.L. VAN BRUNT — poet, editor, critic; books, *Uncertainties* and *Indian Territory* (The Smith/Horizon Press), and *Feral* (The Conspiracy Press); a native of northeastern Oklahoma, lives in New York City.

RALPH WALBRIDGE — poet; born and raised in California; held cue-cards in Hollywood for Bob Hope and Jerry Lewis, among other culture-figures of our time; carpenter, roustabout; has lived in New Mexico since 1971.

DAVID RAPHAEL WANG — poet, translator, editor of *Asian-American Heritage* (Washington Square Press); books, *The Intercourse* (Greenfield Press) and *Rivers on Fire* (Basilisk Press); born and raised in China, lived until recently in Texas.

WINSTON WEATHERS — poet, fiction-writer, playwright; books include *The Lonesome Game* (short stories), *Indian and White: Sixteen Eclogues,* and *Messages from the Asylum* (poems); co-author of four writing textbooks; a native of Oklahoma, lives in Tulsa where he teaches English and the graduate creative writing workshop at the University of Tulsa.

RAMONA WEEKS — poet, prose-writer, co-editor of *Inscape* and The Baleen Press; book, *The Lincoln County Poems* (Konocti Books); anthologized in a *A Part of Space: Ten Texas Writers*, in *American Literary Anthology No. 2*, and in *From the Belly of the Shark*; a native Texan, lives in Phoenix.

JAMES L. WHITE — poet, fiction writer; books, *Divorce Proceedings* (University of South Dakota Press), *A Crow's Story of Deer* (Capra Press), and *The Del Rio Hotel* (Territorial Press); born in Indianapolis, Indiana; has taught writing to Navajo people in New Mexico and Arizona, lives now in Minneapolis.

JAMES P. WHITE — writer, poet, editor; stories in many periodicals; founder and co-editor of Texas Center for Writers Press; raised in Arlington, Texas; currently in Dallas on leave of absence from the University of Texas at the Permian Basin, where he is Director of Creative Writing.

JAMES WHITEHEAD — poet, prose-writer; book, *Domains* (poems) (L.S.U. Press); novel, *Joiner* (Knopf); born in St. Louis, grew up in Mississippi, lives in Fayetteville, Ark., where he teaches in the creative writing program at the University of Arkansas.

PETER WILD — poet, environmentalist; books include *The Good Fox* (Adams Press), *Cochise* and *Chihuahua* (Doubleday); lives in Tucson, where he teaches English and creative writing at the University of Arizona.

STANLEY CARROL WILLIAMS — prose-writer, editor of *Hellcoal Playbook Series*, co-editor of *The Pawn Review*; stories in *The Pawn Review, New and Experimental Literature* and *The Bicentennial Collection of Texas Short Stories*; a native Texan, lives and teaches in Odessa, Texas.

KEITH WILSON — poet, writer; numerous publications, including books, chapbooks, anthologies, magazines; mentor of many Southwestern poets; a native New Mexican, now resident poet, New Mexico State University Writing Center, Las Cruces.

BRYAN WOOLLEY — novelist, prose-writer, poet; novel, *Some Sweet Day* (Random House); *We Be Here When the Morning Comes* (non-fiction) (Univ. Press of Kentucky); associate editor and columnist for the Dallas *Times Herald*.

WAKAKO YAMAUCHI — prose-writer, playwright, painter; stories in AIIIEEEEE (Howard University Press), in *Yardbird Reader III, Amerasia Journal,* and *Greenfield Review*; lives in Gardena, California.

PAULA YUP — poet; presently a student at Occidental College, Los Angeles.